THE LEICA IN PROFESSIONAL PRACTICE

BY

H. STÖCKLER

THE LEICA

IN PROFESSIONAL PRACTICE

by HEINRICH STÖCKLER

in collaboration with leading professional

and scientific photographers and specialists

62 four-color plates and 200 monochrome illustrations

FOUNTAIN PRESS · LONDON

U. S. Representatives:

Rayelle Publications, 76 West Chelten Avenue, Philadelphia 44, Pa.

English text of the original German edition,
Die Leica in Beruf und Wissenschaft, prepared for publication
in the British Editorial Offices of the magazine *Leica Fotografie*
by W. Edward Roscher.

Printed in Germany by Brönners Druckerei (Inh. Breidenstein),
Frankfort on Main

Table of Contents

Preface

SOME MAY be perturbed at the thought of yet another book on the Leica camera. There has been a steady stream, at times rising to a flood, of so-called literature on the subject—but oddly enough there is no good American or English language book on the applied uses of the Leica. This book aims to fill that gap.

Various writers on the subject of Leica photography have touched on this, that, or the other use of the Leica camera. It is clearly impossible for one author to cover the whole field. In general, there has been a drift towards stereotyped productions which begin by explaining the camera controls and indicating the uses of the better known accessories and lenses. Center sections are then devoted to more or less competent surveys of developing techniques for miniature films, and the books are usually rounded off with a selection of Leica pictures conforming, in technical quality or artistic merit, with the individual author's own tastes or photographic aptitudes. The Leica itself is a kind of *deus ex machina* around which this well-worn plot is hung. Precisely the same device may be used to hang an identical plot round any other camera, according to preference or the dictates of an author's pocket.

No such considerations play any part in the production of the present volume which is an assembly of twenty-six authentic articles, each written by a specialist in his own particular field of applied Leica photography, and largely illustrated with his own pictures. These articles originally appeared in the German work *Die Leica in Beruf und Wissenschaft*, and they are now offered to a far wider public in English translation.

Why a translation? Why not compile a similar book from American and British sources who use the Leica in precisely the same ways as here described? The answer to these questions is rooted in time and in experience. The adoption of the Leica camera in applied scientific and professional photography is a history of great endeavor; of close and fruitful co-operation between the Leitz

7

works in Wetzlar and many specialist users of Leitz optical equipment, whose experience, garnered over the years, was a vast untapped source of information on applied Leica technique. That combined experience, the property of no one man, was sieved and shaped into its present form by Heinrich Stöckler, who has been a member of the Leitz organization for more than twenty-five years. All the resources of that organization were available to him in editing this work. Such a combination of factors is unique.

However, this compilation does not pretend to be exhaustive and no claim is made that the survey of all the possibilities is complete. To avoid repetition, it was found expedient not to include some of the material available from certain very specialized sources, notwithstanding the fact that some most interesting work had been done with the Leica. Special publications dealing with these applications are available. The reader is referred to *The Leica in Science and Industry (Leica in Wissenschaft und Technik)* where they are all listed. Within the last year the Leica has been used for aviation accident investigation and for research into the genetic effects of atomic radiation, but papers are not yet available for publication. These, incidentally, are two new British uses of the Leica camera.

It was not the original intention to describe apparatus and accessories because these are dealt with in detail in the various Leitz pamphlets and brochures. Nor was it proposed to discuss the technique of Leica photography because this has already been the subject of a great number of excellent publications, such as Emmermann's *Leica Technique*, Dr. Paul Wolff's *My Experiences with the Leica* and Theo Kisselbach's *Pocket Leica Book*. However, we have been urged to include a short description of apparatus mentioned throughout the book and to state briefly the basic principles of Leica technique. A chapter devoted to this introduces the present volume, but in writing it the author has assumed throughout that the reader is conversant with the current literature on the subject, and is himself able to use the Leica camera. Even the advanced worker might find it occasionally useful to refer back to text-books, because the available space permitted only a brief discussion of the theme.

It will be noted by those familiar with the English Edition of *Leica Fotografie*—a magazine on miniature photography edited by Heinrich Stöckler—that the development of Leica films is again dealt with from the point of view of gradation, rather than that of grain. The battle against the coarse grain of very fast films has been fought and lost. The battle against the steeper gradation of slower films has been fought and won. These two sentences sum up a quarter of a century of trial and error. Here we are not concerned with the history of those experiments—only with their final result, which is given in brief outline.

The body of the book covers too vast a field for summary. A glance at the Index or at the Table of Contents will indicate the breadth of subject matter. There is something for everybody, ranging from the more spectacular uses of the Leica camera in photo-journalism to color photomicrography of plant cells in polarized light. Each author has been allowed latitude to make his own recommendations and suggestions. Though these may sometimes seem to be at variance with each other, they are never wholly contradictory. It is inevitable that different workers in such varied fields will discover and apply slightly varying methods; that their personal preferences will also vary; that their choice of equipment will differ to suit their own needs. It is left to the reader to decide what suits him best, basing his methods and his choice on knowledge derived from the experiences of others. Today the Leica is being used increasingly in scientific and professional photography. It is the object of this book to encourage that trend and to offer useful practical suggestions for applied Leica technique.

It has been a privilege and a pleasure to translate this work. It has also been a challenge which could not have been met without the active co-operation of the Leitz organization in Wetzlar and the able help of the Microscope Department of Messrs. E. Leitz (Instruments) Limited, London, W. 1., and of Mr. C. A. Smith, formerly Managing Director of Leitz, London. Some of the authors, notably Prof. W. E. Ankel, Dr. J. Franz and Dr. H. Pfeiffer, have made most useful suggestions which are gratefully acknowledged. Particular thanks are due to my friend and colleague, Heinrich Stöckler, for his encouragement and support throughout the many months of this undertaking; and to my wife for typing the manuscript and checking the proofs. The aim was to make this book a facsimile of the original in another language. If errors of translation have crept into the text the responsibility is mine alone.

W.E.R.

Reigate Heath, Surrey. July 1955

the constructor of the Leica

Applied Leica Technique

by H. Stöckler

Editor-in-Chief "Leica Fotografie"

MINIATURE photography, born with the Leica more than a generation ago, has staged a revolution. It has made photographic reproduction possible in a whole series of new fields and provided a powerful stimulus to the rank and file of pictorial photographers. It has just as much—a fact which should not be concealed—contributed to a certain leveling, if not lowering, of standards. In retrospect one can establish that zealous protagonists have proclaimed with unbounded enthusiasm that the miniature can perform all the tasks of the heavier, larger camera, and do them better. On the other hand, the sceptics, who have made themselves increasingly heard of late, are of the opinion that precise performance is impossible with the miniature, which merely encourages promiscuous exposure and waste of sensitive material. They hold the view that serious professional photography is thinkable only with larger camera sizes.

As often happens, the truth lies somewhere between these extremes, but it is well to heed the warnings so often uttered by the sceptics. Enthusiasm is commendable but it must be paired with thorough mastery of the craft if worth is to be lasting. The best yardstick of the worth, or otherwise, of a photographic print is to look at it a few years later. One must admit that much chaff must be separated from the wheat that remains and so we find proof that it is just as difficult to do lasting work with the miniature as it is with any other kind of camera.

One might go further yet and maintain that in the case of the miniature the manipulative processes of photography demand much greater care than with the larger sizes if the aim is to produce comparable work of first-class quality.

The size of the original negative, scarcely larger than a postage stamp, demands that quality must be superb in respect of frame utilization, definition, fineness of grain, and gradation, because this small negative must in every case be enlarged at least five diameters, and often much larger, if the print is to have "pictorial" quality.

Not much need be said about mechanical and optical precision if the camera is a Leica. The name LEITZ is the guarantee that here the ultimate has been, and continues to be, achieved. If, then, when evaluating the results of years of photography, we find much, going under the name miniature photography, that is unsatisfactory or not up to the high standards required for professional use, we must turn elsewhere for the reason.

A careful examination of this problem will reveal that it is essential to work according to certain basic principles if good results are to be attained.

The essential points are each discussed briefly below but, as stressed in the Preface, it is assumed that the reader is familiar with the use of the Leica as laid down in the Instruction Leaflets and that he has a working general knowledge of photography. The available space enforces brevity, so no attempt is made to give the subject comprehensive treatment. Apparatus and technique are discussed mainly in so far as they are suitable for professional use, with the emphasis on highest quality. If, as on development, comment is confined to but a few formulas, this does not mean that there are no other methods which would lead to a similar result. But in more than twenty-five years of practical work, and after very thorough experiment and test, the present writer has found that some very old and simple methods are not worse, and often considerably better, than all that has since been evolved or suggested. Accordingly, the procedure recommended is not just one of several possible methods but often the best of these.

The Leica

Before the war there were six different models, from the Standard (Original) Model to Model IIIc.

These cameras are no longer made, but some of them can be converted to the present day f series. The current production program embraces the following models:

Leica I f without built-in (provision for clip-on) rangefinder, interchangeable direct vision mirror finders, focal plane shutter $^1/_{25}-^1/_{500}$ sec. and time exposures, synchronized for expendable and speed flash. Threaded lens fitment which accepts lenses of various focal lengths. This model is all that is required, for instance, in photomicrography.

Leica II f as above but with built-in coupled rangefinder and built-in view-finder, both of which increase the rapidity of operation.

Leica III f has in addition the $^1/_{1000}$ sec. setting for very fast-moving subjects and slow shutter speeds down to 1 sec., useful for indoor and color photography, portraiture and copying.

The model preferred will, of course, depend largely on the use to which it is to be put. Top performance can be obtained with the simplest Leica model; the better ones merely allow the same result to be obtained with greater convenience in use. Important to remember is the possibility of having Models I f and II f converted, if later desired, into Model III f.

Leica M 3 is the latest model in the series. It differs radically from all previous Leica cameras and has so many new constructional details that there is no possibility of having earlier models converted. The most important differences from earlier Leicas are: built-in rapid lever-wind for shutter and film transport; quick-change bayonet mount for lenses; built-in bright line measuring view-finder (combined rangefinder and viewfinder) with automatic bright line field delineation for lenses of 50, 90 and 135 mm. focal lengths; automatic elimination of parallax; subject visible in almost natural size; non-rotating shutter speed dial for all speeds from $^1/_{1000}$ sec. to 1 sec., and B; coupled photo-electric exposure meter; hinged rear panel for easier loading; simplification of flash synchroniz-ation by elimination of Contact Numbers; separate points for expendable bulbs and flash tubes; built-in self-timer; automatic frame counter; film reminder in rear panel; new metal cassette which can also be used in other models.

Threaded Leica lenses can be equipped with a bayonet adapter ring to fit the Leica M 3. Work on the construction and continuous improvement of other accessories goes steadily on.

With the Leica M 3 it is possible to work more quickly and conveniently than with former models. This is a particular asset in certain professional applications, such as press work, portraiture, wild-life photography and when traveling or going on expeditions. The technical considerations dealt with in the following chapters apply as much to the Leica M 3 as to the other models.

The Optical Equipment

At the time of writing there are nine different lenses from which a choice can be made. A 50 mm. lens would certainly be chosen as standard equipment. In this group there are four such: Elmar f/3.5, Summitar f/2, Summicron f/2 and Summarit f/1.5.

The old and well-tried 50 mm. Elmar will suffice for most purposes since it has reasonably high light-transmitting power which has to be reduced, by stopping down, for almost all exposures. Lenses of higher light-transmitting power should really not be described as universal equipment for the miniature camera. Apart from their high price the mere fact that the reserve is there tempts users to an unnecessary use of the largest aperture with consequent loss of optimum photographic quality (restriction in field depth, much more critical focus). One might almost speak of a craze for fast lenses. Statistical inquiry has revealed that more than 70% of all miniature exposures are made at medium apertures so that the use of very fast lenses should be confined to the occasions for which they were designed: sport, reportage, press features. Only when subject movement is so fast that the shortest exposure might call for a large aperture (sport), or when existing light is so poor yet an exposure *must* be made (press), or in cases where both these conditions obtain (theater photography, children in the home), should the full aperture f/2, or more if necessary, be used. But modern synchronized flash apparatus allows us to use even moderately fast lenses under such adverse conditions, and at a medium aperture, with consequent gain in overall image quality and depth of field.

The uses of the other lenses are already fairly well known and are usually determinable by their focal lengths. A useful basic equipment for professional and scientific purposes would comprise the wide-angle 35 mm. Summaron, the 50 mm. Elmar and the 90 mm. Elmar in conjunction with a laterally correct universal viewfinder.

The 135 mm. Hektor lens used on a short mount with the mirror reflex housing deserves special mention. Apart from being almost ideally suited to portraiture it is also adaptable to a variety of uses in all applied scientific fields; indeed, one might say with little risk of contradiction that this combination—especially when used with the Leitz focusing bellows—is really *the* equipment for all the applications discussed in this book. The combination of 135 mm. Hektor lens, reflex housing and bellows, offers all the advantages which opponents of miniature photography are so ready to dispute: utilization of the entire image field; ideal viewing conditions (upright, magnified image on ground glass screen) and the ability to observe (living) subjects and vary focus continuously within extreme limits of accuracy right upto the instant the exposure is made; best perspective because of the narrow acceptance angle (19°) and correspondingly greater camera/subject distance. Used with the bellows device the focusing range of the Hektor and mirror reflex housing extends from the infinity point right down to macrophotography. This apparatus can be applied to all but one of the photographic fields—copying, for which a horizontal position for the matter and the use of a short focal length are, of course, the preferred methods. It is almost superfluous to add that all Leitz lenses are "coated"—a process which considerably reduces flare and to some extent improves the light-transmitting power of the lens. The reduction of flare results in very considerable increase in image contrast, a factor which underlies the subjective impression of improved definition which is, of course, a decided advantage in all types of photography other than portraiture, for which a diffusing screen may easily be fitted over the lens.

Accessories

Comment will be confined to those which are necessary from the point of view of scientific or professional photography.

In the first place, it is well to stress the importance of using a *sunshade or lens hood*, which is certainly not rendered superfluous by lens coating. It improves the clarity of the image, and not only in back light. Since in miniature photography the quality of the end result is often determined by factors of this kind nothing should be neglected which has proved itself of positive value. Looked at in this light the sunshade is a valuable aid.

Filters

Filters are important in both pictorial and scientific photography. They owe their value to certain inadequacies in sensitive materials, which are often unable to convert the natural colors of objects into a gray scale of tones corresponding to the visual brightnesses of the original. Although the claim is sometimes made that modern panchromatic emulsions record colors in correct tonal differences, it will be found that the use, particularly, of a blue-reducing filter is essential. One need but compare two prints of a sunny landscape with cumulus clouds against the sky; the one made from an unfiltered negative and the other made from a negative exposed through a medium yellow filter. The latter presents a greater range of tones; it appears brighter and more pleasing to the eye. In pictorial photography the medium *Leitz Yellow Filter No. 1* is entirely suitable for *all normal purposes*. It combines adequate blue absorption with a sufficiently small exposure factor (approx. $\times$ 2). For special effects an *orange filter* with a rather higher exposure factor (approx. $\times$ 3—4) and increased blue absorption might be desirable (e.g., on high mountains under sun, but with fairly extensive cloud formations revealing sky in small patches only). It is hardly necessary to add that filters for use in miniature photography should be perfect optical flats.

Red filters and others play a comparatively subordinate role in pictorial photography, although they can sometimes be used to produce very striking effects. Red filters are used primarily for penetrating distant haze in long-distance photography.

In pictorial photography under tungsten illuminants (e.g., portraiture) filters are, in general, unnecessary provided a panchromatic film with reduced red sensitivity is used—this because such illuminants have a lower short wavelength (blue) emission than daylight and are rich in red. If very fast and highly red-sensitive film is used for portraits a blue filter is the appropriate one to place on the lens, but in such cases (film studios are an example) it is often preferable to use special make-up because the very high filter factor offsets the speed of the film.

For scientific photography other rules must be applied. Here "inaccurate tone scale reproduction" of colors is often desirable or even necessary. One must know the effect that filters will have, namely, that hues of the same or similar color to the filter will record light in the positive whereas the complementary colors will record dark. Here, of course, the spectral sensitivity of the emulsion and the spectral composition of the illuminant must also be taken into account. Quite remarkable and interesting variations in the rendering of color are feasible in the hands of the accomplished worker, who will find it possible both to record faithfully and to exaggerate color contrasts; to eliminate or to accentuate individual tones or spots or patches, as desired. This kind of thing is being done daily in medical and forensic photography and also in straight copy work, and will be dealt with under the appropriate headings. Photography of the infra-red and of fluorescing screen images also comes under this heading, as do also the possible uses of filters in color photography: for adjusting the balance of artificial light type color film to daylight and *vice versa*, or for the elimination of the pronounced color cast that is often to be expected when color film is exposed to light of a spectral composition for which it is not balanced (morning, midday, and evening sunlight, especially in high mountains). Finally there are polarizing filters which are used to repress or eliminate reflections from shiny surfaces, but their effectiveness is unfortunately limited by the angle of incident illumination.

Other small accessories

Supplementary lenses are now regarded as old-fashioned since they often impair the image quality of the taking lens. It is better to use lens extension for close-ups, such as the *optical near-focusing device "Nooky"*, or simple intermediate collars or rings in conjunction with the *sliding copier* or the mirror reflex housing. Alternatively, variable extension is provided by the bellows device. This apparatus is already adequately described in the manufacturer's literature.

A good *stand* is always an important piece of equipment. Leitz unfortunately do not manufacture a stand suitable for miniature photography. Paradoxical as it may sound, a good heavy stable stand is often a necessity for the small and handy Leica. The usual telescopic light metal stands which collapse into a small space are really quite unsuitable for the purpose. Even the U-shaped metal stands suffer from a certain amount of vibration which makes it impossible to get an absolutely sharp image. For professional purposes the heavy twin-tubed Linhof camera stand, designed for heavy cameras and, therefore, perhaps a little ungainly in appearance, has proved very suitable, as have also the stands manufactured by the Schiansky Co. The *ball and socket joint* on any stand used should be at least as solid as the Leitz "Kgoon". Absolutely reliable and synchronizable *flash apparatus* has become increasingly important to the professional Leica user. Leitz market a very reliable clip-on *synchro-flash gun* for expendable bulbs of many different makes. But where flash is in constant demand for professional purposes it is naturally more economical to use portable or mains power packs for tube discharge: the so-called speed light. Langham

Photographic Instruments Ltd. make a whole series of these, from multi-head studio equipment to ring illuminants for oral work. Flash is important not merely to the press man but equally in many other applied uses (police work, medical and, in particular, ophthalmic and surgical photography).

Exposure Meters

These are very useful little accessories but their value is often over-estimated. Under standard conditions of light every professional or applied worker will, on the basis of careful experiment and test, have acquired sufficient experience to estimate the correct photographic exposure. An absolutely accurate exposure is neither possible nor desirable because the "correct" exposure is very largely a function of the method of development employed. Every photographic emulsion also has some degree of exposure latitude. If—to be precise—there is no "exact" exposure, then optical and photo-electric meters can only serve as an approximate guide and their readings will often need correction—so-called "calibration"—to conform to the exposure requirements of any given method of processing (development). Every practising photographer will soon discover that on just those occasions when he might feel a need for an exposure meter (low levels of illumination, extreme contrasts), the types of reflected light meter generally available today will usually fail to give an approximate reading either because they are not sufficiently sensitive or not sufficiently selective. There is, however, a British meter—the Ilford S.E.I.—which is selective to half a degree of arc.

Exposure meters might be regarded as essential for color work because the exposure latitude of color film is quite restricted.

Care of the Leica

It will be evident that the user must be thoroughly familiar with the manipulative control of the Leica camera and well versed in the instructions supplied with it. Such a valuable precision instrument must be handled with care. Dropping or knocking it severely could easily upset the alignment of the rangefinder and in such cases it is recommended that the camera be thoroughly checked by accredited Leitz agents. It is, however, quite unnecessary to subject the camera or its interchangeable lenses—as sometimes suggested in some photographic

18

manuals—to tests for accuracy of adjustment or optical quality, since the very detailed inspection of each instrument at every stage of manufacture is a much more exacting control than any user test.

Eyepieces and object glasses of the viewfinder and rangefinder should be kept clean because accuracy of rangefinding is often dependent on this. The outer surfaces of lenses should also be kept free of dust and, particularly, of finger marks because these soften the definition of the image. On the other hand, unnecessary cleaning or rubbing of these highly polished surfaces should be avoided to prevent scratching. If it is necessary to clear dust off the lens, breathe on the glass surface first and then wipe off gently with a soft cloth. Front and rear dust caps are provided to prevent dirt accumulating on these surfaces when not in use. The rear dust cap has another important function, namely, to prevent damage to thread or bayonet mounts caused by careless handling, for example, knocking the thread fairly hard against a table top when changing lenses. If unprotected, the end of the focusing mount might be damaged, with resultant inaccuracy of focus setting by means of the rangefinder.

Leica cameras should never be oiled or dismantled.

Definition

The secret of pin-sharp Leica negatives? Extensive tests carried out under exacting conditions reveal that the Leica lens is capable of a performance which is unmatched by that of any modern sensitive material. No film can do it justice, so we must look elsewhere for the causes of poor quality, about which complaints are justified and not infrequent. In the following paragraphs an attempt is made to lay down the basic requirements for optimum definition.

1. Choice of Sensitive Material

It is fundamental to emulsion manufacture that the lower the speed of an emulsion the finer will its grain be and the better its resolving power. Accordingly, fast film would not be used if the aim is to obtain maximum definition. But since it is often impractical to make all exposures on a slow film, one should choose as the standard all-round material a panchromatic film of medium sensitivity (16—32 arithmetic or 24°—27° logarithmic)*.

---

* For comparative speeds see page 25.

19

2. Use the full Frame

Many negatives are not so sharp as they could be because too great a camera/subject distance has been chosen, involving a high degree of enlargement from a small part of the negative. When making the exposure remember to fill the frame with the subject. It is better to use a lens of longer focal length than to approach too near because of the ill effect nearness has on perspective.

3. Focusing, Aperture and Shutter Speed

Focus setting must be accurate, especially when using lenses of long focus or at big stops. Medium stops are to be preferred in most cases because they permit greater depth of field. Stops that are too small do not further improve the overall definition of the image. Shutter speed should be chosen to give good shadow definition (shadow reading). But with reversal materials (color) exposure should be for the highlights (highlight reading). Too great an exposure spoils definition and increases graininess.

4. Gentle Release

The manner in which the camera is held and the method of releasing the shutter both have a considerable influence on the definition of the negative. Maximum sharpness is guaranteed when the camera is absolutely rigid on a vibration-free stand or any such similar firm support, and the exposure is made by uncapping the lens. In free-hand use the aim should be to hold the camera dead steady — and that is far easier said than done. A simple test is revealing. Make ten consecutive exposures of a poster with the camera held in the hands in the normal manner, using the same shutter speed throughout. Compare the negatives so made under a strong magnifier or in the enlarger. They will not all reveal the same degree of sharpness. Nor does it make much difference if the shutter speed used was $^1/_{40}$ sec. or $^1/_{1000}$ sec.

The lessons to be learned are important. The steadier the stance (legs fairly wide apart, camera wedged firmly against the head or cheek, breath held if necessary) and the gentler the release action (complete absence of vibration during the exposure), the sharper the resulting negative will be: the principle is the same as for shooting with a rifle. Similar precautions should be taken also when using the faster shutter speeds. At high shutter speeds the shutter is not speeded up. It is only the slit between the blinds that is narrowed, but speed of traverse across the frame remains constant.

20

Camera shake is a very frequent fault in miniature photography. Users of miniature cameras are apt to forget that the conditions of exposure are much more critical than with larger sizes. This is so because every miniature negative must be considerably enlarged.

The Film

Another factor of primary importance in miniature photography is the quality of the film. It must combine fast speed with complete absence of grain, high resolving power, soft gradation, and good optical sensitization. But this has always been a pipe dream because film manufacturers have not yet succeeded in combining all these qualities. The steady increase in emulsion speeds has been bought at the price of worsened resolving power and coarse graininess. This cannot be claimed as an advance. The use of very fast films should be avoided or at least confined to those occasions where it would be impossible to make a picture without them. Most practical work can be done with a film of medium sensitivity (32....27°). New research holds promise of a drift towards even slower films which are processed in developers specially suited to them.

Grain

For years this was *the* topic in miniature circles; or better: how to avoid it. But there just is no such problem if procedure is correct. It is absurd to try to eradicate by tricks with the developer a fault that is inherent in certain types of film.

Remember: fast film, coarse grain; slow film, fine grain. Further: every true fine grain developer—i.e., every developer which artifically reduces the size of the coarse grain of some emulsions—does so at the cost of that emulsion's speed. Why not use a film of lower speed and develop it normally ? Result: at least the same effective speed but incomparably better definition.

Development

The methods of development have been exhaustively described and are generally known. Their object is to make visible and reasonably permanent the latent image produced by the photochemical action of light on the emulsion; and to preserve in this image certain characteristics important in the production of the positive. Grain size must not be increased and the gradation of the negative must be soft. The definition of the image can be impaired by the nature or method of development.

True fine grain developers, i.e., solvent developers, must be left out of consideration for the reason given in the previous section. Developers that have proved eminently suitable are:

Rodinal (Agfa), Perinal (Perutz), Azol (Johnsons) diluted 1:50 at a temperature of 65° F: 8—10 minutes development (with intermittent agitation) for films of medium speed (32....27°).

If a higher sensitivity is desired from the same film (sport, press work, theater) it is only necessary to raise the concentration of the developer and prolong development; e.g., dilution 1:30 for 15 minutes at 65° F. In this way it is possible to increase the speed of the film by a factor of four and reduce exposure time to a quarter; but it is important to note that the "correct" exposure for this modified development must be carefully judged, otherwise negatives that are too thin or too dense may result. In other words: this method should be attempted only by the experienced.

If films of low sensitivity are used—films which have an inherently steep gradation—it is recommended that the times of development given above should be halved, or even cut to a third under certain circumstances.

Color Photography

These processes are still being constantly improved. Side by side with the older reversal processes which yield direct transparencies for projection, various color negative processes have been developed with the object of producing a color picture on paper.

The negative color processes yield, on exposure and development, a color negative in colors complementary to the original. The color print or transparency is obtained from such a negative by printing it onto positive tri-pack papers or films. It is also possible to make monochrome prints from such a color negative by printing it in the normal way on bromide paper—a very elegant solution of many problems.

But the most important advantage of the negative color process is the freedom it gives the operator to control the subjective color rendering of the print by interposing appropriate filters between the negative and the light source when contact printing or enlarging—a factor of considerable importance in the elimination of color cast, the control of which in reversal processes is not always possible, as many have found to their regret.

None the less, for miniature photography reversal color materials must be preferred because they yield much sharper pictures. For lantern slide lectures, an important feature of many scientific and educational establishments, the reversal color transparency is also better because of its greater brilliance and hue saturation.

In much applied photography color film is now essential. Think only of the better demonstration of the colored object in biology or botany, in medicine, in forensic photography, or in the study of art. For exposing a color film the reader is referred to manufacturers' instructions and also to the extensive literature on the subject. Here it need merely be stressed that only those illuminants should be used for which a color film is balanced and that mixed lighting of different color temperatures should be avoided. Because of the restricted exposure latitude of color reversal materials reasonably exact exposures are necessary (here an exposure meter is essential). Great subject contrast should be avoided, so keep the lighting soft. Some special applications of color and how to use it are given in some of the following chapters but for technical information on color film there is other appropriate literature.

The Darkroom

Finally, a few hints on how to arrange a private darkroom for miniature work.

The walls should be painted as light as possible—not black—because they cannot reflect any but the light from the darkroom safelight. The floor is best laid with tiles or compressed asphalt. Wooden boards or linoleum do not long withstand attack by chemicals. It is of basic importance to have a "wet" and a "dry" section in the darkroom: sinks, trays, and faucets should be arranged along one wall, and along the wall opposite there should be a table for dry work, such as loading film, enlarging, etc. The trays should measure at least 16×24 inches and be sufficiently deep. Three trays should suffice if the sink itself is used for washing and intermediate rinses. Developer and fixer trays should be on either side of the sink. It should not be considered a luxury to have this wall fitted with glazed tiles for at least half its height from the floor up.

Such tiles are not merely easier to keep clean—they last much longer than distemper. Above the dry-work table and also above the developer tray there should be darkroom safelights for direct and indirect illumination. Each lamp should have a 15—25 watt bulb and a safelight screen of the type Agfa No.113 D or Wratten OA series (OB in England). Practise handling films in total darkness. This saves the cost of dark green safelight screens and prevents possible fogging of panchromatic films. Above the fixing tray there should be another wall light with a blue "daylight" bulb or opal bulb behind a flashed opal or frosted glass screen. This illumination is used to evaluate the quality of the prints being made. Attention should be paid to the provision of an adequate light-trap at the entrance to the darkroom. A heavy curtain arranged in a half-circle round the door will often suffice, but if there is room an S-shaped light-trap might be erected. Special provision should also be made for adequate ventilation of the darkroom.

Darkroom equipment will be largely a matter of personal need. Trays should be made of some plastic material. Funnels, beakers, and print forceps should be made of stainless steel. A dry press and a print trimmer are always useful.

It should be noted that work in a well laid out and adequately lit darkroom is far less tiring and progresses much more quickly than in the dim and musty rooms that are sometimes used for the purpose. For the lay-out here described a room from six to nine feet square will be found large enough.

Comparative Ratings of Systems most in use

Din	ASA	Sch	
7/10	3	17	The adjoining table lists comparative speed ratings of three of the systems most in use. In Europe DIN and Scheiner ratings are fairly
10/10	6	20	general. In the British Isles B.S.I. logarithmic and arithmetic
12/10	10	22	ratings were introduced after the war. The logarithmic ratings correspond closely to the Scheiner speeds of the adjoining table while
13/10	12	23	the arithmetic are identical with the ASA ratings popular in the
14/10	16	24	United States, where the newly devised ASA ratings (American Standards Association) are slowly supplanting the GE (General
15/10	20	25	Electric) and Weston Speeds. It should be noted that exact conversion from one system to the next is not possible, since the methods
16/10	25	26	of measuring sensitivity vary from system to system. It might therefore be observed that comparative ratings published from time to
17/10	32	27	time in the photographic press vary, sometimes considerably, one
18/10	40	28	from the other. The adjoining table makes no claim to absolute
19/10	50	29	accuracy of conversion, but seeks merely to give approximations which have proved successful in practice. In the comments on ex-
20/10	64	30	posure meters it has already been mentioned that it is absolutely
21/10	80	31	necessary in one's own work to calibrate the meter for the conditions of development favored because, without this, the speed ratings of
22/10	100	32	films have only a very relative value.
23/10	128	33	

N. B. Throughout this book film speeds are given in arithmetic and logarithmic ratings—arithmetic first, followed by the logarithmic figure, thus:—
32...27°

The Photo-Journalist and the Leica

by Hannes Rosenberg, Munich

ILLUSTRATED magazines carrying the typical photographic picture sequence have been appearing for generations, but it is only recently that a German Institute has been founded to train young people for the calling of photo-journalism. This curious innovation merely underlines the fact that professional training, though it might be of some help, plays but a subordinate part when compared with natural aptitude for the task. Before the Second World War, anyone who felt he had the makings of a photo-journalist went as an apprentice or an assistant to a publisher or established feature photographer and tried his luck. This was soon found to be by far the best method of weeding out suitable human material for the future. The high percentage of those who just did not make the grade, despite competent instruction, was proof enough that personal aptitude was of greater moment than mere theoretic knowledge.

Prerequisites

It can, in general, be said that an apprenticeship provides training which is merely technical or manipulative. But the budding photo-journalist soon learns that technical skill or craftsmanship are not in themselves sufficient to his ends. For him skill is merely a means to an end—it is only a foundation on which he builds—because his work is full of problems which exercise his personality far more than they do his photographic skill. He is not a government official, artisan, or salesman coping with a routine job but is faced with daily change of location and of situation. Every fresh situation calls for the treatment appropriate to it. The first requirement of outstanding journalistic success is the ability to enlist the active help of the people who are the subject of the pictures. Many a news shot derives its journalistic value often from the fact alone

Fig. 1: Surplus women. Among adults of marriageable age in Germany there are only 100 men to every 170 women. Since the war women have had to bear one of the heaviest burdens on the populace.

The picture sequence so popular in Germany has been developed in the U.S. into what is known as the "Photographic Essay". This seeks to examine, in the style of a leading article, the various aspects of any interesting theme and, whenever possible, to suggest solutions or remedies. To do this in pictures requires wide and up-to-date knowledge on the part of the photo-journalist. He must work up his story in written outline before making the pictures and he must provide detailed and well-written captions. Here space prevents elaboration of the theme.

Fig. 2: War widows take over the duties of the absent head of the family. They are now the bread-winners and must provide for the support and education of their children.

that it depicts a place or a person inaccessible to the jobbing press photographer.

The photo-journalist must be a good mixer, at ease in all the varied strata of humanity and able to cope with any situation that may arise. At every fresh assignment, at every new meeting, he has a different problem on hand.

Here are a few examples: he may be called upon to make pictures of a film star or to interview a famous bacteriologist; he may have to photograph a simple hard-working woman with hordes of children, or he may need a picture of a certain group of people to fill out his report. Such variety requires the varied approach, the adaptable nature.

But the photo-journalist may also be confronted with a situation which he can in no way arrange or influence to suit his purpose. He is driven to accept the numerous little accidents or accents of an event, as and when they may occur, to give his reportage a quality of timelessness transcending mere hot news value. He must improvise and make decisions inside the fraction of a second. The atmosphere of an occasion is the thread on which his pictures hang together, but the smallest detail, a seeming nothingness, may make all the difference to the impact of a record and transform it into a living, gripping picture sequence. During a tennis match in Cairo, game-set-and-match point was decided by a ball which hit the cord and ran along the top of the net before dropping over. A photographer of the *Berliner Illustrirte* reconstructed that fateful instant and sent his art editor a large picture of a tennis ball quivering on top of a net. It was promptly published.

These examples suffice to give some idea of the type of approach a photo-journalist must have if he is to be successful in his calling. Apart from the ability to see and to compose he needs a good all-round education, curiosity, persistence, and a talent for organization. Outlining the sequence of a publishable theme, drawing up his plan of action for the occasion, must be done long before he is confronted with the actual living stuff. It is important to know what it is that interests the editors of illustrated magazines and to think up the type of story that will stand a good chance of acceptance. In private and professional life there is a steady demand for new ideas. If the photo-journalist can offer people something that is imaginative, novel, attracting attention, he is already half way there. But having taken the pictures his work is still not done. He must caption them in sufficiently racy and informative fashion, sometimes even write a fully descriptive text. Thus he helps the editorial department of the magazine to decide on lay-out and becomes himself a valuable colleague.

It will be evident that relatively few people are capable of discharging these duties of a photo-journalist. Many try to follow this calling, but few succeed. There are, of course, exceptions—especially if a man has a decided talent for photography. Then he can specialize in landscape or architecture, in commercial photography, in advertising, in stage work or in the history of art, but he is already outside the small circle of those who deserve to be called photo-journalists.

The Rise of Photo-Journalism

Not for several decades after the discovery of photography did it become possible to print photographs in magazines and newspapers. *Die Gartenlaube*, an illustrated of those early days, published hand-made engravings based on contemporary photographs. But when, towards the end of the 19th century, it became possible to make cuts direct from the original print, a new calling came into being—that of the professional photo-journalist.

We know from old reports that many a traditional studio photographer did not dare to venture on the open streets with his huge contraption. A demand arose for smaller, handier cameras, and some quite odd designs, to be worn like a hat or on the tie, appeared but were unsuitable for professional use. Since then the development of cameras and illustrated magazines has kept pace and each has often influenced the nature of the other.

These old magazines are too staid and colorless for our tastes. The pictures were provided by court photographers, engaged couples, globe-trotters and amateurs who confined themselves to groups, to portraiture, to architecture, and to landscape. That it had become possible to publish a photograph was itself sufficient inducement, and remained so for many years, for readers to buy illustrated magazines.

The First World War brought current affairs to the foreground, but the single

Fig. 3: Three women share one cooker.
Fig. 4: Women's hostel: the long queue to the kitchen (montage).
Fig. 5: Mothers in employment.
Fig. 6: Many housewives regard themselves as captives to the daily round of household chores.

3

4

5

6

Figs. 7—12: What does the modern man expect of his wife? In our troubled times a marriage is built up on joint effort. A man's wife is not merely a good housekeeper and a good nursemaid; she is also a lover and a companion who helps him in his own work or contributes to the budget by taking an outside job.

photograph—although content was becoming better and more "newsy"—was still an editor's mainstay. Sequence had not yet been born.

But films were becoming faster and made the photographer largely independent of existing light. Dr. E. Salomon pioneered the interior shot and his was the well-known photo-reportage, "Famous Contemporaries in Unguarded Moments". Brüning, Stresemann, Briand, were photographed during their conferences. Dr. Salomon was always just where the great statesmen did not expect to find him, so they decided to prohibit publication of his conference pictures by cabinet decision. But the photographs that had been published in the *Berliner Illustrirte* made these statesmen so popular that they shut an eye to their own ruling.

Hardly a single photo-journalist of the Twenties was a trained photographer. They all began as amateurs and got pleasure from experimenting with their cameras. A new experience had become theirs and it found its crowning achievement in the making of the action shot—life photographed on the run. In 1925 sequence shooting—series of pictures of a happening—became a new outlet for the photo-journalist. It was developed by a team, many of whom are now famous photographers: Hans Baumann, Walter Bosshard, Eric Borchard, Alfred Eisenstaedt, Harald Lechenperg, Helmut von Stwolinski, Otto Umbo and the Chief Editor, at that time, of the *Berliner Illustrirte*, Kurt Korff. A series consists of several pictures of the same theme. On the principles that underlie the writing of a descriptive text it was proposed to present visually the essentials of an event in the sequence in which they occurred. Harald Lechenperg was the first to apply the new system on his travels abroad. In 1929 he took, in addition to a 9×12 cm camera—and much was he chaffed by his friends—a Leica with him to India. He believed that the journalist with a camera must have a more alert and concentrated vision than the journalist with a pen. His efforts to illustrate his copy with pictures of timeless value led him to the conclusion that photography must come to grips with everyday experience. At that time the Leica was the only available camera that got right in. Returning from his Indian tour Harald Lechenperg brought back so incisive a survey of the Indian

Fig. 13: Goodbye to Europe. For many young girls marrying into the New World seems to be the only possible answer to the dilemma of the German woman.

Fig. 14: For older women who must live alone there is often no escape from public assistance.

Fig. 15: Young girls in their late teens can look forward again with confidence to the full life which lies across the protecting barriers of girlhood. For their generation surplus womanhood will be no problem.

scene that, despite technical quality poor by modern standards, his pictures filled the pages of the *Berliner Illustrirte* and a whole book besides. His brother photographers—all members of the Ullstein Verlag which had long set the pace in German journalism—changed overnight to the Leica.

After 1933 many leading lights of this publishing house—among them the chief editor, Kurt Korff—emigrated to the U.S. There, in 1936, they helped to found the magazine *Life*, the most widely distributed and well-known illustrated magazine in the world today. The sequence idea which had originated in Germany was taken over and further developed to a point at which press photography was set an imaginative problem—that of the so-called "Photographic Essay".

Photo-Journalism Requires the Miniature Camera

Oskar Barnack, the genial inventor of the Leica, lived to see the developments described above and followed them with keen interest. Before the First World War he had come to the conclusion that professional and press photographers needed a miniature camera if photography was to be freed from the shackles of the customary lifeless and "posed" picture. In 1914 he built his first experimental model and with it made a very impressive snapshot of events on the first day of general mobilization. Ten years later the Leica went into series production and appeared on the market. But a single technical problem tended to restrict wide use: the grain of cine-film was very coarse and the Leica had many opponents solely for that reason. Almost immediately film manufacturers throughout the world devoted themselves to the solution of the grain problem in miniature negative films, itself an indication that they had glimpsed a future for the Leica. Art Editors, receptive and broad-minded, recognized the true worth of the little camera and often preferred to publish the spontaneous, telling picture although the print was grainy. It soon became customary to regard technical quality as subordinate to content. Coarse grain, and sometimes even camera shake, could at times provide an impressionistic effect. The preference given to such pictures let loose a quip among press photographers: an unsharp or distorted print was dubbed "another for the *Berliner Illustrirte*". The time had come for illustrated magazines to pay more attention to picture content than to print quality.

Today the technics of miniature photography have been more or less perfected and the original shortcomings of the film have been largely eliminated. After

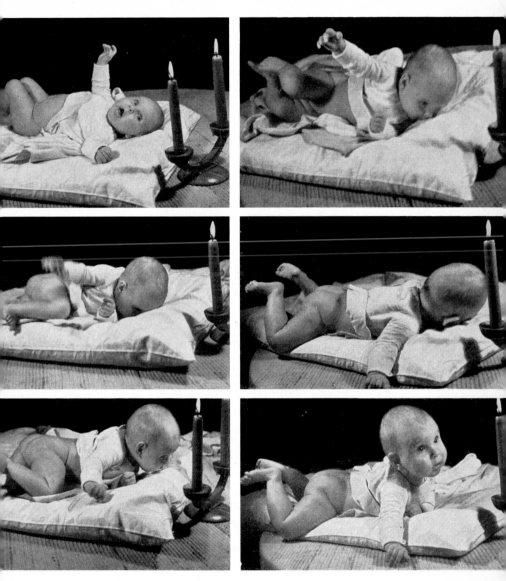

Fig 16: The rapid movements of a lively baby, as rapidly captured on film, are testimony to the eloquence of the picture sequence. They mark the first elementary steps from the single picture to the story in pictures. Stories can be edited as desired to skip a time intervall or jump from place to place to suit the taste of editors or the importance of incidents.

37

the Second World War—and spurred on by the print quality of American photographs—the demand is now for stimulating content *and* good technical quality.

However, the paraphernalia of photography seems to be bogging it down once more. It is not only in America that the photo-journalist has begun to travel round with a general staff (cars, assistants, flash apparatus, even searchlights) and rival the bulk of equipment needed for the old daguerreotype. There is a very real danger of destroying spontaneity. It would be well for the modern feature photographer to consider carefully what minimum apparatus is absolutely essential for his needs. By confining himself to necessities he has greater freedom to get on with the job.

For really universal application the photo-journalist needs a universal camera which can be effortlessly operated in any kind of situation or circumstance. The demand for fast, interchangeable lenses and lightness of equipment can be met only by the miniature. For corresponding speed and range the size and weight of lenses increases as the square, and often as the cube, of the negative size.

Fig. 17: Black Market.
Camera hidden in a brief-case; 35 mm lens at f/4, $^1/_{40}$ sec., on fast film, 128...33°, in dull weather towards evening.
Fig. 18: Currency Reform.
Bad light. Full aperture of the 35 mm wide-angle lens.

Fig. 19: Father Christmas keeps pace with the times.
Speed lamp, 50 mm Elmar; exact image field with clip-on finder.

Fig. 20: Ice-Hockey—the body-check.
Sports shot in poor existing light (outdoor); 90 mm Elmar, f/4.5, $^1/_{200}$ sec., on Kodak Super XX film.

When, shortly after the 1914—18 war, Dr. Salomon published his sensational interior shots, taken with his Ermanox f/1.8—the lens diameter was three inches!—and with a braked focal plane shutter, the day of the Leica had dawned and it took but a very few years for it to satisfy all requirements. The photo-journalist could devote his whole attention to what was going on around him and be free from the constant distraction of attending to the needs of his equipment. Even today the technical possibilities of the Leica have not been fully extended. The resolving power of Leica lenses is still considerably higher than that of the best film.

Equipment and its Uses

A photo-journalist's equipment is naturally more extensive than that of an amateur, but he need not take it all with him on every assignment. Lenses (in their leather cases), sunshades, filters, exposure meter and films can be quite conveniently carried in the four pockets of a wind-breaker without losing track of their whereabouts when needed. In the case of the Leica M 3 the sunshade fits reversed over the lens for easy transport in the ever-ready case, which also accommodates the Leica Meter M in the coupled position on the camera. Since filter diameter has been standardized for bayonet clamp lenses in the three most used focal lengths there is a further reduction in the number of accessories that need be carried loose. Camera bags which take the following equipment have often been found most useful:

Leica with 50 mm. Elmar (or Summicron, Summitar or Summarit), 35 mm. Summaron, 90 mm. Elmar (collapsible in bayonet mount), 135 mm. Hektor; direct vision or universal finders, sunshades, filters, exposure meter, loaded cassettes, and perhaps also an optical near-focusing device.

The Leica in use should be carried round the neck with one or other of the lenses named on the camera. Certain special fields may call for additional equipment. For sports photography or the photography of wild life in natural surroundings, to name but two applications, the 200 mm. Telyt will bridge distance and shoot in rapid sequence, especially when used with the Leica M 3 and its rapid lever wind for film and shutter transport.

That the camera reporter can manage with a modicum of equipment was demonstrated immediately after the Second World War. Many photographers had nothing more than a single—often borrowed—Leica with but a solitary additional lens, yet they managed to get some very gripping pictures.

Often there are situations when it is better to pass off as just another spectator and to have the camera ready for action under the coat or jacket. Many a telling snapshot has been made in this way when the obvious approach was impossible; often with the camera lens just peeping through a button-hole or else held on high with both hands and aimed with faith and hope. On such occasions the 35 mm. wide-angle lens is always a splendid stand-by which seldom fails to get a good picture, even when incorrectly set (for focus or framing). The Leica has also proved its value at social gatherings and in providing so-called "society" material in circumstances which would preclude the possibility of a press man with his miscellaneous assortment of "hardware" escaping notice. How much easier to use the f/1.5 Summarit with fast film—a combination that preserves the atmosphere of a room in existing light, surpassing by far in accent and quality the flatness of flash. A practised photographer will know how to expose at slow speeds from $^1/_{10}$ sec. down to even half-a-second at just those instants when the camera is steady between pulse beats. It is the short focal length of the miniature lens that beats the difficulties of unfavorable light, and at an aperture of f/1.5 it is possible by careful selection of picture area to avoid the limitations of small field depth. The relatively great depth of field in short focus lenses tends at times to make the subject appear as if "stuck to the wall". With two simple actions (open up the lens and reduce shutter speed) it is possible in most cases to achieve a satisfactory separation of the subject from the backdrop.

Before the miniature became known in America, reporters over there made their pictures with large cameras fitted with flash. On the occasion of a Presidential Reception given by President Roosevelt all the press photographers armed with flash awaited the signal to shoot since it was forbidden to disturb the proceedings by flashing during them. During the wait the photographer McAvoy made with his Leica, and against strong light, a series of shots which mirrored the occasion and which President Roosevelt later described as his favorite pictures. They became so sensational that press colleagues demanded the ban of the miniature at White House occasions on the grounds that the competition was "unfair". Leonard McCombe, one of the best known *Life* photographers, is forbidden, by contract, to use flash. In many difficult situations the miniature camera offers him the only means of abiding by these terms. But do not think that flash is always to be avoided. There are occasions (out of doors at night) where only flash can make visible much that even the eye could not detect. Here the light weight of the Leica is an asset because it is possible to serve the camera with one hand while the other, in the absence of an assistant, holds the flash-head out at arm's length (important when long focal lengths are used). Modeling is improved and the impression given that the picture was made by existing light. Ideally, of course, two flash-heads should be used and positioned like modeling lights to preserve a natural effect. A long synchronizing cable is needed. The easy transport of Leitz synchro-flashguns for use with the f series Leica and the Leica M 3 is ideal for such work. Even the bulbs can be carried with them in the pockets.

For theater, stage, and circus photography under arc-lights, free-hand work from the auditorium presents no difficulty because actions like leaps and somersaults can be shot at $^1/_{200}$ and even $^1/_{500}$ sec. The best lens for this purpose is the very fast Summarex because of its long focal length.

What the Photo-Journalist Expects of his Camera

No one has yet invented a pair of spectacles which, by pressing a button, will take a photograph of what the eyes see through them. But the Leica comes closest to this desirable state of affairs. With finder to the eye the picture area is clearly seen. With the Leica M 3 both eyes can remain open, observing action before it enters and after it leaves the bright line frame. The built-in finder serves all the main focal lengths and compensates automatically for parallax. Lever-wind and release button are operated by right thumb and forefinger while the lens is focused by the left hand—adjustments which are made without interfering with the line of sight or distracting attention from the subject.

Interchangeable lenses – quick-change bayonet mounts for the Leica M 3 – make the photographer independent of standpoint. Lightness of weight with simplifield controls and all settings visible from above, fast and slow shutter speeds on a single dial, very rapid film wind and several dozen exposures to a loading are essential for fast, unimpeded photography. The Leica has always come closest to the ideal and now that the Leica M 3 has made its début the photo-journalist has a camera which is even easier and quicker to operate.

What the Leica Expects of the Photo-Journalist

Quick and reliable as the Leica is, it also demands something of the photographer. Often enough the camera falls into the hands of people—especially amateurs—who will not take the trouble to handle it correctly. The photo-journalist approaches it from a rather different angle but the vast differences in the quality of Leica pictures reaching editors' desks are pointers to the different capabilities of different Leica users.

There is the press man who is heavy-handed and "snatches" the release—but the Leica must be held steady like a gun and the release, like the trigger, must be gently squeezed. When movement is very fast the camera can be panned. This blurs the background and gives an impression of great speed. But to handle the Leica as it should be handled when things are happening quickly and must be followed with equal speed, it is essential that the photographer should be familiar with the camera and able to make all adjustments without having to think about them.

There are some who still send their editors coarse-grained prints but with modern medium speed film there is no need to have graininess. An 8×10 in. Leica enlargement should be indistinguishable from a print made from a large negative. The prerequisite is that the Leica negatives should be exposed and processed with care. Exposure, developer temperature, and duration of development are strictly interdependent, notwithstanding the greater latitude of many modern films. Standardize procedure: the only variables are the stop and shutter speed; everything else should be kept reasonably constant. There are exceptions to the rule but they apply only to poor existing light exposures and to negatives exposed to speed flash. In both these cases it is generally necessary to prolong development, but without increasing temperature. Developer solutions should not be worked to death. It is preferable to bear the slight extra cost of discarding early than risk bad negative quality. Finally, miniature films should be kept scrupulously clean.

These are all considerations which should suggest themselves so it cannot be said that work with the Leica calls for any special care. If these few steps are taken the Leica will more than repay such attention to detail. Clean, methodical work will bring success, which depends as much on the man as on his Leica camera.

The Leica Portrait

by Hans Saebens, GDL, Worpswede *

IT IS THE YOUNG photographer who turns to the Leica with serious intent. Times change, new ideas and new people come to the fore, but the experience of the older generation is not without its own validity. It is not the size of the negative or the size of the camera which conditions success but simply the ability of the man who uses the tool. Miniature work requires an agile mind and considerable imagination. Being a fruitful field for the new idea and the new approach, criticism of subject matter should be strict and standards of technique high. To the careful observer of developments in camera and film production it is clear that the technique of using the miniature is much more subtle than that required for larger negative sizes. The camera is no toy merely because it is small. The small negative also requires the serious approach and the careful thought that is bestowed on larger sizes. But miniature photography is even more exacting because all the negatives must be developed together in a single strip and cannot later be individually treated—a point that must be weighed before the exposure is made. Since the interdependence of exposure and processing has been fully discussed elsewhere it is unnecessary to repeat good advice already given. Let us only stress two points: cleanliness and precision. A processing temperature of 65° F means just that, and not 66° F; a processing time of five minutes means exactly 300 seconds and not five minutes and a half.

In portraiture the photographer should make an essential likeness of a sitter; clear, yet without whatever obvious defects of line or feature or expression a face

---

* GDL = Gesellschaft Deutscher Lichtbildner or Society of German Photographers, roughly equivalent to F. P. S. A. or F. R. P. S.

Picture on p. 44: Father Keetmann.
Photo: Toni Schneiders, for data see text.

may present. To do this in professional portraiture is not always an easy task. The largeness or smallness of the camera is of no importance, though the Leica has the advantage of making a quick series of exposures possible. A few quiet words, a sudden question, a well-timed call, bring about fleeting changes in expression, all of which are just as quickly captured. The contact prints examined under a strong reading glass clearly reveal the negatives suitable for enlargement.

Making occasional pictures of friends, who willingly co-operate, is one thing. It is quite another to be confronted with complete strangers for twenty minutes or so at a time. Every portrait photographer develops his own methods of breaking through shyness and putting his sitters at ease. His methods are peculiar to himself, conditioned by his own temperament and approach, so no rules of procedure can be given. The portraits we see in advertisements, in magazines, in books, are all specially made with a particular object in mind. They are not to be classed as everyday portraiture. The models are carefully selected for their photogenic looks and invited to sit—often even paid a fee. It may occasionally be possible to produce similar work on the commission of a private sitter, but by and large it is unlikely.

The portrait "Father Keetmann" by Toni Schneiders gives an excellent indication of the precision of Leica portraiture. (135 mm. Hektor, f/9, $\frac{1}{2}$ sec., 32...27°, stand, windows right and left, one 500 W. photoflood angled from above front to brighten shadows.) For skin texture the picture is a treat, and it is precisely this that is required in such a portrait. But we do not always want it so. For a male head showing character this portrait does it very well. But Toni Schneiders would use a different approach to the portrait of a lady.

In the portrait of a young girl by Helga Meyer the degree of sharpness is quite sufficient. (85 mm. Summarex, f/5.6, $\frac{1}{4}$ sec., 32...27°, stand, two 500 W. photofloods.) Here it would be undesirable to show every pore. It would destroy the delicacy of the picture. The treatment is simple, the pose effective and the lighting good.

Picture on p. 47: Portrait of a young woman.
Photo: Helga Meyer, for data see text.

Picture on p. 48: Prof. L. Böhler of Vienna.
Photo: L. Rübelt, GDL, for data see text.

Picture on p. 49: The painter Hermann A. Raddatz.
Photo: Hans Saebens, GDL, for data see text.

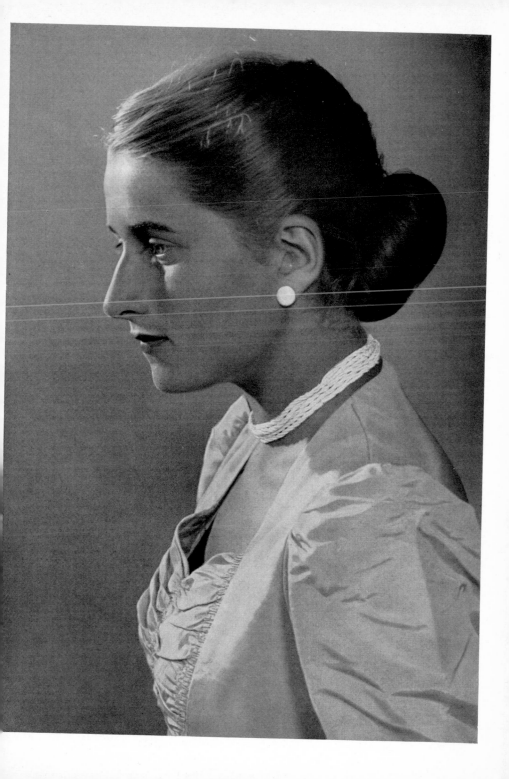

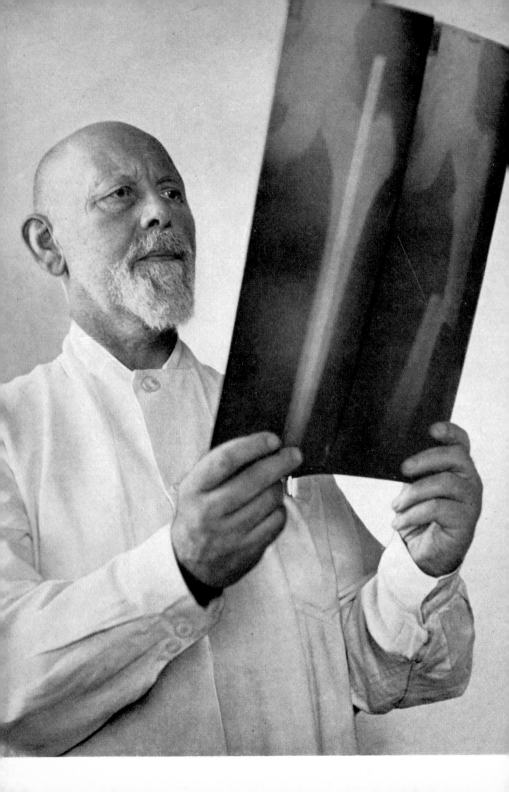

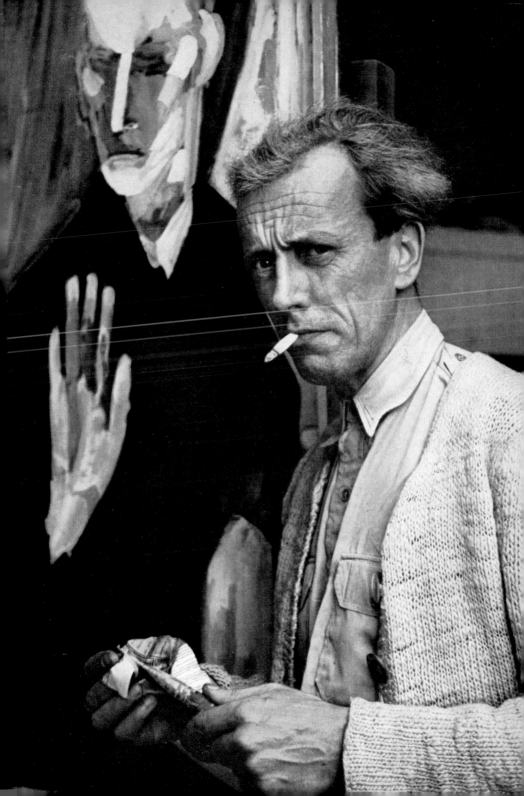

Lothar Rübelt's telling picture of Prof. Böhler is a typical 50 mm. focal length portrait taken near a window. (50 mm. Summitar, f/2.8, $^1/_{10}$ sec., 32...27°, free hand.) The relatively restricted depth of field has been used for the face, and the softening of focus towards the hands does not detract from the effect. The attitude of concentration is a good one, the lines have been well managed and the dark and light masses well disposed.

The very lifelike portrait of the painter, Hermann A. Raddatz, is quite unretouched and reveals the slight testiness of a highly-strung individual. (50 mm. Summarit, f/5.6, $^1/_{20}$ sec., 32...27°, free hand, daylight through the studio window.) The picture was snapped suddenly at the end of a portrait sitting when the painter was addressed by name and looked up. Not posed but waited for, and snapped at the right instant.

Hannes Rosenberg's picture of a *couturier* is a typical wide-angle shot. (35 mm. Summaron, f/5.6, $^1/_5$ sec., 32...27°, daylight and one photoflood.) The subject is in a completely natural posture, at ease among his circle of helpers who, with photographic forethought, have been positioned merely to suggest atmosphere— a carefully considered composition. Observe that only the principal subject looks directly at the camera. The nine girls are all looking elsewhere. Anyone who can make such a quiet but incisive picture of a group of ten people must have a wealth of experience to draw on and a flair for arrangement.

Oskar Kokoschka is said to have declared that his portrait by Dr. Walter Boje is the best photograph ever made of him. (50 mm. Summarit, f/5.6, $^1/_{10}$ sec., 32...27°, stand, daylight and two 500 W. photofloods.) The fascinating thing about this picture is the observant, somewhat expectant look of the great painter, whose eyes follow the face of the beholder. Although the arrangement of lights and the low camera position break all the rules, the expressive power of this picture indicates what little bearing text-book knowledge has on practical work.

Manfred Hausmann in his study in Rönnebeck on the Lower Weser. (50 mm. Summarit, f/4, ½ sec., 32...27°, stand, early twilight.) Here the intention was

Picture on p. 51: Couturier.
Photo: Hannes Rosenberg, for data see text.

Picture on p. 52: The painter Oskar Kokoschka.
Photo: Dr. W. Boje, GDL, for data see text.

Picture on p. 53: The poet Manfred Hausmann, in his study.
Photo: Hans Saebens, GDL, for data see text.

not to make a portrait but to depict the poet at work in his study. The point of principal interest on the left of the picture is balanced by the objects on the right.

Those desirous of depicting the subjects of portraiture in fairly wide and well arranged surroundings would use one of the 50 mm. focal lengths, either the 50 mm. f/3.5 Elmar or the 50 mm. f/2 Summicron. More often the 90 mm. Elmar f/4, or the 85 mm. Summarex f/1.5 will be preferred because these miniature focal lengths have proved themselves most suitable for portraiture and the subtle emphasis of detail. Used with the Leica M 3 the framing of the 90 mm. Elmar is very much clearer, the image is almost in natural size and parallax is under automatic control. With the somewhat shorter focal length of the very fast Summarex lens, overall definition is considerably greater at medium apertures. At maximum lens opening skin texture is clearly revealed in the plane of focus with a delightful blending of the whole picture area so characteristic of this very fine Leitz lens. This subtle blending is so fine that it is lost in reproduction and visible only in the photographic print. Of recent years the 135 mm. Hektor f/4.5 has been increasingly used in portraiture, preferably in its short mount with the ground glass screen of the Visoflex housing. As with the 200 mm. Telyt f/4.5 an upright ground glass image, laterally correct if the pentaprism magnifier Peego is used, makes this a very attractive combination for portraiture in color. Used with the Leitz focusing bellows the range of the 135 mm. lens is extended from infinity down to 1:1 reproduction: one of the widest ranges in the Leica System. The popularity of these long focus lenses with ground glass screens is based on their success in portraiture. Leitz have, therefore, introduced a new Hektor lens of 125 mm. focal length and relative aperture as high as f/2.5 for use exclusively with the ground glass focusing screen of the Visoflex housing. This lens is supplied in short mount only and cannot be used direct on the camera. Its large aperture is, of course, an added advantage in portraiture.

In miniature photography the full utilization of frame size was never given sufficient attention until the use of long focal lengths with ground glass screens made it a matter of common practice, and of considerable ease, to fill the frame to the full.

The use of the long focal length in portraiture—with or without ground glass screens—solves the problem of backgrounds because the image is large and focus falls off rapidly behind. With 90 mm. and 50 mm. focal lengths a good background is essential to the success of the picture. It cannot be too quiet.

A 100 W. lamp behind the sitter and aimed at the background will provide the necessary impression of distance from the figure.

For studio portraits, where the level of illumination may be 1500—2000 W., the exposure for a film rated at 32...27° would lie between $\frac{1}{4}$ and $\frac{1}{10}$ sec., according to stop selected. A stand would be used. Whenever long-focus lenses are used for portraiture there is always a greater risk of camera shake and focus is more critical. It is, therefore, necessary to use a really rigid stand equipped with a smooth-working ball and socket head to permit accurate adjustment or unimpeded movement of the miniature camera. When portraits are made with speed lights at least two flash heads will be needed to provide satisfactory modeling of the subject. The Leica can then be used free hand. A synchronizing lead at least 20 feet long will allow the necessary freedom of movement. For portraiture by speed light the flash heads should not be aimed at the sitter. Reflect the light off white screens suitably placed. One of these acts as the main light and the other as the fill-in. Hardness is thus avoided. In England, Langham studio equipment as used by the London Polytechnic can be supplied to order with as many as five flash heads. Built-in modeling lights make the positioning of the flash heads a simple matter. This method is particularly suited to child portraiture and to fast color work. With f models having red synchro-dials, and with the M 3, shutter speeds are as high as $\frac{1}{50}$ sec. with studio speed lamps.

Leica portraits should be enlarged onto smooth matt or fine luster surfaces. Glossy surfaces are good advertisements for clean workmanship but they are unsuitable for knifing. Straight, unspotted enlargements will seldom satisfy the discerning client. Small blemishes caused by enlarged specks of dust must often be spotted out; skin blemishes may need beautifying; wrinkles may need subduing or complete removal. Women over forty do not as a rule have their portraits done in order to display the ravages of time. Some careful retouching of the throat, of the corners of the mouth and around the eyes will always be necessary. It needs but a few touches of the knife to soften folds in the skin and make the print more acceptable or pleasing. By retouching we do not mean the uniform spraying of a coat of paint over the face to produce those dead pan female visages so popular in some quarters. On the other hand, reality is sometimes harsh and there is little point in producing portraits which please no one. But there are faces—even among women—in which every crease or wrinkle tells of character. None of these should be removed. The experienced portrait photographer will know where to draw the line in these matters. He will also know what can be softened by careful positioning of his lights and just where retouching will be unavoidable. Good retouching is a matter of patience but the difference between a straight print and a retouched Leica portrait, clean and spotless, is convincing enough. With spots and blemishes removed, treating the surface with colorless wax or varnish will hide all trace of spotting and knifing and lend richness to the blacks. Such a portrait well mounted survives the most critical inspection.

Leica Photography in Advertising and Commerce

by Fritz Brill, GDL, Hofgeismar

THE SCOPE of Leica photography in advertising and commerce is certainly not restricted nor confined. It has many technical possibilities which are a constant incentive to perform and fulfil the high standards expected in commercial practice. The nature of commercial and industrial work demands that photography must be both versatile and accurate: it is the function of such photographs to emphasize quality. But beyond this, commercial photography sets a premium on the new idea and the original approach. The commercial photographer must have a progressive outlook. He must be conversant with the most recent technical advances in photography and he should be able to suggest to photographic manufacturers what improvements may be needed to fill gaps he might find.

Such being the case it is no wonder that the Leica, with its deceptively easy universal applications, should be at the center of discussion whether its use in commercial photography is an advantage or not. The question is sometimes elevated to the status of a problem by those who habitually associate first-class print quality with large camera sizes. It would be idle to pursue that subject here. The fundamentals of commercial photography are a host of individual problems which defy any standard classification, so it would be wrong to come down in favor of any given negative size. It is curious that in the many discussions about camera sizes no mention is ever made of the correct use of lights. The pictures selected to illustrate this chapter were chosen because of the specially difficult photographic problems posed by the subjects. They demonstrate quite conclusively that the correct management of lights is far more important than the negative size.

One of the more serious pitfalls for the commercial photographer is the fact that his pictures reach the public they are meant to impress or to entice only in the form of a printed reproduction. He must assess his work not from the origi-

Fig. 1: The Straight Record

With this record shot of two hygrometers we have an example of the type of surface which causes great difficulty in work that is not retouched. These bakelite surfaces, moreover, span a range from clear white to glistening black and the fine calibrations on the dials are under glass. It is evident that Leica technique can provide first class material for the engraver.

Bellows and 135 mm Hektor stopped right down. On Perutz Pergrano 10...22°, developed in Windisch W 665. Illuminant: Osram HNT tube (daylight fluorescent).

nal photograph but from the end product, which in every case suffers disruption into the half-tone dots of the printer's screen, with inevitable loss of photographic quality. It is his task to give his originals such a high degree of brilliance and contrast that they remain highly effective pictures even after the deformation they suffer in half-tone reproduction; and this without the aid of air-brush retouching which merely destroys the quality of texture. Such is the highest goal of the commercial photographer. To reach such a level of efficiency it is absolutely essential that the technique of lighting the subject should be completely mastered. It cannot be sufficiently stressed that this lies at the very heart of all photographic achievement.

It is not without importance in the right approach to commercial photography, and in the choice of photographic apparatus and accessories, that one should be quite clear in what fields he intends to specialize. The photographic depiction of wares, that most important handmaid of advertising, requires that an article must be depicted to its best advantage, in most convincing form and without any distracting picture elements. For this purpose the sliding copier for the Leica, with its ground glass focusing, is an ideal component, especially when a sequence is required. Its range extends to macrophotography so that even small objects can, when necessary, be magnified on the negative. In commercial work this can often be a strikingly successful way of showing the connexion between objects and emphasizing in the picture the quality or the characteristics of very small parts. The Leica used in conjunction with the bellows device, which is also very well suited to this type of close-up work, masters such tasks with consummate ease.

Another type of commercial is the functional shot which relates any given article to the circumstances in which it is used. This type of picture is often printed on the inner pages of brochures. Machinery and its uses, or advertising shots depicting the conditions under which a product is manufactured, would fall in this category. Such subjects can vary considerably in size and area. Great attention must therefore be paid to the correct choice of focal length and to the prevention of distorted or falling verticals. The Leica with its extensive range of lenses in widely varying focal lengths will be found quite exceptionally adaptable to such use.

Side by side with these two main branches of commercial photography we have the stylistic advertising shot and the surprise effect picture . The first of these is designed for use without any special explanatory text, but the presentation

must be sufficiently forceful to compel the attention and endure in the memory of the observer.

The effect photograph might be described as a surprise approach to the client. It is used for insertions in newspapers or magazines and also on the title pages of leaflets and brochures. Such pictures are usually the result of executing some novel idea with superb photographic technique. The sliding copier, the adapter for single frame exposures and the flash synchronizing apparatus for the Leica are here the tools for the job.

Leica photography intelligently applied spans the great breadth of commercial work. It distinguishes itself in particular by the fact that the available accessories can be used separately, or together, to vary approach and provide perspectives which are both a challenge and a spur to ever better advertising.

Fig. 2, page 59: The Stylistic Commercial
The objects were arranged to give the advertisement style. The association between the objects is not strained though the glass vase is in unusual surroundings. Appearing with a firm's trade mark or name this picture can be used without text for newspaper and magazine insertions or on the cover of a catalogue. In this picture the nature of glass which, like bakelite, demands a high degree of photographic skill, is clearly indicated by the weight and quality of the substance.
With sliding copier and 50 mm Elmar stopped right down. A slow panchromatic emulsion and an Osram projection lamp. (Data not available.)

Fig. 3, page 61: The Functional Advertisement
To keep the picture as natural as possible this type of functional shot is best made by flash. In the present case the picture is quite a good advertisement for a gadget that not only cooks eggs but also deals with the shelling of them, and it was made with just three flash heads and no other light. Two Blaupunkt "Reporter 52's" were synchronized with the Leica Synchrocontacts. One of these was used for the foreground and another as a side light. The shadow of the child on the background was cast from behind onto a sheet of paper by means of a slave unit (third flash head) also made by Blaupunkt.
Combination of bellows device and sliding copier with 135 mm Hektor stopped right down. On Perutz Pergrano 10...22°, developed in Perufin.

Micrography
in Industry and Commerce

br

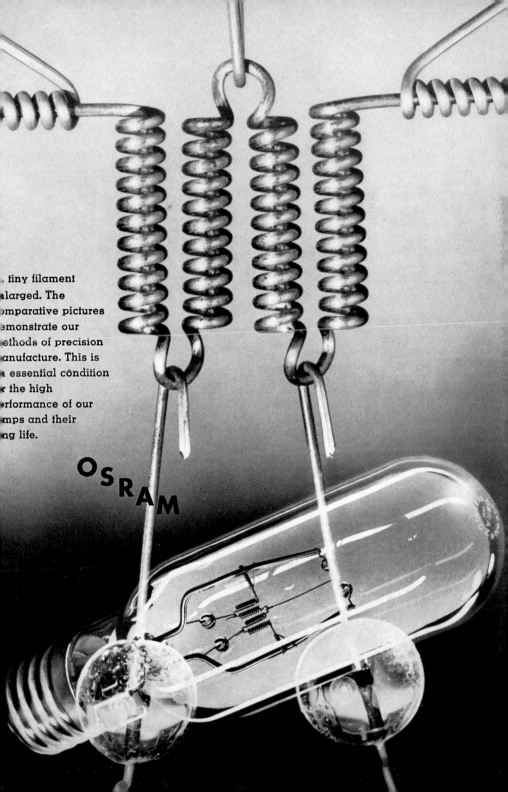

tiny filament enlarged. The comparative pictures demonstrate our methods of precision manufacture. This is an essential condition for the high performance of our lamps and their long life.

OSRAM

Fig. 4, page 63: Photomicrographs as title-page pictures for a brochure.
Photomicrography for advertising purposes demands a very high standard of performance from the equipment. Such tasks are carried out with the utmost precision by the Leica and its micro-attachment "Mikas" used in conjunction with a Leitz microscope. This composite picture was made with such equipment. The color picture on Agfacolor tungsten film is a × 80 magnification of a transparent microtome section of the igneous rock olivine-gabbro as seen in polarized light. It is superimposed on a × 2000 magnification of a pigment smear on a monochrome emulsion.
Monochrome material: Agfa Agepe developed in Faber-Reprogen.

Fig. 5, page 64: Document Copying for the Advertiser.
In advertising there are many tasks and one of the most frequent is the copying of pictures, drawings, and script in order to reproduce copy in different ratios of reduction for a montage. Now, it is not an easy matter to photograph script correctly, but if a fairly steep gradation negative material is used and development is appropriately modified the Leica will be found to master even such work.

The illustration is an advertisement that was made for a publisher by means of a single Leica negative. There is considerable depth in the copy, which exhibits strong contrasts and presents the additional problem of incorporating fine script and half-tone copy in a single photograph. It is a picture which demonstrates particularly clearly the extremely high capabilities of the Leica and its Leitz lenses and is a tribute also to the excellent performance of the Focomat enlarger.
Sliding copier with helical focusing mount and 50 mm Elmar stopped right down, on Ilford Microneg film developed in Windisch W 665. Illuminant: Osram low voltage lamp. Tests with German sensitive materials revealed that Agfa-Agepe film produced the most comparable picture of the same subject.

Fig. 6, Page 65: The Surprise Effect Newspaper Insertion.
This effect photograph, from a single negative, was made by means of double exposure and varying image/object ratio. For the first exposure the lamp itself was photographed at about two-thirds natural size with the upper half of the picture area covered. The filament of the same lamp was next photographed on the same negative in fairly considerable magnification by means of macro-accessories.

The photograph clearly illustrates the fact that it is entirely possible to maintain, with the Leica, accurate dispositions of negative area for the purpose of superimposing correctly positioned additional images by means of double exposures. The photograph illustrates the high resolving power of the lens which has brought out all the detail of the drawn wire filament. Both exposures were made with the bellows focusing device and the 135 mm. Hektor stopped down to f/22 for the lamp and to f/16 for the filament.
Sensitive material: Agfa-Agepe film developed in Windisch W 665. Mixed lighting: Osram HNT tube (daylight fluorescent) and low voltage lamp. Filament with Osram Xenon gas tube.

The Leica in School and Classroom

G. Schmidt, Director of Education

THE VALUE of visual aids to instruction is undeniable. Whenever it is impossible to produce the original natural object for examination by a class, the picture takes its place. Among the most important of such pictures is the photograph, with its clear objective record and great accuracy of detail. But visual aids do not dispense with the old-fashioned requirement of private study and application. The photographic visual aid is rather a means of completing and expanding the curricula of set courses of study.

Much quiet work is done, especially by teachers and lecturers, in deference to the urge to expand their own knowledge and perhaps specialize in given fields. The desire to make records of their researches leads almost inevitably to the use of photographic means. In many cases such collected photographic material becomes a most valuable way of expanding the lecture or the lesson, particularly because it incorporates the element of personal experience and achievement. But it is an aid and not an end. It channels knowledge and reveals avenues for further study.

Not so very long ago opinion was divided on two questions: one of cost and the other how best to overcome the difficulties of the photographic process. Now both these questions have been largely answered by the advent of the miniature camera, with its universal application, great precision and considerable economy of sensitive materials.

When the opponents of the miniature (and there are still some!) point to the extreme care required in miniature work the answer surely is that the need for greater cleanliness and care in school photography is itself of educational importance. The Leica System has the great advantage that it can be expanded, by means of suitable accessories, to cover the entire range, from telephoto work to photomicrography. The Visoflex mirror housing, the sliding copier and the universal focusing bellows merit special mention because of their many applications both in the field and in the workroom. The excellent and time-saving Reprovit has many wider applications but it is a relatively static piece of equipment, although of universal use indoors. Earlier accessories should not be discarded merely because they are old. The supplementary lenses, for instance, are still very useful for certain types of work.

More important yet than all this very excellent apparatus is the ability to track down suitable subjects for photography and to devise a methodical system of follow-ups. Here practice and experience soon teach much, but it really is essential to be fairly critical of one's results and to strive to cover a field as completely and as well as possible. The illustrations in photographic and other magazines are often a useful guide to the best treatment of given themes.

Projection

For schools and universities the fact that miniature negatives can be almost indefinitely enlarged on paper is of less significance than the possibility of making transparencies for technically excellent projection, even in large classrooms and lecture halls. Miniature transparencies can be made for but a fraction of the cost of large lantern slides. They reveal in definition and fineness of detail the full capabilities of highly corrected miniature lenses. The popular home projector "Prado" deserves special mention because of its moderate price. Even small schools could easily afford one. Its merits are also that it is easy to manage, convenient to move about, consumes little current (150 W.) and can be used with existing Leica lenses for projection. The VIII S 375 with its three condensers and the Prado 250 with a special aspherical condenser have a higher efficiency because of the greater wattage. They are more suitable for projecting color transparencies onto large screens because color needs a higher light output to bring out the brilliance and luminosity of hue. These models can also be used with Leica lenses, but for details readers are referred to the appropriate pamphlets issued by the manufacturer.

Commercial projection screens are characterized by the high reflectance of the treated surface. To cut down expense screens can, if need be, be home made, but their reflectance will not be so high.

The screened image should not be too large. The size of the picture should be related to the throw of the projector and the size of the room. Pictures that are

Fig. 1: Lesson. 28 mm Hektor. Photo. A. Künzl, Reichenberg.

too large are distorted for those who sit close up to the screen and lose their concentrated effect.

Gone are the days when it was customary to project transparencies in long strips of film. Today it is general practice to use the two-inch square glass lantern slide. This also allows individual control of density and gradation in processing.

Geology and Geography

Anyone who is interested in the natural sciences would well be able to use the Leica with great success in the geological survey of his own home territory. Often enough it will be necessary to make pictures of transient phenomena or to illustrate clearly in pictures some carefully prepared find. For this purpose the Leica with the standard lens and one or other of the devices for close-up work will be found entirely satisfactory. Special mention should perhaps be made of the focusing bellows for close-up work. Used in conjunction with the 50 mm.

Elmar lens and the sliding copier it allows continuous uninterrupted focus over a range extending from a reduction of 1:20 to a magnification of ×2.5.Used with the 135 mm. Hektor and Visoflex housing the bellows device permits continuous and uninterrupted focus from ∞ to 1:1 reproduction. Since differences of hue are often important in the study of geological specimens, the use of color film is strongly recommended.

Geological investigations form a basis for the understanding of the geographic landscape picture and the nature of the country-side it depicts. It might well prove a very pleasant and instructive occupation to seek to illustrate by means of photographs how the shapes of living organisms, or the distribution, depth and position of stretches of water are strongly influenced by geological conditions, which also largely determine the nature and extent of human occupation of a country-side. Watersheds and ravines, evidences of volcanic activity, erosion, outcrops of rock, country rising in terraces, moors and boulder-fields, moraines and other relics of the Ice Age—all these are most instructive subjects which, if photographed on outings and excursions, provide the material for piecing together a picture of the local terrain. They relate it to the wider country-side and lead to what is really a true picture of the landscape. Lest this should be but the technical product of an unthinking lens it behoves one not merely to isolate form but to depict it in relation to the factors which conditioned a particular formation. Thus it happens that mere technique is vanquished by its own laws and a picture is created which, when enlarged, would look well on the wall of a classroom. For such pictures it will often be found desirable to use a lens of long focal length (135 mm. Hektor or 200 mm. Telyt). A satisfactory separation of planes and reasonably correct rendering of skies sometimes present difficulties, particularly in flat country, which are overcome by intelligent use of yellow filters.

The aspect of a country-side is very considerably influenced by the nature and distribution of flora, and especially of forest. Experience has shown that classes conducted on the spot by qualified forestry experts, who conduct school children over wooded estates and explain their own duties, have always been of great interest to the sons and daughters of city-dwellers. To keep such interest alive there is really no better medium than the photograph taken on the spot.

Fig. 2: Danube gorge near Kehlheim (Franconian Jura).
35 mm Elmar, f/6.3, $^1/_{60}$, 32...27°, graduated yellow filter. Photo: H. Wagner, Wetzlar. —→

Fig. 3: Garden-spider (Epeira diadema) lies in ambush.
50 mm Elmar with No. 3 supplementary lens, f/18, 2 secs., in weak sunlight. Photo: G. Schmidt, Wiesbaden.

Zoology

Pictures of birds and animals in their natural surroundings require patience and some knowledge of the limits to which one can safely intrude on their territories without driving them away. It is also necessary to know something about their habits, to know where they are to be found at certain times of the year or day, else photography of wild life becomes a very hit-or-miss affair. In bird photography, for instance, it is as well to know when the birds are least disturbed by the presence of the camera (usually shortly before or after laying), their feeding habits and behavior in different weather conditions, and so on. This knowledge must be related to the best times of the day for photography and how these times may alter in Spring as foliage sprouts and casts shadow.

Bird photography is very largely conditioned by the nature and place of the nest. If the nest is breast-high, as is often the case with the thrush or blackbird, or if it is on the ground (redbreast, tree-pipit, wood-lark, etc.), it will be possible to work with the optical near-focusing device "Nooky". But since the camera

Fig. 4: Song-thrush at nest. 200 mm Telyt with mirror reflex housing, f/6.3, $^1/_{60}$ sec., in weak sunlight from about 12 feet. Photo: G. Schmidt, Wiesbaden.

must be fairly close to the subject (as near as 20 inches in the case of some small song birds), good camouflage must be provided for both camera and stand. Such blinds are simple to make by erecting a small tent of drab material around the camera and fastening it with press-studs. Openings are left for the lens and camera controls, but since lens reflections are often very disturbing to the birds it is as well to provide a longish cardboard tube which fits over the lens mount and also acts as a sunshade, but without intruding on the field of view. The tent should be equipped with external loops or netting for holding twigs and foliage in position, so giving the blind a natural appearance. Such an erection should be fairly stable even in quite fresh breezes and with careful positioning of the foliage camouflage there should be little danger of leaves or twigs bending into the lens field. If a shiny metal stand is used it should first be daubed with matt green paint (a fairly heavy wooden stand will generally be found most satisfactory for this type of work). For ground-nesters the camera can be hidden in a heap of dead leaves or foliage which has been placed near the nest some days before in order to let the birds grow accustomed to it. Experience shows that birds and animals are much less afraid of well-camouflaged apparatus than they are of the presence of the photographer. He must therefore keep at a distance and remain hidden, yet be able to observe the nest through field glasses and release the shutter from his own hide. Long wire-releases grow increasingly less reliable with length. They should not be trusted at lengths longer than about 20 feet because it is almost impossible to avoid some curling or kinking when laying them out of doors. Electric releases will be found most reliable if rubber-insulated twin flex is used and the contacts are always kept clean. For distances up to seventy feet or more the current supply from two torch batteries in series will be found ample. A button-switch in circuit will operate the shutter release.

If the nest is well above ground level in a tree, the Leica should be fixed to a neighbouring branch by means of a special tree-stand or suitable clamp for holding it in position.

Interchangeable long-focus Leica lenses considerably ease the difficulties of bird photography. Since they allow comparable ratios of reduction at greater taking distances, which increase proportionately with increasing focal length, the almost inevitable disturbance is reduced to a minimum: the bird will return sooner to its nest and the chances of success rise. The Visoflex housing used with the 200 mm. Telyt lens is an ideal equipment for the nature photographer. If need be the shutter can also be operated electrically from an even greater distance from the nest, but it will usually be found possible to make a blind in which the photographer can wait with the camera at the ready. This has the great advantage of permitting operation of camera controls, such as film wind and shutter re-setting, without having to betray one's presence after every exposure. It is even more exciting to stalk one's prey with the camera. In covering a given area there may be many a day when not a single exposure is made but the opportunity for observation is ever present and much that is noted will often prove useful knowledge later.

Although it should not be necessary to add that a nature photographer's name should be sufficient guarantee of the authenticity of his pictures, it does some-times happen in this field of photography that faked or carefully posed pictures are allowed to masquerade as the real thing. The teacher should instil in his charges the need for honest and objective work and help them to appreciate the peculiar charm of pictures which can lay claim to be authentic nature docu-mentaries.

Fig. 5: Stamens of a willow (Salix caprea). 50 mm Elmar with revolver head and 1:1.5 intermediate collar, 2 minutes af f/18, illuminated with Monla lamp and opal diffuser. Photo: G. Schmidt, Wiesbaden.

Fig. 6: Muscular tissue in the abdomen of a mosquito.
Revolving stage, intermediate collars, polarizing filters; gypsum compensator Red I. Objective No. 6 with × 10 periplanatic eyepiece and ground glass screen; Agfacolor film, 35 secs., with Monla lamp.

Botany

The botanist's approach to his subject differs from that of the zoologist. None the less it should also be his aim to use the photograph to promote the ends of nature preservation. The good photograph will also preserve for later generations knowledge of species doomed to die out.

The world of plants is rich in possibilities for general pictures and close-up views which reveal, as it were, the personality of a flower. Equipment will also be simpler than for the animal photographer. No very long focal lengths will be required. In many cases the standard Leica will suffice but for close-ups "Nooky", already mentioned, or a ground glass screen will be found most useful. The bellows device with the Visoflex reflex housing is particularly suited to the work. Here the small rectangle of picture area on the ground glass screen fulfils two functions: picture composition is simplified and the limits of field depth, even with the lens stopped down, are clearly noted. The frame should whenever possible be used to the full. Because depth of field is important in this type of close-up work it will generally be necessary to use small lens openings.

One to one reproduction requires greatly increased exposure time and exposures go on increasing so rapidly with increasing magnification (see tables in the relevant manufacturer's pamphlets), that work out of doors is often impossible because of the wind. The bellows, by the way, are scaled for lens extension, image/object ratio and exposure factors to be applied, so that tables are not needed when working with the Leitz universal focusing bellows. Long exposures can be made indoors under artificial light. The cut plants should be left awhile to get used to their new indoor conditions, nor should they be placed too near powerful lights.

It is no waste of time to try out various lighting effects, which can vary from the bundled beam of a single Monla lamp to the even illumination from all sides provided by the Reprovit. Various types of illuminant can also be mixed, spot and photoflood, and positions of the sources varied. Quite surprising effects can be obtained with skilfully positioned lights. The distribution of light and shade is really the basis of pictorial effect. Exposure times vary not only with the ratio of reduction or magnification, but also with the color of the specimen and its distance from the main light source. The correct exposure is at first a matter of trial and error, but one soon gains experience. A good photo-electric cell intelligently used will prevent many a disappointment. The outer lens surface should be protected from light falling directly on it by means of a sunshade. In passing, it may be mentioned that the bellows device can be equipped with a reciprocating bellows in front of the lens. This is a most effective way of shading the lens from stray light; since its extension can be varied at will lights can be placed almost directly opposite the camera, if desired. To brighten shadows in a subject ordinary white reflectors made of a sheet of writing paper can be used, but often an even better way is to use a variable light source (rheostat). Backgrounds should not be too close to the subject in order to prevent the casting of unpleasant shadows, and the color of the background should be selected to harmonize with the color of the specimen. A pure white background would almost never be used, while a jet black one will be found generally effective for color work only. For monochrome perhaps the best color for backgrounds is a neutral gray, not too light. The botanists who prefer to compose their pictures on ground glass screens will, of course, be using one or other of the devices already mentioned. The sliding copier might be found inconvenient for use out of doors when specimens are close to the ground and would necessitate a very low stand and a cramped posture. Better by far under these circumstances is the

Visoflex housing with vertical or angled magnifiers for observing the ground glass image. The fact that it can be used only with fairly long focal lengths, such as the 135 mm. Hektor, is hardly a drawback since such long focus lenses emphasize the main subject against backgrounds that are well out of focus. For this reason the lens should not be stopped down more than necessary to provide sufficient depth of field for the whole specimen. Intermediate collars, or, better still, the continuous extension of the bellows, allow bigger image/object ratios than are possible with the lens alone. For outside work a sunshade is always necessary, even when there is no sun! By cutting out stray side light it increases the contrast and brilliance of the image. In this connexion it should perhaps be mentioned that direct sunlight is not always the best illuminant. Light haze over the face of the sun gives a better, diffuse illumination which is particularly suited to the requirements of color photography.

The teacher who is also a photographer will experience a thrill in coming across rare specimens and being able to photograph them, but his main efforts will be bent to the task of making pictures of more usual subjects. This can be specially instructive if the pictures are made to illustrate the specimen as a living thing which must adapt itself to its surroundings and carry on a ceaseless struggle with enemies of the species. It is interesting to observe in this connexion how two separate faculties may overlap because such photographic material is also of value in the study of heredity.

Children who grow up in towns should not be credited with the ability to distinguish between even our most important domestic crops and plants, nor to name the trees in our forests. A photographic series illustrating our trees in leaf and bare, our crops and the differences between them, is instructional matter which goes straight to the point and is not without interest to the teacher, who may find himself confronted with some nice little problems in photography, such as illustrating the structure of an ear of wheat. Here he will be glad of the ground glass apparatus in tackling such difficult subjects, because its range extends well into the sphere of macrophotography. For image/object ratios greater than 1:1—i.e., for magnifications—it is preferable, for optical reasons, to use the 50 mm. Elmar reversed (front of lens towards emulsion) in an intermediate collar or with the bellows. But for those who lay emphasis on particularly sharp and brilliant images the excellent Microsummar lenses are recommended. These lenses are particularly suited for work under conditions where the image size is required to be larger than the object.

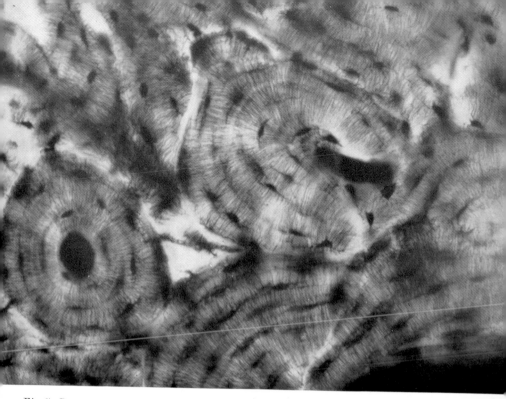

Fig. 7: Cross section through a bone of a cow. Fibrin stained by Weigert's method.
Objective 4b, × 10 periplanatic eyepiece, micro-attachment, yellow-green filter, ground glass screen, Adox film 32...27°, 10 secs.

The teacher finds himself in the fortunate position of combining his work with a hobby. But even in photography it is necessary to work to a system if results are to be consistent. Those who dabble at it only will not achieve much. Finally, here is a thought it might be well to expand: the isolated picture shows a plant at rest in some particular stage of its existence. It is only a mere moment in the life of the specimen and is therefore a very restricted record. To infuse interest into the subject of plant life, to reveal growth in all its vitality and to illustrate how vegetation takes possession of available living space, there is no better method than spaced series exposures of growth, development and decay. The miniature might have been made for this.

Photomicrography

Any rigid vertical column equipped with a dove-tail camera slide and rack and pinion fine focusing adjustment which remains always in the position set by hand (the Leitz Aristophot is such a column) will be needed. It should, further, have some means of positioning a variable condenser system or microscope on the base plate beneath the camera. A rotating object stage is a convenience in ordinary use and a necessity for work in polarized light. Even better is a mechanical revolving stage, and any of the simple screw-on types will be found quite satisfactory for most purposes. A ground glass focusing device will be needed and the choice of type is a matter of personal preference. I favor the light sliding copier. This is fitted to an upright column with removable base plate and is fixed to the microscope by means of a conical intermediate collar which makes a light-tight join. To ensure constant conditions of exposure a special microscope lamp is used (Leitz universal lamp "Monla"). Should there be interference from the grain pattern of the ground glass screen, a light smear of varnish or thin oil will reduce it almost to vanishing point. Focusing should be controlled over the whole area of the ground glass screen and not merely by means of the aerial image seen on the clear glass center section. With such apparatus exposure technique is very simple. The microscope is positioned on the base plate in a manner which allows it to accept the tubular end of the conical intermediate collar. To view the microscope image with the eye the sliding copier with intermediate collar is raised up on the column and swung to one side. When examining the microscope image attention should be paid to correct centering of condensers, if these are being used, and to even illumination of the entire field of view at the desired magnification (here the Köhler principle of illumination is of help). With low power objectives it may be necessary to remove the front lens of the condenser system, or even to dispense with the entire condenser system under certain circumstances (if Microsummars are used). With microscope objectives of designation 3b and above a periplanatic eyepiece should be used to lessen curvature of field*. When the parts of the preparation to be recorded are correctly positioned on the object stage and sharply focused, the sliding copier is swung back over the microscope and lowered onto it to make the light-tight join. Before focusing the image on the ground glass screen check that the tube of the conical adapter is in the right position. It must be right up against the microscope stop provided, if the image as seen and focused on the ground glass screen is

---

* Since this text was written Leitz have announced the production of a new Flat Field microscope objective.

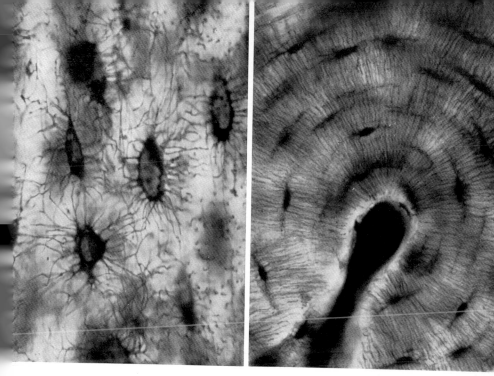

Fig. 8   *Fig. 9*

Fig. 8: Cow bone: individual cells and intercellular structure. Fibrin stained by Weigert's method. ¹/₁₂″ oil immersion, × 4 periplanatic eyepiece, micro-attachment, yellow-green filter, ground glass screen, Adox film 32...27°, 25 secs.

Fig. 9: Cow bone: cross section of a single osteoblast. Fibrin stained by Weigert's method. Objective ¹/₇″ Fl., × 4 periplanatic eyepiece, micro-attachment, yellow-green filter, ground glass screen, Adox film 32...27°, 15 secs.

to be sharply recorded in the film plane. When using powerful microscope objectives with the sliding copier and without the lateral eyepiece and special micro-adapter (see below) the hand should not be rested on the sliding copier while exposing. Bearing this in mind it will be found that the manual adjustments are quite simple and applicable also to other types of ground glass focusing screen. The only real difficulty is to determine the correct exposure time, but because of the shorter traverse of the image forming rays to the film plane (square law) the exposure for the Leica size will be considerably less than for plate cameras. No rules of thumb can be given because of the many variables in various types of work. It is therefore advisable to keep records of exposures made in order so to acquire the necessary experience for constant quality.

In photomicrography the special micro-adapter, Mikas, for the Leica will be found much more convenient to use than any ground glass screen. Once a few trial exposures have been made it will be seen that very rapid work can be done with it, even with living specimens. But the uses of this micro-adapter are confined to photomicrography, whereas sliding copiers and other types of ground glass screen can also be used in other fields.

For record work by transmitted bright field illumination photomicrography still offers considerable scope. Dark field illumination is also particularly instructive in schools. It is perhaps insufficiently known that, in addition to immersion systems, there are simpler dry systems for low and medium power work suitable for schools. The exposure apparatus remains, of course, the same as for bright field.

Schools might not always have adequate facilities for the preparation of microscope sections. More often it will be desirable to view small objects in a natural state and for this purpose it will be necessary to use an incident light microscope. A very suitable adapter for this purpose is the Leitz Ultropak attachment, but even without it photomicrography by incident light would be possible with any microscope provided low power objectives are used, because they permit greater working distance from the specimen. In such cases it is best not to lay the specimen on the object stage, which is often unavoidably dusty and tends to throw back reflections, but to glue it to a small piece of wood or else transfix it with a needle which is used to hold the specimen in position against a matt dark background. In this way disturbing shadows cast by incident side light can be avoided in the picture area. The illuminant would be the Monla lamp which can be adjusted to throw a beam in any direction. If dark shadows are cast to one side it will be necessary to brighten them with the aid of a second light source. The limits of field depth are, of course, very fine even for low power objectives, as will be seen from a glance at any appropriate set of tables. In the resulting record these limits appear to be even narrower than when viewed directly through the microscope because it so happens that these particular conditions are favorable for demonstrating the power of accommodation of the human eye.

Many objects cannot be quite satisfactorily recorded either by transmitted light or by incident light. In transillumination they appear as silhouettes, lacking surface detail, and in incident light they tend to give off undesirable reflections. This is often the case with small living aquatic specimens, for which a combination of both types of illumination will often be found very satisfactory. Incident light is provided by the Monla lamp while a second light source transilluminates the specimen. To obtain well-balanced illumination the lights could be controlled either by rheostat, or by varying the distance of the light sources from the specimen, or even by using the diaphragm control. For small living creatures instantaneous exposure will often be necessary, but since the use of very bright illuminants, with great heat output often injurious to the specimen, may prove undesirable, recourse must be had to very fast film in spite of its coarser grain. Often it will be possible to restrict the movements of the living specimen by adopting suitable measures (raising the viscosity of the medium in which it is placed, confining it between cover glasses, or applying light pressure to a single overlaid cover glass supported at the corners on small blobs of plasticene, etc.).

With plants and creatures polarized light also reveals differences in structure with a brilliance that cannot be attained by the use of dyes, even in cases where the details to be made clearly visible, such as muscle tissue, may lie under chitin. The specimens are fixed in neutral formalin or in alcohol (acids or alkalies should not be used) and then sealed in the customary way with Canada balsam. Inexpensive polarization filters are used to polarize the light. The apparatus is set up as for a normal transilluminated record but with one polarizing filter positioned in the filter holder under the iris diaphragm of the substage, and a second polarizing filter as analyzer above a gypsum compensator which is rested on the eyepiece and has a mount for the filter. The respective vibration planes of the polarizing filters can be crossed by rotation. The field then appears in a red or magenta color due to the presence of the gypsum plate. Fibres and vascular structures appear in excellent optical differentiation, varying from blue-green to yellow in color according to the setting of the crossed planes. The exposure should be made on color film without the use of additional filters. Exposure times are critical and best determined by trial. For objective No. 2 with a ×10 periplanatic eyepiece, an iris diaphragm about 3 mm. across, the Monla lamp as light source and a × $^1/_3$ micro-adapter, the exposure time might vary between 10 and 20 seconds.

Photomicrography can quite easily be fitted into any curriculum and perhaps the best place for it would be in the natural history and natural science classes. For instructional purposes the color transparency is at least as good an exhibit as the original dyed and prepared specimen, particularly so when projected, because its effect is then quite impressive. From the point of view of system there is also much to be said for the projection of color transparencies because the lecturer can use these records to illustrate his subject rather than run the risk of spoiling in micro-projection the original slides which often require long and careful preparation. The method is applicable to many fields, such as anatomy, histology, heredity, to name only those subjects which derive from the behavior of living cells, their sub-divisions and their fertilization.

The town child's ignorance of the work of the farmer or the woodsman can be really quite appalling. Photographs of meadow, of field, of wood and their uses are valuable not merely as an introduction to the work of other members of the community, but can be made the starting point for a whole series of questions relating to the structure of an economy or the historical development and hereditary characteristics of a people. For the making of the systematic photographic record in such work there can, of course, be no rules. In some cases close-ups will be needed, in others the long distance lens. But for a beginning it can in general be said that a standard focal length should initially suffice. Used with the Leica it will find many other applications in school work.

Side by side with the record of the life and work of the various sub-divisions of the community, it is instructive also to make photographic records of old customs and rituals, of costumes and architectural styles. Here color film is unrivaled.

Education does not begin and end in the classroom. School outings and smaller conducted rambles over the local country-side, sports days, parents' days, and even the holidays are essential to the mental development of children. They are also a direct challenge to photographic skill and a testimony to the quickness of the Leica.

There can be no doubt that the miniature, once greeted with a tolerant smile, is more than just a refinement of technical precision. The world has opened up to its lens.

To bring the world into the classroom is the privilege of the educator.

The Leica in the Hands of the Explorer

by Dr. Karl Schmid, Rio de Janeiro

IN ICELAND in 1934—it is an enduring regret—I had to do without it. I was faced with the choice between compass and camera.

What pictures they might have been! Volcanic eruptions under an ice-cap. A pillar of fire rising several thousand feet into the air, bursting through a mass of glacier ice at least 1500 feet thick and covering an area about half the size of Wales. In this mass of ice the eruption blew a hole six miles long by four wide, melting every scrap of ice within. Molten lava and boiling water spread out under the ice-cap on a front of some thirty miles, breaching a gap this wide in the edge of the glacier and creating a flood which was competently estimated to be as broad as the mouth of the river Amazon—at least at its height. During the whole of that summer blocks of ice from the disrupted ice-field, each higher than a house, lay scattered about the south coast of Iceland. The water had bored nine great tunnels through the ice-cap and the local children found it great fun to slide through them for considerable distances under the glacier.

I experienced all this without a camera. The visual impressions of the moment were thus perhaps more acute, but details fade as time recedes. This was my very first journey to Iceland and offered a record that should have been a permanent one. But since it was my first journey of exploration I had to decide on the compass—it was necessary to life. Without a compass it would have been impossible to find the way across the ice and the gaps torn in it by the volcano—through fog and blizzard, over fields of volcanic ash deeper than a man's height, and carried by the wind far into the interior of the ice-covered country. In such conditions the compass needle is far more important than a camera, but as luck would have it the compass packed up. As long as visibility was good we kept to route with the aid of isolated landmarks lunging out of the ice-cap, but in mist or storm the needle danced every way, upset possibly by the magnetic storms which accompanied the volcanic activity.

Richer by one experience but with one illusion the less, we roamed in circles for hours and days, almost until exhaustion. Had there not been a sudden shaft of sunlight, piercing at just the right moment the enshrouding fog, it is possible we would never have extricated ourselves from the maze of fissures across that expanse of ice.

In the following year I did succeed in making pictures of another volcanic eruption. I had sold the compass that let me down and by odd-jobbing in my spare time I collected sufficient cash to buy a Leica. But those films went up in a different kind of eruption—in a bombing raid to be precise.

But that is putting events in wrong order. That "dream of my youth" went first with me to South America—on a rough and tumble trip as we later found. To begin with, everything went quite well and according to plan. But we did perhaps take life almost too seriously. I said almost—fortunately we had with us, on that mountaineering and scientific expedition to the "White Cordilleras" of Peru, a few light-hearted companions who remained cheerful in spite of setback and near exhaustion; always, and as it proved rightly, optimistic about the results of that original expedition into the South American Andes.

When the war broke out in 1939 the scope of our travels was widened, the circle of companions grew and interests became more diversified; we joined up with a German film expedition working in the highlands of Bolivia on archaeological surveys of the ruins of the pre-columbian Tiahuanacu—perhaps the oldest city of the New World. We followed traces of the Incas along the banks of Lake Titicaca to the Holy City of Cuzco and the mysterious Machu Picchu. There were expeditions to the source of the Amazon and finally a perilous journey by raft downwards from the upper reaches of the Amazon into Brazil. We had cut across this giant continent, from the Pacific Ocean across the Andes to the blue nostalgic waters of the Atlantic.

A detailed account of our experiences would fill several volumes. Here com-

Fig. 1: Illustrating the scientific work of the German Andes Expedition—surveys for the cartographer by theodolite and camera. The "Cordillera Blanca" is probably the longest single range of mountains ever surveyed outside Europe with an accuracy rivaling that of the charts published by the Alpine Club. The charts made by this German expedition were used recently as the basis of further exploration undertaken since the war by American and joint Franco-Belgian expeditions to the same region.

Fig. 2: In the coastal region. Two old German sailing ships, engaged in the nitrate runs, lying in the harbor of Callao. In the foreground blossom of the thorn-apple (Datura stramonium).

ment must be confined to photographic requirements. On all these journeyings my equipment consisted of a Leica IIIc with 50 mm. and 90 mm. Elmar lenses and a 35 mm. Elmar wide-angle lens. Once I owned a motor-bike—a 750 cc. BMW which was nicknamed the "Fleeting Stag" by my friends. I knew that it had to be filled with gasoline whenever it spluttered to a stop and that sometimes it needed oil. The rest was a closed book and that was perhaps the best advertisement for the machine. Here I have to write about "The Leica in the hands of the Explorer", and much the same applies—I cannot go any too deeply into the technical problems of photography. This for the simple reason that there were hardly any. I bought the film in bulk for cheapness' sake, fed my Leica with it and went about much as I do at home. As a hard and fast rule one might perhaps care to note the following: if you remove the lens cap from your Leica there is little else you need do—whether in Greenland, or on the Amazon, in deserts or by the sea. Is not that also a good advertisement?

But perhaps I have over-simplified. There is climate to consider ... performance to be tested ... manipulations to be made... there are difficulties and possibilities ... But the reader will be his own best judge.

To return to my theme: five times within as many months I lugged my Leica up to the summit of some 20,000-foot Andean giant that had never before been climbed. "Lugged" is the right word. At these heights weight is a telling factor and some have been known to cut off the handles of their tooth-brushes to keep it to a minimum! For the same reason any large camera must remain at the foot of the mountain. I daresay that a fifteen-foot flagstaff could be man-handled up and planted on the summit, but I have supposed that people are more or less normal. In the event it turned out that even under such extreme conditions the Leica performed beautifully every task it was called upon to do. The pictures were not merely for the press, or taken for the sake of the personal record. They had to fulfil a scientific function by providing adequate material for the study of glaciology and accurate photographic surveys for the cartographer. Pieced together they provided a picture of the remotest and most inaccessible Andean valleys—records that were translated into the contour lines of the map.

Fig. 3: Misti—the symmetrical cone reveals the volcanic nature of this mountain.

Loading stoppages, shutter trouble? Not a sign of it. At 65° F below zero it would be unwise to touch any metal parts with the tongue—it would freeze on! Every boy who has ever tobogganed down the Alps knows that. — And two days later? Why, the same Leica was busy photographing humming-birds at $1/1000$ sec., as they darted, with wing beats too rapid for the eye to see, from one exotic bloom to the next in their search for honey.

In the dust storms of the uplands and on the sandy wastes of the West Coast the camera rested on my chest in its ever-ready case, with the spare lenses in the saddle-bag or in the pocket. Grit inside impeding the shutter? It would not have been extraordinary, but I had no trouble which made exposure impossible. Lucky? Perhaps, and I still shudder to think of the predicament of a sudden folding up. It is a wise precaution to have a second body in reserve on such expeditions. But there is no point in coddling the camera, in keeping it carefully packed up against external ravages. The one-piece Leica body, without bellows and other such moving parts, is itself the best protection against outside influences and will stand up well to rough treatment—it is, after all, the whole purpose of the project to be able on the instant to photograph the condor that suddenly sweeps across the track, or the vicuñas—those camels of the clouds—or the coca-chewing native. It is essential to get all these varied impressions onto the film strip—and they would not have got there if this robust little camera had not been always "at the ready".

There is a small point I always recall with pleasure—and not unimportant though it is rarely stressed by travelers. Simple multiplication will tell you how important it can be to the thoroughness of the photographic record on such expeditions. I mean those moments when it is just too much trouble to bother with a camera. With a Leica these moments are reduced to a bare minimum. Towards the end of a tiring day, as one jogs along on the back of a mule, it may be necessary to dismount two, three, four, five times in quick succession in order to photograph some particular feature or thing. With the Leica in the saddle-bag or round the neck, a couple of adjustments—at the outside three—and the picture is there. A few yards further on there may be an even better view, revealing more clearly certain things of interest to the scientist. The Leica is so handy on just such occasions and the economy in film is considerable.

I had come to terms with my stubborn mount on this matter. I had only to stand in my stirrups to get a better look at some view or follow the movement of some animal when my mule stopped dead, as if rooted to the spot. A light shudder trembled over its body, a pause while the camera clicked, and then the next unhurried step forward. That animal got to know just what was expected of it every time I made for the left saddle-bag—the one in which I kept the 90 mm. Elmar. I am still wondering how I could have made a stand fit the mule for a heavy plate camera. With the Leica it was unnecessary and, thank goodness, I did not have to dismount into the rough on either side of the narrow bridle-path where thorny bush rose nearly breast high.

With the Leica—it was a generally known and acknowledged fact—we brought back by far the highest percentage of successful pictures. Was that because it is "ass proof"? And I do not mean merely that mule. I include myself and would make so bold as to include us all! Do I hear someone say that there is nothing to go wrong if you are a "photographer"? Try it sometime at the end of a wearying day, when you are dog-tired and wish you were snugly in bed in your own home.

It is very rare for a member of an expedition to be concerned solely with photography. The scope is usually too wide and the available numbers too small to permit such luxuries. The man who is detailed for photography must simplify—ruthlessly. And yet he must, if he is to get a bird's eye view of what progress is being made, photograph everything—the landscape, the people, their work and amusements, their customs, rituals, methods, uses—everything that typifies, that welds the pictures into a living documentary record. And everything under difficult circumstances, quite literally sometimes with only one hand while the other boils the pot or scribbles the log. In my view it would be impossible without the miniature camera. True, there are many. But why should I pick an imitation when I can have the real thing? Of all miniature cameras the Leica is the oldest, the most tried, the best constructed and, in spite of its captivating beauty of form and mechanical precision, it is robust, has extremely good performance and is versatile in use. The recent model M 3 merely underlines these facts while simplifying and speeding up the means to the end.

My rules—and I am rather proud of them—are: 36 well-exposed negatives on each strip, with no double exposures and no "blind" shots. Depth of field excellent—small wonder with a 50 mm. focal length. Impressive height in mountain scenery with the 90 mm.—the frame utilized to its edges. With the same lens portraits of the natives rich in detail, modeling, perspective. And should one slip into an Indian hut, swarming with chickens, guinea-pigs and children, or enter some decaying monument—then the 35 mm. wide-angle. Where for-

merly explorers spent days sketching ornaments the Leica with its synchronized flash and versatility of application gave quick, superlative records surpassing in quality and reliability those made with other cameras, which are also carried along on expeditions comprising several members, each with his own set of predilections. With my three lenses I had three specialized cameras in one hand. This small camera, which accompanied me on all my travels from Greenland to the Equator, from San Francisco to St. Petersburg, has mirrored the world with vital emphasis. It has kept a chronological record of my scientific work and, side by side with the intrinsic value of the record, it has enriched my own experience and provided comparative data of a kind which molds knowledge and is not without influence in the development of the man and his way of life. Thus it transcends the purely optical function of apparatus made available by the genius of modern methods. For me this lovely little thing

Fig. 4: (top): Condor, king of the high Cordilleras.

Fig. 5 (bottom): Huaca—an ancient Indian idol. Fired and painted clay. From a private collection in Lima.

Fig. 6 (right): A descendant of the Quechuas, but with intermingled Spanish blood (note beard). A native of the mountains.

had acquired a being all its own and it became almost another companion throughout the long years of travel; a solace to fondle in the lonely hours.

But back to realities: To one more technical aspect of expeditions of which neither the famous inventor of the camera nor the present inhabitants of Wetzlar have ever dreamed ... the camera that looks into the hearts of men! It was this way: After a ten hour ride over the burning Sierras we arrived, famished and dead tired, at a small Indian pueblo or settlement. We had not reached the day's goal and had to make the best of what looked like being a cold and hungry night. A small hut was placed at our disposal by the village elders and the curious inhabitants crowded round in a tight circle.

Food!

Have you any bread to sell?—No hay, there is none.

Have you eggs?—No hay, we don't have eggs here ...

Question and answer repeated themselves through other variants. We had aimed to reach the village lying lower down the valley. Here we were literally without a scrap of food.

Dejectedly I began to play with the Leica hanging from my neck, when one of the bolder little boys stepped forward and pointing to the camera said: "Mister, is that one of those machines with which you look through mountains? ..." A Gringo (American) had been there, he explained, who owned one of those maquinas. My companion looked at me with tired, amused eyes ... we could get one over, too!

Jumping up suddenly he pointed at the startled villagers who began to shrink back. "Yes, yes!" he shouted. "That is just one of those maquinas with which one looks through mountains ... and through the sides of your pest-ridden Chozas!" "There!" he continued suddenly, "There! I see that you have eggs at home, and you"—turning to another—"you have bread!" Silence hung over their dark faces and their hunched shawl-covered shoulders. One made a movement towards the door, but my friend leaped across to bar his way and cut off retreat. They began to exchange frightened glances, but my companion suddenly raised his voice to a bellow: "Yes, you s.o.b.'s, if you don't know I'll tell you that this maquina is even more wonderful. With it I can look into your black hearts. And when I do that I find to my horror that there are cattle thieves among you!" (A farmer whom we had met the day before had told us of the thefts and that suspicion lay on these out-of-the-way hillside pueblos.) "I tell you now", continued my colleague, forcing a tremor of anger into his voice, "I tell you, we shall hand you over to the police, and all the rogues and thieves among you will be dragged off to appear before the President. I have only to look into this little maquina to know all", and he threatened them with the Leica held above his head. The men present became uneasy, but Edward's voice continued on ... "But I will protect those who now go home and fetch us bread, butter and eggs". With that he stood aside and let them pass out into the dark night ...

Would they come? We were not at all sure ...

But they did, and we sat up till after midnight before a huge pile of bread, butter and eggs. Oh! You sceptical Europeans, you have no idea what magical qualities your machines and instruments possess for backward peoples!

But let us turn from the metaphysical to the practical value of Leica equipment on expeditions. Are not the modern accessories, such as mirror reflex housings, bellows devices and telephoto lenses up to a yard or more in focal length, all a little too delicate? A South American once said to me: the Leica is a camera that you can slip into an inside pocket, but to use it you need a truckful of accessories. As cracks go, it's not a bad one, but it is just a crack. Accessories increase the scope of the camera and the more you have the wider the applications of the instrument. Not everyone needs all the available accessories and for my kind of work I am most interested in a long focus lens of big aperture for the photography of animals and humans in their natural state. To widen the scope of such a lens, the bellows device with mirror reflex housing are admirable accessories for close-up photography. Thus equipped, a fortnight spent in any one of the villages on the Amazon would provide sufficient material to keep press and scientist amused and occupied for many a long day. In my opinion these accessories are essential to every expedition and they should be kept in a good stout watertight tin trunk of the officer pattern. As far as I can see, not much has changed over the last decade in the requirements of explorers and if the call should come again, which pray God it might soon, to up and off to the Cordilleras, the Pampas or the Green Hell, I should merely assemble the same old equipment that stood me in good stead more than a decade and a half ago, on my first journey of exploration through Iceland. I should take the 90 mm. Elmar, the 35 mm. Summaron and the 50 mm. Elmar or Summicron (now that we have this excellent new lens), and instead of my old IIIc I should take, naturally, the Leica M 3 and a speed lamp to bring sunshine to the dark earth under virgin forest.

For anyone who does serious work with it the Leica today is perhaps even more reliable than ever it was, certainly more convenient and quicker off the mark; and with even fewer accessories now that the M 3 has the vital ones for interchangeable finder fields and automatic parallax correction built right into it. The M 3 is a truly unexcelled camera which accepts my old lenses via a bayonet adapter.

But let me pause for a moment to do honour to my all too quickly departed first Leica. Ten years it spent with me on all my journeyings through every clime and it got its fair share of jolts, but it never once let me down no matter whether the temperature was sixty below or soaring in the hundreds of humid heat; never in sandstorm nor in blizzard. Five times it went to the top of a 20,000-footer only to plunge down again into the tropical heat of the Amazonian jungle. Five hundred films passed through it so the shutter must have functioned faultlessly some twenty thousand times.

Now let me relate briefly the story of my second Leica—a Wehrmacht Leica—

Fig. 7: A raft or so-called Callapo, made of balsa, is swept along by the Rio Beni at a good 20 knots.

Fig. 8: On the way to the Lagune Santa Ana—herds of llama, sheep and alpacas tended by native girls. Height about 15,000 feet. The source of the Santa Ana lies about as high as Mont Blanc in the Cordilleras of Raura. In the foreground, semi-domesticated llamas typical of the Andes.

because "now it can be told". In October 1944 an overwhelming force of American Marines, with ice-breakers and a flotilla of destroyers, overcame the small detachment of weathermen stationed by the Wehrmacht on Greenland's east coast, somewhere in the region of 76° N. Latitude. Our orders were to destroy everything on discovery, but I just could not find it in me to bash that Leica, lying snugly in its ever-ready case, against the inviting block of granite that rose out of the surrounding ice. Instead I found a place for the little treasure in my greatcoat pocket. While crossing to the ice-breaker I could have let it slide under the cold green waters—and should have according to orders—but I just was not able to do it.

On board, and stark naked, I passed through the usual decontamination procedure determined as ever; and when asked about the camera I declared it as my own. Dreadful moment! The enemy had all the trumps but, I must say, he played fair.

A few days later an officer came to my bunk. Barefaced I maintained: "yes, it is my own".

He could take it away from me ... What could I do? I would never get it home again, perhaps not even as far as the Prisoner of War camp.

He was right. So I shrugged my shoulders.

He did so want a Leica. He even offered to buy it from me.

I pricked up my ears at those soft American intonations.

But I had not wanted to sell it. It was not for that reason I had brought it with me. It was just that I could not destroy it. But I had to admit to myself that the man was right.

During those weeks he made three offers. My mind was made up; but what would I do with cash? A dark presentiment arose in me that Dollars might be useful after the war. Since there was no reason to doubt the integrity of an opponent who wished to trade, I made a suggestion: he should take the camera and I would write to him after the war. He gave me his address and I had no difficulty in committing it to memory. If I needed the Leica to make my living he agreed to send it back to me. Otherwise he could keep it and pay me what he thought was right. I, in turn, gave him the address of my cousin in New York ...

Two years after: he had kept his word. And one of the consequences was that during all that time my little boy could tuck into quite a few CARE packets ...

And now I live in Rio de Janeiro with my third Leica—a little changed in profile but clearly recognizable and already a trusty friend. It has done some fine work for me, but neither of us will be quite happy until we have both seen the whole of South America ... as I am sure we shall.

Stalking Game with the Leica

by Dr. Arthur Lindgens

As a small boy I went hunting with my uncle and it was not long before I had bagged my first. Hunting and stalking lay in our blood and I early began to attempt stalking game with the camera. For Christmas in the year 1905 someone presented me with a copy of Schilling's famous book *With Flashlight and Rifle*. It has become a text-book for those who stalk with a camera. Although the equipment was primitive, Schilling made some really excellent pictures. Later many others followed in his footsteps, of whom Bengt-Berg was perhaps the best known. But the photography of wild life, which had up till then comparatively few exponents, rapidly became popular among hunters with the advent of the miniature camera, because here lightness and ease of manipulation were coupled with the possibility of making fast sequences. With a good rifle it is easy to bring down an animal on the run, but not nearly so easy to photograph it. Light, for one thing, is important because you can still take aim in conditions which make photography impossible.

There was always an air of mystery about wild-life photography, but it is really quite straightforward. Rules, of course, can be made—but they seldom apply. Experience is the best teacher and each must pay for his own lessons. It is absolutely necessary to be complete master of the equipment used. Hunting instincts should be well developed and the habits of wild life should be an open book. It will be necessary to know the country over which one stalks. The beats should be reasonably well stocked with game, and luck—an important ingredient of success—will do the rest. The best pictures will doubtless be made from a blind near the game tracks. It is only necessary to take up position fairly early and wait quietly and patiently for the time the animals are known to pass. In my experience the machan, or shooting-platform up a tree, is not the best of positions for photography because, however firmly erected, it is always liable to

Fig. 1: Stag in the prime

Fig. 2: Stag in the rut

sway a little, which leads to unsharpness, especially when a telephoto lens is used. Apart from this, the view is always downwards and the pictures suffer in consequence. I find it best to be on the ground in a well-made blind, which is not difficult to construct. There are bound to be small thickets or a few trees fairly close together. Throw a roll of wire round the trunks and erect some camouflage netting, leaving wide apertures at a height of at least $1\frac{1}{2}$—3 feet. This is important because, when raised to this height, the camera does not take in the immediate foreground, which would otherwise appear blurred. It is quite useless to attempt photography from a hole dug in the ground because half the picture will be cut off by out-of-focus grass and leaves in the immediate vicinity of the camera lens at ground level, or unsharp foreground would take up too much of the picture area. For wild life work it will be necessary to use a long focus lens. I have been very well served by the 135 mm. Hektor and the two telephoto lenses for the Leica—the 200 mm. and 400 mm. Telyts. But the larger the lens the firmer must be the camera stand, because the slightest vibration, such as that caused by a gust of wind, will become apparent as blur in the subject. In spite of its weight I have found that the Askania stand was best for the purpose, although I did need someone to help me carry it.

Those who engage in the photography of wild life are often asked from what distance they can take their pictures. The answer is that modern developments in photography have made it possible to take a picture at least from the same distance that one could bring the animal down with a rifle. With the powerful telephoto lenses game can be photographed easily from distances of 200—300 yards. Stalking game with a camera is a thrilling sport and the more experienced I become as a tracker the greater I find that thrill. Today I rate a good wild-life picture higher than a good shot with the rifle.

But the amount of waste in near misses was high. That was the price I had to pay for the experience I now have. I began with little equipment. Buck and stag were carefully stalked. With a shot I could have laid them low but the distances were too great for photography. I persisted, but the pleasure of getting there with the camera lens was often dashed when the picture revealed the surrounding trees and countryside with the animal little larger than a blob somewhere in the picture area. Things began to improve when the Leica appeared and Leitz made available their excellent telephoto lenses. Everyone who stalks with a camera should remember a fundamental principle: once the game is there within distance just go on exposing without regard to the number of

Fig. 3: A magnificent bull bison (Upper Silesia)

Fig. 4: An old hind with her fawn in the Danube Basin.

Fig. 5: Wild boar (Upper Silesia)

pictures made. Economy of film is false economy, because it will only be from a series of pictures that one can select the single shot, or the few, snapped just at the right moment and typifying the particular animal in front of the camera lens.

On page 74 we have read about the uses of the remote electric release. Here also the remote release, especially when coupled with a flash-head, will be found necessary to surprise shy customers.

I find it pleasant to recapitulate and turn up old memories in my collection of pictures. They come alive much more vividly in the picture than they do by looking at the rows of trophies I have accumulated over the years. The eyes wander back over the Pripet Marshes, through Poland, Hungary, Roumania and Austria. Here there are some pictures of black grouse (facing), capercaillie, bustard; of wild turkey, of duck, of geese; there I see others of chamois and elk, wild boar, bison and stag. Red deer have always been my special favorites. In the course of my stalking life I have made countless pictures of stags; in velvet, in the prime, in the rut. I am often amazed even now to recall in how short an interval of time these pictures were taken; there were days when three hundred or more exposures were made before midday when stalking black grouse or capercaillie.

In the fields and forests of my own private shoot it was always fun to photograph the roe-deer. It was always so peaceful on the flower-carpeted meadows before the stalk began. And what a touching picture to see a doe with its young come out into the open among the flowers, or prance away in graceful bounds when alarmed. They are fairly easy subjects and even the beginner should have no difficulty with a 135 mm. Hektor lens.

Often, too, I have tracked pig; in the snow, and in their mating season, just as I had followed the stag in the rut. On one occasion I was waiting for a magnificent stag while hidden in my blind near a wild apple. I knew he was there because I could hear him call in the forest, but days went by before he appeared. Instead, a tough young wild boar came every day straight past the blind to eat the wild fruit. Just as if he knew there was no danger, he often remained still for quite a while in front of the blind and gave us the opportunity to photograph him from every angle. (Illustration on p. 105.)

In the dark forests at the foot of the Beskids in Upper Silesia I spent countless happy hours stalking stag. Their rut coincided with that of the bison, which were protected in these parts, so I spent many a pleasant afternoon stalking these huge beasts with my camera. (Illustration on p. 103.)

Fig. 6: Black Grouse (Pripet Marshes)

Evenings we would descend into the broad meadows of a valley where the red deer were scheduled to appear. The nights were cold and the days cloudless. Light ground fog formed early on those lovely evenings. To right and left on the thickly wooded slopes we could hear the stags bellow across the valley. Slowly, a very fine specimen came towards us through the mist, calling out the while. It was a beautiful, an unforgettable, sight. (Illustration on page 101.)

At the same season of a different year I was in the low-lying plains of the Danube basin. The challenging calls of the stags were just as loud, but we were eaten alive by mosquitoes at dawn and dusk of every day. Netting, gloves, anti-gnat ointment, furiously puffing pipes, were of no avail. To stay, to flee, was the constant struggle waged within us. We stayed. We sat among the reeds on a low platform erected on the bank of a tributary of the great Danube. Bellowing challenges reverberated on either side. The great stags thundered and antlers tossed. We heard the sound of battle as clashing antlers met. There was a sudden rustling of reeds to the left as twilight faded. An old hind with her fawn began to ford the shallow feeder-stream directly in front of us. The light was going, but with a large aperture the picture was still possible—but one had to be quick. (Illustration on page 104.)

On another occasion in Silesia I wanted to photograph a stag in the prime. These beasts are always at their best before the rut. I built my blind near a good game track and spent many a long day beside it. There was no wind. The beasts could pick up the slightest sound from great distances, and in every direction. I wrapped the Leica body in a woolen garment to deaden the trip of the shutter. A fine young specimen with a good head came slowly down the game track straight towards us; ever closer until he got within photographic range and we were able to make excellent pictures of him. The shutter tripped dozens of times. He grew suspicious and would not approach closer but stood some distance away from the hide for nearly half-an-hour. Changing one Leica body for another was carried out without a sound. More than 50 exposures were made. Then something frightened him—he had probably heard us—and he tossed his head and was gone in a flash. (Illustration on page 100.)

Part of my camera bag in Europe has been published in the books *Wild, Bild und Kugel* and *Sorgloses Leben* (Franck'sche Verlagshandlung, Stuttgart). The African pictures have appeared in the book *Afrika aufs Korn genommen*, a romance of rifle and camera through East Africa, published by Verlag Paul Parey, Hamburg. Altogether, about 600 pictures have been published; but a

Fig. 7: Magnificent bull elephant in the Tana Basin (Kenya)

small part, though the best, of my work with the stalking camera. I trust that this short contribution to the wider theme of this book on the applications of the Leica will have been found sufficiently interesting to encourage kindred spirits who use only the rifle to try the camera as well. Once they have tasted the pleasure they will, like me, become passionate devotees of this sport, which has the charm of perpetuating the simple pleasures of the chase, in fog and wind, in snow and sunshine; and holding fast for ever those brief glimpses of nature from which we compile our records of her creatures.

Photography Under Water

by Dr. Hans Hass

IF WE LOOK down on the sea from a high cliff and observe the great waves breaking on the beach below we might feel that the sea is hostile, dark, mysterious; and so we might imagine that the world under the sea is a dark, unreal one. We do not suspect that it can be sunny, magical. But if the sea is glassy and the sun high there is really very little difference between the brightness above and below the water; little difference between exposure times for under-water photography and photography on dry land. In general it might be necessary to increase exposure by one or two stops, according to depth below the surface of the water. The following rules of thumb will be found satisfactory:

5 fathoms open up 1 whole stop
10 fathoms open up 2—3 stops
15 fathoms open up 3—4 stops

No detailed knowledge of the optical laws governing reflection and refraction is necessary to realize that photographic conditions will vary considerably between high noon and late afternoon. Under water, the changes of light that take place in the course of a day are, if anything, of greater significance for the photographer than the same changes taking place on land. Mid-morning to mid-afternoon, that is, from 10 a.m. to 2 p.m., when the sun is at its highest in the heavens, will usually be the best time for under-water photography. Conditions from 8—10 a.m. and from 2—4 p.m., though not so good, will not be impossible. But outside these time limits it is always gloomy under the surface; what light there is, is very strongly diffused and there is little or no modeling of shapes.

The second factor governing the quality of light under the surface is the nature of the waves on it. Completely placid surfaces will be found only on ponds or small lakes, but the sea is in constant movement. On the rare occasions when the surface is glassy the sun's rays are uniformly refracted and illuminate the bottom quite evenly so that there is no impression of being under water. But when the surface is rippled the sun's rays are refracted into a pattern of light and shade which ripples over the sea-bed. We see that we are under water.

The normal waves of the sea are good for under-water photography because they scatter light in all directions. This helps to brighten deep shadows under the surface. The effect is most pronounced in fairly shallow waters. The deeper one descends the wider and less sharply defined is the refracted pattern of light and shade, and sometimes also of color. The rippled effect disappears below a certain depth and all the light is then uniformly diffused.

In stormy weather the waves roll over the surface at constant intervals. Their passage can be observed on the sea bed by the alternate bands of light and dark periods which might be compared with the sudden changes in the quality of light as clouds scud across the face of the sun, hiding and revealing it at intervals. Crested waves and breakers off shore cause foam which the sun's rays penetrate with difficulty. Under foam-covered surfaces the face of the land under water presents a dull monotonous aspect comparable with the appearance of landscapes just before the sun rises, or at dusk, or under gray, featureless skies.

In addition to the nature of the waves, the depth of operation also governs the photographic quality of available light. If the water is turbid or muddy brightness decreases very rapidly with depth. In rivers or harbors where there is always some pollution complete darkness reigns a fathom or so beneath the surface. But in clear water the loss in the intensity of light is much more gradual and it is unnecessary to make any big aperture adjustments until a depth of 6 or 8 fathoms is reached.

Shutter speed is as important as aperture. A good compromise between the two will eliminate the risk of camera shake but unnecessarily high shutter speeds should be avoided because they are bought at the price of decreasing depth of field. Some kinds of fish are always in a hurry. This decrees a reasonably fast exposure, but it is not subject alone that governs the shutter speed to be used. The weather is also an important factor. In fine weather and with calm seas it is difficult enough to hold the camera absolutely steady because of the slight rocking action of waves or ground swell. In rough weather this is much worse

Dr. Hans Hass preparing to descend

112

and dictates fast shutter speeds. From considerations such as these we find that in calm weather and for slow-moving objects an exposure time of $1/50$ sec. can be given. But to avoid all risk of shake I generally work at half this speed, with the shutter set at $1/100$ sec.

The shutter speed should be reduced to $1/200$ sec. if it is desired to make a photograph of the millions of bubbles that surround a man as he dives into the water. I have often used this speed in stormy weather or when battling with a large fish that has been speared. But the light must be good. For some under-water photographs even $1/200$ sec. is not fast enough. The sudden reflexes of a speared fish are so quick and convulsive that even $1/500$ sec. is not fast enough to freeze movement.

Estimating distance is one of the acute problems of under-water photography. When looking through the glass panel of a water-tight face-mask things appear to be much closer than in fact they are, and the under-water camera lens is subject to the same effect.

The reason is that the refractive index of air is quite different from the refractive index of water, which, in the case of the sea, varies also with salt content and temperature. By carrying out a number of photographic tests I have established that the conversion factor lies between 0.66 and 0.75. This means that the lens distance scale must be set between 25 and 30 feet for an object that is in fact 40 feet away, in order to obtain a sharp image.

If conditions are bright enough a yellow filter is recommended to counteract the effects of diffused light. With color film use a polarizing filter.

The photography of fish proceeds as follows:

I slide up as close as I can, estimate actual distance and convert this to apparent distance by mental arithmetic. The resulting figure is set by touch on the distance scale and it is sometimes difficult to do this quickly enough. The closeness to the fish and the need for a fast shutter speed often result in the available depth of field being restricted to a few inches. It is necessary to work fast. The

Picture opposite: Frogwoman, graceful as a mermaid, glides from one outcrop of coral to the next, resting occasionally or waiting quietly for the fish to come close.

Picture on p. 116: Diver investigates the sunk and heeled- over Italian ship UMBREA There was danger that the dynamite on board might explode by spontaneous combustion

Slender Spider Crab (Stenorhynchus).

Photo: Dr. P. Juster on Kodachrome.

Common Starfish (Astropecten aurantiacus). Diameter 18-inches.

Photo: Dr. P. Juster on Kodachrome.

estimate of distance must be fairly exact, the conversion rapid, the setting quick; and the release must be made almost in the same instant because fish do not wait: they are constantly changing their positions.

Lastly, a word or two about the finder, because this can cause trouble. It is not a practical proposition to use ground glass screens under water; nor is it possible to use the optical viewfinder on the camera because the face-mask prevents the eye being brought sufficiently close to the eyepiece.

I have therefore had a frame finder mounted on the water-tight camera chamber. This gives accurate picture area and cross braces mark the center of the field. A sight behind the frame is equipped with two small knobs placed one above the other. The upper knob is used for sighting when objects are very close. The lower one is used when objects are more than six feet distant. In each case the knob is brought to the center of the frame for sighting.

I must admit that I have spoilt several pictures by bad framing, even when using this special finder. This is perhaps the only drawback of unbounded enthusiasm. I was often very excited and quite unable to keep cool, calm and collected at critical moments when the good exposure could have been made. I have also been fascinated by many interesting happenings below the surface and omitted to photograph them simply because I forgot.

Dr. Hans Hass with a large sea-hedgehog. It looks more dangerous than it is. This porcupine-fish has blunt quills.

Note :

Those interested in under-water photography might like to note that the new water-tight chamber used by Dr. Hass for his Leica camera is manufactured by the AKG Co., Ltd., Vienna XV (Akustische und Kino-Geräte G.m.b.H.). This under-water camera chamber is illustrated below. It is equipped with external knobs which operate the Leica controls. An under-water speed light is manufactured by the same firm.

Aerial Photography

by Dr.-Ing. Werner von Langsdorff

A CHAPTER on aerial photography in this book on applied Leica technique may at first sight appear out of context because long distance photography and miniature film seem irreconcilable opposites. On closer investigation it will be found that the Leica offers not merely a rich assortment of possibilities for aerial pictures, but has already been applied to aerial photography with considerable success.

Since aerial work can hardly be described as a simple application of photography it will be necessary to go into the matter in some detail. Let us get it straight from the outset that making pictures from aircraft in flight is not an occasional pleasant pastime. It is a serious business which provides much useful knowledge and might well be the beginning of further important developments in human affairs.

The idea of making pictures from the air is almost as old as photography itself. Attempts had even been made by Daguerre and we find that practical use was made of the aerial photograph as early as 1859 during the battle of Solferino, and again in 1870 during the siege of Paris. Much pioneer work was done by Tissandier (1886) and Adams (1892), but it was during the First World War that the great value of the aerial photograph was clearly recognized and an attempt made to systematize the applications of aerial photography.

In the nature of things, attention was at first confined to obtaining information on enemy dispositions and terrain, fortifications, lines of communication, gun emplacements and the like, in order to divine the intentions of the opposing commanders and so adopt suitable counter-measures. It also became necessary to apply the arts of aerial camouflage to one's own positions and ultimately to use the aerial photograph for the correction and extension of map information.

These varied uses of the aerial photograph have since been considerably extended. With increasing operational altitudes photography replaced eyesight and it was found to be much more reliable than mere memory of the various observations made during a sortie. It was thus not surprising to find aerial photography being put to excellent use after the war in the surveying of territories and the planning of economic ventures. The aerial survey provides quickly and cheaply all the information needed for the control of rivers and soil improvement, for planning dikes and work on land reclamation, for afforestation and prospecting for mineral wealth, for controlling the growth of cities and the development of new settlements, and much else besides. For example, the planning of the German *Autobahnen* was carried out largely by means of aerial survey. Then there was the surprising discovery that the aerial photograph was of service also to the archaeologist because it revealed to the eye, through the arrangement of shadows and the discoloration of the earth's surface, shapes and configurations not otherwise detectable, which gave valuable clues to the location of ancient settlements, burial grounds and the like.

It can with truth be said that the aerial photograph is now indispensable both to the pursuits of war and of peace. But it is a specialist sphere demanding specialized knowledge. Not every good photographer can count on making good aerial pictures.

It might therefore be appropriate to set out below the most important considerations governing good aerial photography. In all average photographic work the photographer can rely on a fairly wide luminance range and pronounced differences of hue. The difference in brightness between, say, a patch of sky and some foreground detail in heavy shadow, is so great that it is not always an easy matter to span the interval. The aim of the photographer is to record these brightness differences on a negative in such a way that reasonably good gradation is preserved throughout the whole of the tone scale.

In aerial photography the converse is true. Subjects are at a great distance; one might almost say that they are all at the same distance from the camera. Accordingly, the luminance range and the differences of hue presented by the subject are exceedingly small. Moreover, the great intervening distances introduce the effects of aerial haze which, due to the dispersion of short-wave light, brightens up shadows to a point at which the albedo differences are very small. On almost any flight it will be observed that the vivid colors of the earth's

Fig. 1: Constance from the air. Photo: Siegfried Lauterwasser.

122

surface decrease steadily in saturation with increasing altitude. Similarly, the differences between light and shade grow less until eventually a point is reached when a veil lies over the face of the earth below. This is due to the fact that air, in great depth, is not a fully transparent medium, but causes light to be dispersed by suspended dust particles, water vapor and other impurities which scatter light diffusely in all directions.

It is demonstrated at every sunrise and every sunset that the rays of the sun passing obliquely through greater atmospheric distances are robbed of their blue and violet components. The higher the content of atmospheric impurity the redder the sun appears. Because of this blue absorption any white object observed through a deep layer of air appears to be yellowish or even orange in color.

These impurities tend to congregate at the lower levels of the earth's atmospheric envelope. At great heights there are fewer impurities so that here the light is much richer in blue and violet. It will therefore be apparent that the aerial photograph will exhibit less subject contrast when the camera angle is flat. In good weather conditions, especially in the absence of wind, it will be observed that a bluish haze seems to veil distant landscapes—most noticeable when distant mountain ranges appear to be blue. But if we have a warm, dry wind, like the Föhn or the Sirocco or the Chinook, winds which evaporate moisture, we should notice the effects of selective diffraction of the light rays penetrating to the earth's surface. The lower the impurity content of the air the clearer do distant landscapes appear.

Another point to note is that the air, as a turbid medium, must reflect some of the light incident on it. Once again it is the short-wave blue and violet rays which are reflected much more strongly than the yellow and red of the longer wave bands. This also explains the blue color of the sky. We have seen how bright objects lose their blue content through absorption. The effects of reflection are that distant dark objects are brightened by the rays reflected by the atmosphere and so appear to be blue, and the effect increases with increasing depth of atmosphere.

It is instructive to compare the apparent brightness of a sheet of white paper, held in shadow during a flight, with the darkest shadow of a landscape passing beneath. The brightening effect of the bluish haze is so intense that even a

Fig. 2: The Matterhorn. Photo: Dr. R. Mühlethaler, Olten. Altitude of aircraft 12,350 feet.

black rock cliff in shadow a few miles away will appear brighter than the shadow tone of the white paper in the hand.

This is the reason why pictures taken from the air, with no modification of photographic technique, appear to be flatter, more veiled and less contrasty than photographs made at ground level. Such aerial photography rightly seems but a poor representation of the actual thing.

To obtain better results special techniques must be adopted for aerial photography, but it must be admitted that as yet no satisfactory method has been found to counteract the uniform brightening of shadows by the reflection of light from the coarser impurities in the atmosphere. In conditions of poor visibility there is only a very slight albedo difference between the brightest and darkest parts of an aerial view. On such days aerial photography could scarcely succeed, at least not for civil purposes when some degree of aesthetic quality is expected of the picture.

Conditions are more favorable when atmospheric haze is caused primarily by the reflection of light from very fine particles suspended in the upper air. At high altitudes this type of haze is almost always present on clear days. But the reduced contrast thus caused may be combated by the use of filters; principally yellow filters which absorb blue light. This results in a better differentiation of tones in a distant subject, a fact which can be tested by donning a pair of yellow-tinted flying goggles; but the effect on a panchromatic emulsion is even greater because its sensitivity to blue is much higher than that of the human eye.

The density of the filter is selected to match the degree of haze. The use of unnecessarily dense yellow filters should be avoided also in the interests of sharpness. But even in the clearest visibility it will be found that a light yellow filter will improve the picture, even when taken from only a few hundred feet up. On the other hand, it should be apparent that a yellow filter can only be effective when shadows are diffused by superimposed blue light. If conditions are misty and shadows are brightened by reflections of light of all wavelengths, a yellow filter will be of little use. Orange or red filters should then be used to penetrate mist or haze, but exposure times will be relatively long. Later we shall discuss the use of red filters with infra-red film.

Should one have a choice of filters, or of differently sensitized emulsions, the primary factors to consider will be weather conditions and illumination. The principal aim of the aerial photographer is to eliminate the effects of short-wave diffuse illumination. Since aerial photographs are valuable more for the detail revealed than for the correct tonal rendition of color, contrast filters will be a more or less obvious choice. But they must be suited to the spectral sensitivity of the emulsion used. For instance, green and red of same visual brightness can be recorded as identical gray values on panchromatic film exposed through a yellow filter, thereby losing the contrast of color. But the gray values of these colors can be effectively separated by correct choice of filter and emulsion; exposed to an orthochromatic film through a yellow filter, or to a panchromatic film through a strong green filter, the color green would be reproduced in a lighter shade of gray than the color red. Alternatively, red will reproduce lighter than green if a panchromatic film is exposed through a red filter.

Nothing very definite can be said about filter factors because these can vary considerably with the spectral composition of the light or the spectral sensitivity of the emulsion used. They are also considerably influenced by the nature of development. When using Leica filters attention should be paid to fastening them securely on the lens by means of the thumb-screws if the screw-in type standard for all M 3 lenses are not available.

Choice of film and the nature of development are just as important as optical considerations. It would be wrong to use, for aerial work, the same kind of negative material which has been found satisfactory for photography on the ground. In addition to being merely beautiful the aerial photograph must also reveal a maximum of detail if it is to be of any use. This calls for increased contrast in the emulsion used. For aerial photography gradation must be fairly steep, and since it is necessary to keep exposure times as short as possible (maximum $1/_{100}$ sec., and often much less in view of increasing aircraft speeds) the film must be a reasonably fast one.

The requirement that gradation should be steep must not be exaggerated otherwise the exposure latitude of the film would be restricted. This would in turn require very precise exposures which are not always possible in practice. Films of inherently steep gradation will usually be found least disappointing by those who have considerable experience of aerial photography and of the order of exposure required for any given set of conditions.

Since aerial photographs are generally enlarged to a considerable size the film must have excellent grain characteristics and the highest resolving power. Modern aero-emulsions will resolve lines or points separated by $1/_{100}$ mm. while retaining all other desirable optical characteristics. They are thus quite suitable for the purpose though their performance still lags behind that of the lens.

Fig. 3: Excavations in Peru. Photo: Inge Stölting.

Leica negatives enlarged up to eight diameters (8×10 inches) will reveal increasing detail. At greater enlargement detail already visible will merely be further enlarged.

An additional point of importance is the dimensional stability of the film if the pictures are to be used for survey or cartographical work. Variations of humidity, the influences of development and drying, occasion certain dimensional changes to which all photographic materials, but particularly films and papers, are subject. If aerial photographs are to be used for purposes of exact measurement the film must be handled and processed with particular care, maintaining uniform conditions and avoiding all mechanical damage or stress. Most important of all is the need to effect uniform drying of all surfaces. Local distortion of the emulsion layer and patchy drying cause uneven shrinkage. The degree of shrinkage should not exceed the margin of error permissible in the tolerances of lens and camera. It was a great step forward when film manufacturers succeeded in limiting shrinkage of aero films to about 0.01 of a millimeter, and in no case exceeding a tolerance of 0.02 mm. With such films stereoscopic evaluation of results became possible. With plate negatives which, unfortunately, have other disadvantages such as bulk and breakability, the shrinkage error was limited to 0.003 mm. and rarely exceeded 0.005 mm.

With films uniform shrinkage takes place during and after processing. It is of little significance in the evalution of the record because the error is to some extent balanced by the great ratios of reduction possible with lenses of short focal length. It is, moreover, possible to allow for it in evaluation by excluding the edges of the field when examining the record. With Agfa aero films uniform shrinkage was of the order 0.3 to 0.5%. Further shrinkage taking place during prolonged storage of the completed records was under 0.1% for normal temperature conditions.

In aerial photography plates are only used when the tolerances for a given record must be kept as small as possible.

More generally, special films of high sensitivity and small grain are used. Their optical sensitization must be such that they are particularly responsive to long-wave light. The need for this is apparent from the considerations already discussed concerning conditions of illumination governing aerial photography. The use of panchromatic materials of high red sensitivity restricts image-forming light to the longer wave bands while an appropriate filter eliminates the undesirable short-wave radiations. The high sensitivity to the red permits the use of fast shutter speeds despite fairly dense filters and great operational altitudes.

Such films can be used with success especially in very hazy conditions. Used with a dense yellow filter negatives of good contrast are obtained. Over forested country in these conditions and from great altitudes, an orange filter will be found particularly useful. If the light is good but the impurity content of the air high (much dust), light red filters might also be used.

Panchromatic films of medium speed, 32...27°, are also most useful because of their fine grain and sufficiently extended sensitivity, which allows short enough exposures even when using filters. Other good characteristics of such film are the thinness of the emulsion layer, the increased resolving power permitting big enlargement while retaining definition, and the great exposure latitude which makes over-exposure almost impossible.

Slower films do indeed possess a much higher resolving power with finer grain,

Fig. 4: Lancaster bomber with Bostons in line astern.
Photo: J. Leroy, 90 mm. Elmar, f/8, $^1/_{200}$ sec., on Ilford F.P.3.

but they cannot really be recommended for aerial photography because their sensitivity is not high enough, particularly to the red.

Materials sensitive to infra-red radiation, when used with the appropriate red filter, will penetrate dense haze and even cloud which would prevent photography with other sensitive materials. Unfortunately exposure times are excessively long. When using infra-red film in the Leica adjust focus to the datum line marked "R" on the lens mount.

As already indicated, it is not altogether easy to determine the right exposure for the aerial photograph. The exposure determines the character of the negative, but it is dependent on the speed or aperture of the lens, on the spectral sensitivity of the film used, on the nature and intensity of existing light, on the

130

brightness distribution of the object photographed and on the density and hue of the filter. To these must be added the relative movement of the object, conditioned by the operational altitude, and the acceptance angle of the lens. It should be clear that it is virtually impossible to indicate exact exposure values for aerial photography. A point to note is that certain types of soil and surface absorb light strongly while others reflect it. Forests, cities, moors, have low luminance values, while sand, water and large flat plains are very much brighter. It is a common failing to over-estimate brightness. Note also that when flying low, relative movements are much faster, requiring very fast shutter speeds, so that filters should not be used.

Some reference has already been made to the influence of development. It is advisable to use a developer which quickly penetrates deep into the emulsion layer while the gelatin is still swelling. Development must be energetic and the solution should be fresh. The conditions governing aerial photography have not hitherto required the use of any special fine grain developer. Miethe recommends Rodinal diluted 1 : 12 with the addition of 1 grm. hydroquinone to every 500 ccs. of the dilute solution. I have found this method good.

For printing the aerial record special papers are available. They are highly resistant to mechanical damage and their dimensional stability is good.

The focal length of an aerial camera lens is greater than normal. The longer the focal length the larger the image or the greater the height from which photography is possible. Since enemy action can be expected in military aviation photographic reconnaissance takes place from very great altitudes. Focal lengths of twenty, thirty or even fifty inches are not uncommon for such purposes. For photography from captive balloons in forward areas, focal lengths as great as 120 inches have been used in specially constructed aerial cameras. But the very long focal length is coupled with greatly restricted field of view and consequent difficulty in accurate aiming of the camera.

It would be wrong to suppose that good aerial photographs cannot be made with short focus lenses. Much useful aerial work has been done with miniature cameras like the Leica. Here the primary consideration is the aesthetically good picture, such as many to be seen in the private collections of professional airmen. In addition to this such minatures have yielded useful topographical and scientific aerial pictures. Finally, the Leica is being used increasingly in rapid reconnaissance of an area for quick checking against maps or charts. This will be discussed later.

Fig. 5: Olten, Switzerland. Photo: Dr. R. Mühlethaler, Olten.

In regard to apparatus it should be mentioned that the central or between-lens shutter is not entirely satisfactory for aerial cameras because its efficiency is largely dependent on temperature. Focal plane shutters have proved to be better in this respect. It is an erroneous belief that rubberized blinds are less reliable at low temperatures than metal shutter blades. The contrary is true: careful tests have shown that metal blades fail to function at about –15° F. while the "winterized" Leica goes on functioning satisfactorily down to –50° F.

The Leica will present difficulties only when flying at very great heights. The cold is so intense and differences in temperature so sudden that any normal camera would fail to function. Where, on earth, we use a camera at a temperature of about 60° F., at thirty thousand feet above the earth the temperature in summer can be as low as –40° F. and in winter it can go down to –60° F. or even to –70° F. at great altitudes. All camera apparatus must be adequately protected. Simple kapok linings no longer suffice. Camera body and lens must be kept warm in electrically heated jackets, like a flyer's suit. The film must also be warmed because emulsion supports become brittle and easily damaged under the influence of such extreme cold. Since nitrate supports are often used in the interests of dimensional stability care must be taken to prevent igniting the film. Mica insulation has proved satisfactory.

The aerial photographer will also encounter certain difficulties inherent in his calling: aircraft are unstable platforms in gusty weather and they are never free from engine vibration. The motors should be throttled back on a photographic run, and the pilot should avoid the critical engine revolutions which set up sympathetic frequencies in the airframe. The camera is held free hand—not rested against any part of the aircraft. It is held firmly to the body which here serves the purpose of a shock and vibration absorber. It will be apparent that this is not always easy with an aerial camera, although now they are constructed of light metals. In open cockpits the difficulties are naturally greater, particularly because the slipstream is a further cause of camera shake. If it is cold the difficulties are multiplied. For these reasons it is preferable to use light and handy photographic equipment whenever it is not essential to use a special aerial camera. Because of the large number of exposures possible at a single loading, and the easy manipulation, the Leica in flight will bring back many more pictures than the aerial camera. Enlarging them to 8×10 inches presents no problems, whether of grain or definition, and such pictures are much sought for publication in books or magazines, or transparencies can be made to illustrate lectures.

Now a word or two about the different kinds of picture. *Verticals* are always very difficult because of the pitch, yaw and roll of aircraft and the attendant problems of keeping the film plane dead on the horizontal. Even with cameras that are specially mounted and sprung to absorb engine vibration, the faultless vertical photograph is a rarity. But it is just these verticals which are of very special interest, because they permit observation of all the details in an area. In sparsely wooded country the vertical camera lens reaches right down to the soil on which the trees grow, revealing all that might be concealed under their shelter. Over towns and cities the vertical shot locates everything outside the dwellings and other structures in plan form. Moreover, the vertical record preserves the scale of all the details visible, and so can be used like a map. Finally, the vertical angle takes the shortest route through atmospheric haze and will thus sometimes produce usable pictures when the oblique shot is impossible.

Obliques do not require that the aircraft should fly directly over the target,

133

but a lot depends on the position and elevation of the sun. The main drawback of the oblique shot is that it provides no information on what lies behind the objects depicted, or in the folds of rolling country. For the same reason, however, the oblique shot conveys a better idea of contour and topography. But the record cannot be like that of a map. The area shown is not rectangular, but shaped like a trapezium.

For easy identification of pictures and their subsequent arrangement in mosaic it is advisable to include some prominent feature or landmark in every exposure. When photographing from the gondola of a captive balloon, the alternate swing about the axis of the cable must be taken into account. Exposure should be made at those instants when the balloon is momentarily at rest between oscillations.

The miniature camera can be put to good use in both vertical and oblique aerial photography and provides most of the information desired from an aerial photograph. A Leica, for instance, can be used to provide a vertical survey of a large area at little cost. By vertical survey is meant a series of verticals systematically covering an area and fitting each other with reasonable accuracy. Such a record provides a useful bird's eye view of a territory but the pictures are not necessarily to exact scale.

Such vertical surveys are useful for both military and civil purposes. (Quick checks on the state of the land reveal recent changes, or preliminary investigations of a proposed route show up obstacles to projected road construction.) For such work air speeds should not be too high in order to get full coverage without gaps.

When more precise information is required an aerial map must be constructed from the individual pictures, each to exact scale and fitting precisely. This is done by eliminating the known distortions of each photographic record by methods developed for precise aerial survey during and since the war. Such a composite photographic map can have great military value for plotting the fire of artillery precisely and seeking out targets too small for ordnance maps. A rectangular grid corresponding to the map grid is placed over the aerial record, every point of which thus receives co-ordinates. Such mosaics are also extremely valuable in the briefing of bomber crews for low level attack. Since the war, similar methods have been applied to the aerial survey of Africa, and England has been similarly mapped from the air.

For the production of these aerial mosaics the Leica has been used as success-

Fig. 6: Eastbourne Pier. Photo: Frank Coates, 50 mm. Elmar, f/4, $^1/_{200}$ sec., with yellow filter.

fully as the large aerial camera. For altitudes under four thousand feet the standard 50 mm. focal length should be used and the 90 mm. for greater altitudes. The finder should be the sports type frame-finder to allow viewing the subject clearly without reduction. With the Leica M 3 this is now possible for both these focal lengths through the built-in finder, the bright line delineation of field area being a most suitable means of obtaining on the negative exactly what is wanted.

If it is necessary to gain knowledge of contour and height this can be done by means of stereoscopy. Two pictures made in succession are viewed together through the stereoscope and they reveal topography almost as it is in reality. Seen in 3-D it is possible to tell, for instance, whether a forest consists of old trees or of saplings, and whether a gradient is steep or gentle.

Similar information can also be deduced from the two-dimensional photograph by the lie of shadows. For this purpose it is best to make the exposures by a low sun, either near dawn or dusk. During the war aerial photography by night became commonplace. Flares dropped by parachute were used as the illuminant and experiments were made with very powerful flash sources. Cameras installed in night bombers were also used to record the impact of sticks of bombs.

In the limited scope of this chapter all these and other special applications, such as the aerial panorama, can be little more than mentioned. But even this is enough to give a good general idea of the great advances made in aerial photography of recent years. The impetus was supplied by the technical requirements of war but the knowledge so acquired has already well served the purposes of peace.

The Leica in Archaeology and the Study of Ancient Art

by Dr. Bernhard Neutsch and Hermann Wagner, Heidelberg

A N ATTEMPT to enumerate the immeasurable services photography has rendered in archaeology and the knowledge of ancient art, and to assess its importance as compared with other aids to study, would be at once an invidious and impossible task. The photographic print, the transparency, the engraver's reproduction of the photograph, supplement in marked degree the printed and the spoken word addressed to the furtherance of learning and research. Here we shall not be concerned with the opinions of that small minority who oppose the visual aid because they see only the pitfalls to research which may lie hidden in the photographic print. To such we would merely indicate the responsible and pioneering work done by acknowledged German authorities like L. Curtius, E. Langlotz, W. H. Schuchhardt and, in particular, by G. Rodenwaldt, to whose enlistment of the services of professional photographers we owe the entirely satisfactory pictorial representation of many works of ancient art. In this co-operation they made available the benefits and guidance of their own trained powers of observation and research and so brought knowledge of their specialized activities to circles outside their own small coterie. We believe we can say with truth that most workers in this field themselves use cameras which they regard as a necessary part of their scientific equipment. But this does not mean that the services of professional photographers are superfluous. On the contrary, it promotes better understanding of the problems involved and leads inevitably to a smoother and more fruitful partnership.

For both classes of worker the Leica with its many accessories is an ideal equipment which now dominates this field of photography.

In modern archaeological expeditions, such as the great American excavations on the Agora in Athens, every field archaeologist is issued with a Leica to

Fig. 1: Head of a famous archaic sculpture dating from before the Persian Wars. 90 mm. Elmar.

Fig. 2: The same figure in its wider setting in the Acropolis on the east front of the Parthenon. 90 mm. Elmar. $\longrightarrow$

Fig. 3: South-eastern corner of the Parthenon. 135 mm. Elmar.

record the progress of the digging in all its phases and details, many of which suffer inevitable destruction as trenches get deeper.

With the Leica it is easy to take a series of pictures of the finds made and of the positions in which they were found, relative to the layers uncovered, so providing a valuable pictorial commentary on the scientific notes made as work proceeds.

If time and site permit, pictures of excavations should preferably be made with the camera on a rigid stand, though the Leica is particularly suited to fast free hand photography whenever the rate of progress or the angle of the find make this necessary. Sitings would also govern the use of focal length, which may vary from the extreme wide-angle of the 28 mm. lens to the medium long focal length of the 90 mm. Pictures gain in interest and in value if the finds and the layers are photographed in color (compare figs. 6, 7, 9 and 10).

In certain circumstances (fine art and landscape, or parts of a territory for-

Fig. 4: General view of the Parthenon from the North-west. 50 mm. Elmar.

merly inhabited) the documentary photograph often lends itself to good pictorial composition. For topographical surveys (determining the perimeter of an ancient city or of sacred sites) it might be necessary to photograph from the air. With aerial photographs much is revealed which would remain hidden to the eye from ground level. In both cases the Leica is a reliable aid to knowledge.

For broad landscapes the wide-angle lens would be used and from the air either the standard lens or one of longer focal length. The recent introduction of the M 3 has made it even easier to photograph precisely what is wanted by means of the bright line finder with automatic parallax compensation. The design of this new Leica cuts down the number of separate accessories which would otherwise need to be carried.

The main subjects for photography in archaeology and ancient art are architecture, mosaics, friezes, bas-relief, sculpture, pottery, utensils. Their varying sizes and the photographic problems peculiar to each are easily mastered with

141

Fig. 5: Bronze sea-god in the National Museum, Athens.
135 mm. Elmar with universal focusing bellows.

the Leica and its range of lenses, extending from the very short focus wide-angle to the extreme focal length of the telephoto lens. If it is possible to photograph a structure from a distance, either the standard or a medium long focal length could be used to best effect (fig. 4). If space is restricted the short focus lenses are the ones to use. Interiors, for example, can only be satisfactorily photographed with wide-angle lenses (fig. 6). True, depiction of spaciousness

*Fig. 6: An Etruscan tomb
(Tomba dei Leopardi) at
Tarquinia, Italy.*
35 mm. Elmar in artificial light.

*Fig. 7: Detail from the
same tomb.*
90 mm. Elmar with universal
focusing bellows, in artificial light.

Fig. 8: Grecian vase in the Landesmuseum, Karls-ruhe Focal length 200 mm. with universal focusing bellows; two photofloods.

Fig. 8a: The same vase. Notice the exaggerated curvature of the bowl and the loss of one complete figure from the decoration.
Exposed in a whole-plate camera with 180 mm lens.

Fig. 8b: Detail from the same vase.
200 mm. lens with universal focusing bellows.

in depth, for instance in large dome-shaped interiors (Hagia Sophia), is not always quite satisfactory in two-dimensional photography, but with 3-D the problem is easily solved. Since the Leica can be used with lenses of very long focal length to obtain a large undistorted image of distant objects, this camera has proved extremely useful in the photography of remote architectural detail or decoration (fig. 3). The erection of scaffolding or platforms, usually at great cost, thus becomes unnecessary, a factor which is particularly welcome when on journeys. When photographing statues, a lens of fairly long focus is recommended, because it eliminates distortion (figs. 1, 2 & 5). The handiness of the Leica is also an asset whenever it is necessary to photograph a specimen from the standpoint which the artist had in mind when creating a masterpiece (fig. 5); or to give an impression of how an object appeared from the main or most customary viewpoint—a condition that cannot always be assessed from museum displays.

The photography of paintings and frescoes in confined spaces calls for the use of wide-angle lenses (fig. 6). Surface reflections can be eliminated by use of a polarizing

Fig. 9: Mural decorations as in figs. 6 & 7. 50 mm. Elmar to tungsten.

Fig. 10: Dionysus and the Panther, Delos. 50 mm. Elmar to daylight.

Fig. 11: From copy negative of a drawing in the Heidelberg Museum. Notice the spotty result when exposed to non-panchromatic document copying film.
Fig. 11a: Same subject exposed to panchromatic film through a red filter.

Fig. 12: Stereo-pairs of a counterfeit coin (cast taken from genuine). 3-D shows up clearly the roughness of the surface, the unfinished appearance of hair, eyes and mouth, and the crudities of the cheek. 50 mm. Elmar with universal focusing bellows and single exposures with slight lateral displacement for each picture. Enlarged about eight diameters.

146

filter. A near-focusing device, such as the universal Leica bellows, permits the clear depiction of detail (fig. 7). The same is true for all small objects, drawings and engravings. If the latter have suffered damage from mold or age, and are spotty, a red filter used with a film of high red sensitivity will eliminate the defects in the photograph (figs. 11 & 11 a). In archaeological work the photography of art specimens, such as handpainted Grecian urns, which have peculiar significance in establishing periods, is often a difficult task. As a comparison of figs. 8 and 8a will show, the Leica with a longfocus lens affords the widest possible view of a curved surface and can also pick out fine detail in close-ups (fig. 8b). The purely photographic problems involving the elimination of undesired reflections from the curved surfaces of the vases cannot be dealt with here. The difficulty is sometimes great, but more often than not a polarizing filter will be helpful.

The archaeologist also finds the Leica most useful as a copying camera. Here the point is not to reproduce readily available texts but rather to make copy negatives of photographs or book illustrations of original specimens that are not easily inspected and, if necessary, to use the copy negative for the production of further illustrations in new publications.

If finest grain film is used with the Leica on a rigid stand—I have found the Linhof clamp stand Type 0 very suitable, especially when traveling light—print quality is obtainable that rivals the plate negative for sharpness of image.

The applications of stereophotography to this field have been surprisingly limited. The 3-D picture is the only one which conveys an adequate impression of depth and plasticity of form in architectural detail, in sculpture and relief work, in interiors and the like. With a little practice the stereoscopic effect of twin images can be observed by the naked eye, but for those unable to adapt, various instruments are available for viewing the 3-D picture which can also be projected in depth both in monochrome and in color. Since archaeological subjects are by definition static, a single Leica with a standard lens can be used for the production of stereo-pairs. For distances greater than three feet the stereo camera-slide for shifting the camera body through the required interocular distance is quite suitable. With devices for close-up work (coins, carved stones, intaglio work) the single Leica will perform work impossible with a stereo-camera because of the short camera/subject distances. Pictures are made in succession with a slight lateral shift of the camera for each stereo-pair (fig. 12). The new Leitz Stemar attachment for stereoscopy is a remarkable simplification of the problems involved in stereo work. Interocular distance is variable for close-up and for distant subjects and the pairs can be projected in 3-D with a standard Prado projector fitted with twin Elmar projection lenses equipped with their own polarizing filters.

Color presents its own individual problems, traceable largely to the teething troubles of this new discovery, but it is sufficiently promising to justify intensive work to remove the causes of criticism sometimes leveled at color film. It requires little imagination to appreciate what a tremendous step forward it would be, to be able to reproduce in true natural color such objects as paintings. In archaeology we already have sufficient evidence of the value of photographing layers in color. Color has also been important in the photography of walls and materials of varying hue, as we have seen from the work of Prof. E. Kirschbaum during his excavations under St. Peter's, Rome.

Color photography for this purpose is restricted to reversal processes, which are still the only ones yielding sufficiently satisfactory results (figs. 9 & 10 are reproduced from such direct transparencies). The Leica with its range of interchangeable lenses is a particularly efficient instrument for color work. It is convenient to have a second Leica body permanently loaded with color film to facilitate photography in both monochrome and color. It is merely necessary to switch the lens from one body to the other, a procedure that is now considerably quicker, thanks to the bayonet fastenings of lenses for the Leica M 3 body.

The Leica system of photography is being used increasingly in the photographic libraries of archaeological institutes and foundations devoted to the study of ancient art. The saving in filing space is considerable and the greatly reduced weight of the records is a boon to the traveling lecturer. Various Leitz projectors are available for small rooms or the largest halls, and the quality of the Leica transparency they throw on the screen concedes nothing to the large lantern slides formerly used. Finally, one might mention the greatly reduced costs of the Leica system of photography. Where pictures are produced in large numbers this has proved itself to be a very considerable saving to organizations which are never lavishly supported. Moreover, when one considers the great versatility of the Leica system and the availability of apparatus for adjusting the camera to so many applications, it will be apparent that the Leica adds operational economy to its many other notable features.

The Leica Microfilm in the Service of the Librarian

by Dr. W. Schürmeyer, Chief Librarian, Düsseldorf

THE APPLICATIONS of the Leica in document copying and general library work must be divided under two heads. On the one hand there is the microfilming of existing documents and books and, on the other, the uses of the camera in providing original photographic records. In documentation the division between the two is not a rigid one and there is often overlap. The latter, or productive, application of the Leica may be said to embrace every kind of pictorial record. The collection of such records is often an integral part of the work of a librarian, though they need not necessarily be made by the library staff. Here we can only discuss the applications of the Leica camera and its accessories when used on the premises as an instrument for microfilming. The accent on microfilming is important, but it should be noted by those who prefer the photostat that the micro-record is equally capable of yielding a copy print in original size. This application of miniature photography, pioneered by the Leica camera, has acquired ever widening significance because of the decided economy of materials. Long before fully automatic copying devices appeared on the market, American universities and libraries used the Leica extensively for microfilming. That is why microfilming even today is virtually a Leica technique, though the introduction of electrically driven cameras which can be used only for this purpose gave rise to the view that the Leica had been superseded and was useful only in emergencies. It was a hasty conclusion because the wide choice of ancillary apparatus available for the Leica makes this camera eminently suitable equipment for all the special applications that collectors and users of rare manuscripts could desire.

The work of the librarian may be divided under three heads: collection, arrangement and distribution of documents, books and papers. For various reasons it is not always possible to obtain originals, lapsed editions and the like. In

149

earlier days this was a frequent cause of disappointment to librarians and users of the library, but today there is no need to have any gaps on the shelves. Every librarian is in the fortunate position of being able to supply the lack of original texts and manuscripts of rare or unobtainable publications and documents by the simple expedient of buying the photographed text on strip film or borrowing the books and having them copied by the camera on the premises. Before microfilming became possible, photostat copies in original size were sometimes prepared, but the high cost of this procedure confined its use to cases of exceptional need or interest. Bulk was also a problem in storage. Since the advent of microfilm reading apparatus, which blows up the microfilm record to original size or even larger, if desired, the filling of gaps in library collections is no longer a major problem. The costs of microfilming are so low that even modest libraries can avail themselves of its potentialities. Obviously, no one would wish to replace books entirely by microfilm, but in all those cases where certain books are unobtainable, or can be had only at an impossible price, the microfilm record will provide a satisfactory substitute. By adopting this new method many a specialist library has been planned and built up according to the requirements of its users. Similarly, city libraries and national libraries have been stocked with microfilm records of interesting books or publications in a nation's literature which are not easily procured. In America one publishing enterprise has been started solely in order to make micro-records of all the English literature published prior to 1630, much of which is now very rare and to be seen only in old European libraries or in famous private collections, like the one at Beeleigh Abbey near Maldon, Essex. Copies of these records are supplied to American libraries. The Bibliothèque Nationale in Paris can now supply users with microfilm records of all medieval French MSS. and a large and varied assortment of incunabula. In the British Museum the entire editions of "The Times" newspaper are available on microfilm. In Germany a similar enterprise is in the process of being built up. In the reproduction of old illuminated MSS. color film will in future provide copies which give a much better semblance of the original than the monochrome photograph was hitherto able to do.

The microfilming of daily newspapers is a special application of photographic documentation. Newsprint has a high cellulose content and a short life. But since early newspapers are sources of information which cannot be too highly rated, libraries which are obliged to collect newspapers in large quantities are

Fig. 1

tending more and more to preserve the microfilm record rather than the original newspaper. Microfilm is considerably lighter, it utilizes but a fraction of the space occupied by the original, and it saves the cost of binding. Fig. 1 is a convincing illustration of the comparative sizes of the micro-record and the corresponding bound volumes of a daily newspaper. It shows clearly the much smaller amount of space utilized by the film kept, on the one hand, in two uncut rolls of 400 feet each and, on the other, by the film cut in Leica lengths with each roll preserved in its own container. For reasons of weight and space alone the microfilm library will often be preferred. In an ordinary living-room it is possible to house the equivalent of twenty thousand volumes, each the size of a standard dictionary. Libraries and archives containing valuable MSS. will in future—and this was done during the war—make microfilm records of this irreplaceable material for everyday use while the originals are removed to places of safe-keeping and scientific storage to preserve them from the risk of damage or destruction. Microfilm can be read in a reader, it can be used as the negative from which paper prints can be made, and from it any number

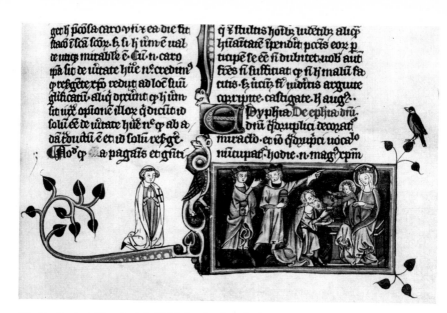

Fig. 2: Part of illuminated MSS. by Jacobus de Voragine from the Golden Legend or Lombardica hystoria, 1324 (Municipal Library, Frankfort-on-Main).
50 mm Elmar with Portable Copier, f/12.5, 2 secs., on 6...20° film.

Fig. 3: As above but made from direct separations using Agfa filters Nos. 40, 41 and 42.

of duplicate microfilm records can be easily and cheaply reproduced. In one sense the film strip can be regarded as a permanent and ever-ready set of drinting plates. It is this feature which makes possible the publication of limited editions of scientific works for which the demand would be small, or could not in the first instance be fully assessed in regard to possible wider interest. Extracts and references could be published in the technical press and those sufficiently interested to pursue the matter could apply for a complete text of positive prints made from the microfilm record of a clean typewriter script. In scientific work illustrated with diagrams and sketches the fairly high cost of engraving is also saved in all those cases where the risk of printed publication is considered too great.

Whereas the librarian would, as a rule, collect whole books, a complete series of magazines, or the entire editions of a newspaper, there are other more specialized tasks where it would be necessary merely to extract certain passages or cuttings concerning the work of a particular foundation or institute. Since in such cases the service is designed to inform users of advances in opinion or method in specialized tasks which may have many ramifications, the cutting out or sub-division of printed matter has certain obvious limitations. The microfilm is a much more flexible record. Copies can be made or renewed in unlimited numbers should the need arise. Whether the film is kept in long lengths or in short strips, or whether large or small photostat records are to be made for filing, will in each case depend on personal factors and on convenience in use. In general it will be found that librarians providing a service to various individuals either within or outside an organization will prefer to keep their collections on microfilm because it is then easier to make better positive copies in any desired size. The lone research worker, on the other hand, who collects scientific literature for his private use only, would prefer the photostat because it is more easily accommodated in his private files. In the interests of economy even positive records are kept as small as possible and read with a reading glass. Should a contact copy or an enlargement of two or three diameters be desired this can be done with little complication. All microfilm and paper micro-records should be prefaced with a clearly legible script, readable by the unaided eye, indicating the source of the document and giving reference to all other microfilmed records held on the same subject.

Microfilm is not merely an aid to collection, it also helps in classification. In all libraries the card index and the bibliography are the basis of classification and search for material required. Through using a machine for cataloguing book titles we have discovered how useful it is to have a printing plate of the index card which allows duplication at any time. Such printing plates can now be made in the form of the micro-negative. The film is cheaper and is stored in much less space than any other material. Another advantage is that the existing title-page of any book can be photographed for the micro-record, thus eliminating copying and setting errors in the preparation of plates. The use of film in indexing and cataloguing has proved particularly useful in all cases where it has been found necessary to duplicate existing records or to assemble in a central library a complete index of books held by different branches of an organization, often situated in different places. Often, also, because of shortage of staff or pressure of work, it might not always be possible to devote much time to the indexing of a large number of new books, or of a windfall left to the library by private bequest. In such cases the microfilm record of title-pages, with the operative word underlined for classification, is an excellent interim measure.

For bibliographic purposes, as also from the point of view of the book lover, it is often of value that the index card should show a reproduction of the original title-page and also of the subject index of each volume. With the aid of the Leica this can be done at little cost in money or time.

At the time of writing we are in a transitional period. It is still fairly generally necessary to make positive paper prints of catalogues and bibliographies from the microfilm records, but direct microfilm readers (see fig. 7) are becoming available. With their aid it has proved possible to overcome the difficulty hitherto presented by the micro-copying of new titles out of strict alphabetic or other order. In future even the roughest arrangement of titles will suffice because photo-electric cells, adjusted for any desired classification of material, signal the correct frame as the film index proceeds at speed through the reading device. The reader is stopped at the required frame which is then read or automatically copied on positive paper, as desired.

The users of microfilm and photo-copies were quicker than librarians to appreciate the benefits of the system. But the wider use of the photo-copy as a means of disseminating the knowledge contained in central collections of books and MSS. was heralded when it became possible to make use of a system whereby the lending library could despatch a microfilm record for the use of the borrower. In recent years the percentage of new books, published at home and abroad, which small and medium-sized libraries have been able to acquire, has steadily

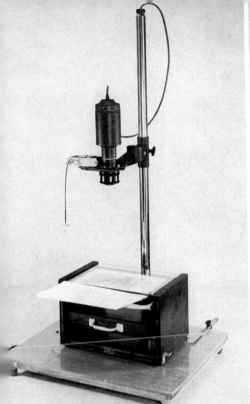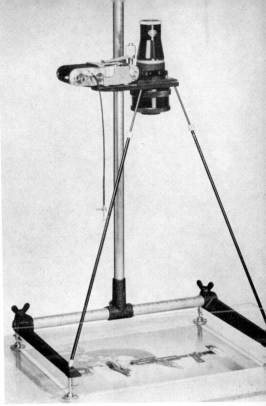

Fig. 4: Leitz Reprovit I with book-holder. *Fig. 5: Leitz Portable Copier.*

diminished. As a consequence borrowing between libraries is on the increase and has already reached proportions which bring heavy work to the great central and national libraries. Here microfilm has been a happy solution of the problem. It is considerably cheaper to send some remote user a microfilm of a magazine or newspaper extract at second-class mail rates than it is to pack up and send him the heavy bound volume containing all the issues for a whole year. It also avoids damage to the original in transit and there is no danger of loss due to accident or irregularities on the part of the borrower. But, most important of all, the original remains in the possession of the central library and is always available for the public who would otherwise be deprived of its use for considerable periods of time. These methods are proving of even greater significance in the international exchange of microfilmed texts, which can be made available at comparatively low cost for any desired book, magazine or newspaper at home or overseas. Even for lending libraries—and to this category

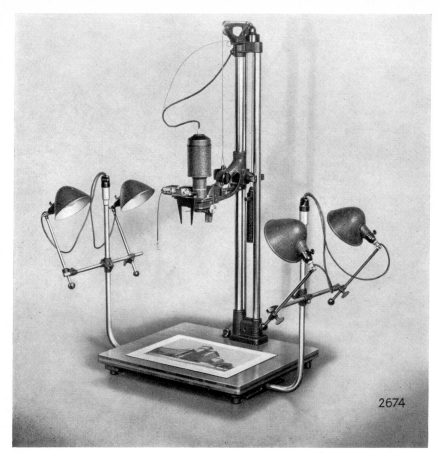

Fig. 6: Leitz Reprovit II.

belong many specialized scientific libraries—microfilm is a useful means of supplying the wants of distant borrowers. Libraries and archives are relieved of the necessity to refuse applications for books which are very valuable, or which are frequently referred to *in situ*, by the simple expedient of the microfilm, which serves the purpose as well.

Formerly, if the photographer wished to reproduce text or pictures, he was compelled by the design of his camera to photograph them in a vertical position. Single sheets were often damaged in the process and it was frequently found

156

difficult to copy simultaneously in this way both pages of an open book. The handiness of the little Leica and its exposure technique, based on easy observation and control of camera settings, have made it possible to devise Leica copying aids which facilitate the copying of single sheets of text as well as whole bound books with the matter in a horizontal position. Since the manufacturer's literature and pamphlets deal in detail with all these Leitz copying devices for the Leica, I shall confine myself to the basic considerations arising out of the many varied applications of such apparatus.

Some of the copying aids for the Leica are designed for use by daylight, while others can be used either by daylight and tungsten, and still others by tungsten light only. Because of the constancy of tungsten sources and the even illumination of the field there can be little doubt that it will be the preferred method to illuminate copying matter by this means. For private use it might not always be found possible to accommodate the rather large copying boards equipped with their own light sources. The individual worker with access to public and private collections might also find it inconvenient to use this method. But this does not mean that he is deprived of the use of his Leica to spare him the tedium of transcription. Simple and cheap devices are made for copying the standard paper sizes, postcard, octavo and foolscap, with the Leica camera. This apparatus can be disassembled and carried conveniently in the brief-case and is designed for use away from home and when traveling.

Other special apparatus (Belun and Behoo) is available for reproductions in natural size or a little smaller. Since the negative image is very little reduced, or not reduced at all, enlargements made from it often provide useful clues to the methods of production or about the physical state of the original.

Particularly reliable equipment which can be used for all copying work is the Portable Copier. It is easy to assemble and when not in use is carried in a small canvas bag. The rigidity of the construction is quite remarkable and might be compared with the stable static devices. To promote ease of operation, precise focus and wide adaptability, it is equipped with a sliding copier and ground glass screen for observation and control of the image. The value of this is the independence of focusing tables. The distance between the supports is also large enough to accommodate most normal book sizes and other copying matter. For private workers and for scientific institutions faced with the need to make many photographic extracts, the Reprovit I, and especially the Reprovit II, are recommended.

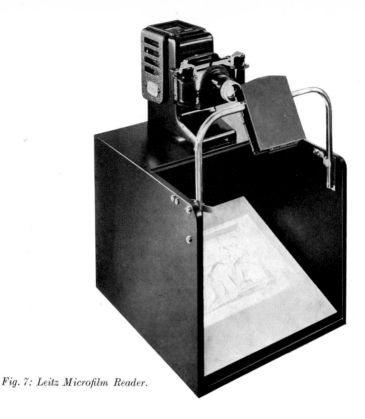

Fig. 7: Leitz Microfilm Reader.

Both these equipments are static and operate over a range extending from natural size (1:1) to a reduction ratio of 1:18. Details of these universal copying equipments for the Leica are contained in the manufacturer's appropriate specifications. What concerns us here is that a special book-holder evenly flattens the open pages of a book into the horizontal plane, no matter where the book may be opened nor how thick it is, thus making possible the simultaneous photo-copying of both leaves on a single frame of the micro-record. Provision is also made for the use of intermediate collars and special lenses which increase the range of these instruments upto a magnification of $\times 6.5$. Since the microfilm can itself be enlarged some ten to fifteen times with very satisfactory definition, the research worker is thus able to inspect specimens at one hundred times magnification. These advantages of the Reprovit II, with which a micro-attachment can be used if need be, make it a most valuable instrument for the close examination of passages difficult to read in old MSS. and aged documents. For the same reasons it is suitable for establishing the authenticity or otherwise of seals and coins, and for examining details of type and the method of making old illustrations. Focus is set not by tables and the like, but by the projection of a test mark onto the matter to be copied. The mark is focused and the book or document is correctly aligned in the rectangular beam which delineates exact lens coverage. This coverage can be altered to suit the size of the matter to be copied.

The equipment can, if desired, be used by daylight illumination, but it is obviously better to make use of the four tungsten sources, provided with reflectors, to ensure even illumination of the field and the absence of all reflections from the surfaces copied.

Sensitive materials suitable for the reproduction of MSS. and printed matter are the generally available slow positive safety films for black and white specimens, or the special document copying films such as Agfa Agepe, Kodak Microfile and Ilford Microneg which are suitable also for the copying, through appropriate filters, of documents yellowed with age.

These emulsions all have the very finest grain and the highest resolving power very suitable for the recording of fine detail. On such microfilms reductions up to 1:20 are fairly easy to obtain with the assurance that the film will allow an entirely satisfactory enlargement of the copy back to natural size. The ortho- or panchromatic sensitization of the special document copying films mentioned is useful when specimens are printed or written in colored inks or on colored paper.

Correct exposure and development are of course understood, but it might be worth mentioning again that half-tone subject matter should be given soft development whereas line drawings need development to high contrast.

Since the miniature camera is such a useful aid to the serious worker in the collection and evaluation of the material he requires for study, it is quite conceivable that the taking and reading apparatus will become as indispensable to him as the fountain-pen and the typewriter are today. Wherever scientific documents are collected the photo-copy improves and simplifies system, replaces unobtainable originals and removes the danger of loss or damage due to repeated handling of valuable specimens, which need no longer be touched. Microfilm, next to the book—which it does not deny pride of place—bids fair to play a leading part in the future dissemination of knowledge which is our cultural heritage.

Uses of the Leica in Bridge Building

by W. Hoffmann, Gustavsburg

Unfortunately there is insufficient space in this book to deal with all the applications of the Leica camera in industry and the engineering professions. As a typical example of its uses we have selected bridge construction, because the following account applies equally to other technical spheres. (Ed.)

THOUSANDS of pictures have redeemed the unremitting second. The photographer is now the diarist of the times. We record in monochrome and color all that is of interest in our private and professional lives. Prints are the *aides memoires* which spare us the strain of recollecting detail.

Photography has become an indispensable stand-by, especially in industry where the photograph and the copy negative have acquired a prominence which is now largely maintained by the quick and economical miniature camera.

Surely one of the finest professions is that of the construction engineer and of construction engineers the bridge builder is clearly outstanding. Let us spend a little time with one of these and observe him as he uses his Leica in the course of his work. We shall see only certain phases of it, yet enough to make our point.

One of the considerations in all modern constructional problems is to relate the design of a projected structure to the particular surroundings in which it

Fig. 1: Company architect's project drawing.
35 mm. lens, f/22, 8 secs., to two 500-W photofloods.

Fig. 2: Architect's model—general view.
35 mm. lens, f/22, 8 secs., to two 500-W photofloods.

is to rise; to make sure, in other words, that the edifice merges in outline and appearance with the heavily populated industrial area or the beautiful landscape of which it is to form a part. Masonry should never offend the eye—the only arbiter in all such cases—but should seem to be an organic part of the wider setting, in a style that is always beyond reproach.

A bridge designer conscious of his obligation to society would therefore proceed somewhat as follows: First, the area in which the bridge is to be erected would be photographed from several different standpoints. A study of these pictures would provide the architect and the constructional engineer with a basis for their designs, all of which would be drawn to scale for a consideration of the best of the many suitable alternatives. (Fig. 1.) Other most important aids in arriving at a decision are architect's models of the general scene and of the details of construction. Here, too, the photographic record, covering the appearance of the structure from all angles, is useful in providing a ready means of establishing the best visual effect (figs. 2 & 3) and revealing novel features of the construction (fig. 4).

In modern engineering new methods of calculating the suitability of a proposed material in terms of the stresses and strains it will withstand, particularly when used in conjunction with other building materials from which it differs in kind, are a feature of most building enterprises. Special testing machines for the experimental determination of endurance (fatigue), resistance to

Fig. 3: Detail of superstructure (architect's model). 35 mm. lens, f/22, 6 secs to two 500-W photofloods

Fig. 4: Model of a prefabricated section of the carriage-way seen from below. 35 mm. lens, f/11, $^1/_5$ sec to daylight.

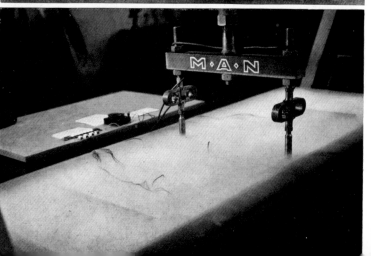

Fig. 5: Joggling and low temperature test of the surfacing for the carriage-way. 35 mm. lens, f/11, 8 sec to one 500-W photoflood

Fig. 6: Welders at work on a section of the carriage-way which has been power-tilted to the vertical for convenience of operation. 35 mm. lens, f/16, $^1/_{60}$ sec., in daylight.

Fig. 7: Slewing cranes float prefabricated sections down to the site. 35 mm. lens, f/5.6, $^1/_{40}$ sec.

Figs. 9 & 10: Sections of the carriage-way being laid by day and night.
Fig. 9: 35 mm. lens, f/5.6, $^1/_{100}$ sec. Fig. 10: 35 mm. lens, f/16, 1 sec.

torsion and buckle are used. Fig. 5 illustrates a method in use for fatigue-testing models of pre-fabricated steel pavements or carriage-ways by means of a joggling machine which simulates the stresses to which the part will be subjected in practice, the test being carried out under the severe conditions of artifically-induced extreme cold. The photographic record of the results of such a test reveals all the required detail for the information of experts and others who often cannot be present at the time the tests are carried out. (B.O.A.C. Comet Yoke Uncle was recently fatigue-tested to "death" in a similar manner at the Royal Aircraft Establishment, Farnborough, and photography played an invaluable part in reconstructing the probable causes of the disaster to Comet Yoke Peter off Elba in January 1954. *Ed.*)

With other types of testing machine, materials are tested for quality in respect of tension and compression by direct push and pull forces applied by special devices like the Haigh equipment.

165

ig. 8: The final section is lowered into position. 35 mm. lens, f/5.6, $^1/_{40}$ sec.

Once all the preliminaries in office and on the testing-bed have been completed, production can begin in the factory and the site can be prepared. Fig. 6 is a particularly instructive picture of work in progress. It shows how one section of a prefabricated carriage-way—a type of construction now increasingly used—is power-tilted to a vertical position to facilitate the work of welding.

A series of photographs of progress on the site is a useful means of keeping all site engineers informed of the dispositions of labor and materials necessary, and gives a clear guide, for example, to the time intervals between call-ups of the cables required at various stages of the work.

The entire progress of construction, which in this particular case was carried out with the help of modern floating cranes, can be followed far from the site with the aid of Leica sequences (fig. 8) which even provide excellent pictures of night work, often preferred because there is no hindrance to river traffic (figs. 9 & 10).

This short account may serve to illustrate how Leica pictures, reproduced here for most part only from sections of the negative, can trace the stages of a great constructional enterprise from the desks of the architect, the statistician and the constructional engineer, *via* the drawing-board and the testing-bed to the workshop, and on through all the stages of erection to final assembly. Lastly, the negatives are often used to prepare transparencies for instructional purposes in the great institutions where the engineers of the future are trained. Their value has been proved.

The documentary record may be almost as long as a short motion picture, but it is more adaptable to the varied uses it will find.

The Leica in the Service of Industrial Accident Prevention

by Fritz Lesser, Chief Engineer, Bergisch-Gladbach

SOON AFTER I was appointed, in 1926, to be technical supervisor of the comparatively small group of people engaged in industrial accident prevention and research in the paper-making industry, I realized that it would be hardly possible to tackle the job without the aid of the photograph. But I also soon learned the difficulties of photography in this particular field. In the first place it is the duty of those who seek to prevent accidents to inspect all the industrial plants under their control, to investigate the causes of accidents that have occurred, and to adopt appropriate measures to prevent future accidents. Photographs must be made during the course of these duties, but it is not the primary object of the inspector to collect a good set of prints. I found my 5×4 inch plate camera an impossible burden on these inspectional tours of factories, which often necessitated climbing over roofs and scaffolding, or ascending to the control cabins of cranes. Soon afterwards I saw one of the early Leicas—this surely was the instrument which would make it possible to set to work in the manner which my calling decreed. So I bought Leica No. 7908 in the summer of 1928, although at that time it still required considerable courage to pay so high a price for a "toy". After several visits to the factory for conversion to later models, this same camera continues to perform its duties right upto the present time.

Towards the end of the Twenties one of the principal applications of photography was to provide pictures of safeguards which had been proved efficient. But this was not always easy in the restricted space of the various machine shops where light for photography was never very good. At that time the relative aperture of the 50 mm. Elmar at f/3.5 was exceptionally high as lenses went, but film speeds were low, so the hope of being able to work free hand was soon discarded. Meanwhile lenses have become much faster and the speeds of

Fig. 1   Fig. 2

Fig. 1: It is obvious that a turbine trash-rake should have a hand-rail to prevent people falling into the water, but it is not so obvious how this hand-rail should be constructed so as not to interfere with the job of clearing away flotsam.

Fig. 2: This was the scene of a serious accident. The chalk arrow (left center) on a stationary part shows the sense in which the roller rotates.

films have risen enormously—but I still carry around a light collapsible stand. It is not as rigid as it might be, but it often comes in useful. The important thing is that the camera fixed to the stand can be carried either on a shoulder-strap or in a brief-case. This allows it to be taken anywhere so there is no risk of losing a picture. It is my experience that the exposure postponed is the one that is seldom made.

The 36 exposures on a strip of Leica film are rather too few than too many. The library grew rapidly and today it contains well over 10,000 negatives which increase at a yearly rate of about 500. True, there are many negatives of the same subject among these—taken not only from different angles or at different machine speeds, but also with varying exposure times. The duplication is not wasteful because negatives are sometimes damaged and the replacements do not have to be made again. Bracketed exposures are a wise precaution because a second at about half the estimated exposure and a third at about five times the latter ensure that one of the three will be good—generally they are all usable: the thin negative being preferable for big enlargements and the dense one for making the transparency. The photo-electric exposure meter is a useful aid, but for really consistent results in poor light, meters like the Ilford S. E. I. Photometer are ideal. In spite of this I still make bracketed exposures of every subject at widely divergent shutter speeds. The cheapness of the film permits this luxury.

Although I worked at full lens opening from the very start I found the depth of field to be quite adequate. In 1928 the 50 mm. focal length was unusually short and the depth of field at full aperture better than with the longer focal lengths I had previously been obliged to use. Maximum definition is also desirable only in the main subject and can be annoying if foregrounds and backgrounds are rendered equally sharp. Prints are often carried around or sent to other interested parties by post. They are never much larger than postcard size (which is also quite big enough for engraving if cuts are to be made for publication). Should there be slight unsharpness, or if the print is grainy, these effects are not unduly disturbing. Graininess disappears in the screen pattern of half-tone reproduction.

Accuracy of focus was improved after the camera was fitted by the makers with depth of field scales round the lens mount, and still further facilitated when a coupled rangefinder was subsequently built in, also by the makers. Dispensing with the tape-measure put up the speed of operation. This is an important point because production is held up whenever it is necessary to reconstruct the causes of an accident in order to make pictures which are posted up on notice boards as warnings to the staff, or used to illustrate accident reports. Speed of camera operation restricts production delays to a minimum. It also reduces the time during which the actors in a reconstructed scene are exposed to the same danger. Concentration, quick thinking and some talent for arranging the props and the workmen are necessary if the resulting picture is to appear quite natural. The manipulation of camera controls should not hold up the proceedings. Settings should be made easily and quickly—and for this there is no more suitable instrument than the Leica. In the interests of safety it is sometimes necessary to stop the machine in order to reconstruct the accident. In such cases it is useful to make a second picture of the machine running, but with no one near it, in order to illustrate the speed of motion; and by careful retouching or montage it will be found possible to produce a final composite print which preserves the impression of danger.

The 50 mm. Elmar has proved an excellent lens, but sometimes even this comparatively short focal length is not short enough in some restricted corners of a factory where it is just impossible to include the whole of the desired picture area because one cannot get far enough away from it. In such cases the 35 mm. wide-angle Summaron lens comes to the rescue and I have found it so useful on so many occasions that I am now using it as the standard lens. Its slight exaggeration of perspective is of little consequence to the technician whose main concern is to get everything he needs onto the negative.

In outdoor work, or sometimes even in large workshops where it may be necessary to photograph a gantry and traveling cranes, lenses of medium to long focal length, like the 90 mm. Elmar or the 135 mm. Hektor, will be needed to show up the required detail and fill the frame. This because there are limits to the degree of enlargement possible from small sections of the negative.

When, in 1929, the first great "Accident Prevention Week" was planned, I was invited to lecture on the subject in a large number of paper factories. It had been my experience that to lecture well on this subject the photograph was necessary to illustrate the spoken word. Earlier attempts to expound the theme without the visual aid had been unsatisfactory from my point of view—and doubtless from that of the audience. But how were these pictures to be shown? Fortunately the "Eldia" contact printer for transparencies was available and the pictures so produced could be projected in strips by the Leitz miniature film projector which had just appeared. The success of these illustrated talks was astonishing. Although screen brightness was much lower than what we expect today of the Prado or even the VIII S 375 projectors, the apparatus was excellent for its time, it was conveniently portable and the audiences were delighted. It was important to be able to carry all the necessary equipment in a small light case, because I did not at that time own an automobile. Today it is pleasant to find that modern Leitz projectors are still light, handy and space-saving because, my car is generally packed with all kinds of

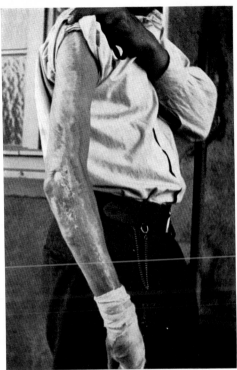

Fig. 3   Fig. 4

Fig. 3: To make this picture without risk to the operative the machine had to be stopped.
Fig. 4: How dangerous the running machine could be is illustrated by this section of a
picture showing the injury inflicted.

other things. All my most important transparencies are now made on two-inch
glass lantern slides. Their life is longer and individual slides can easily be
replaced whenever necessary. A little more attention must be paid to the correct
order of presentation and the correct insertion of the slide in the projector.
Film strips become hopelessly scratched after 40 or 50 showings, but since the
cost of replacement is low they are still useful for some purposes. For instance,
during the Accident Prevention Week in 1934 dozens of such film strips, prepared with some frames carrying appropriate texts to be read between pictures,
were sent round from factory to factory where they were used by members of
the staffs for presenting internal lectures on the subject.

171

The growing negative library, the collection of transparencies and the recurrence of lectures drove me to find a suitable method of storage. In 1928 we had only the boxes in which 25 rolls of strip film could be housed. I have stuck to this method, but were I to begin again it is probable that I would change to strips of six negatives filed flat in tissue or, better still, cellophane envelopes. But to change over from one method to the other is unthinkable! I cannot say that I have had cause to regret the storage in rolls. Negatives that are now twenty-five years old and have been used several times are still not so badly scratched that I could not make quite passable enlargements from them. Once again it is borne in on me that the preventer of accidents needs clear pictures which need not lay claim to artistic merit.

Classification and cross-reference were major headaches. What system should one choose? Fortunately every negative in the archives could be directly related to some particular cause of an accident—whether, indeed, it was one that had in fact occurred, or one which had in some way been prevented from occurring. It was thus simple to base classification on the accident statistics which, by a law of 1926, had to be kept by all industrial enterprises which were then made responsible for taking out accident insurance on behalf of all employees. Since the accidents are classified according to the machines or objects which caused them—something that can be photographed—a similar classification of negatives was easy and proved most useful. But each negative had to carry a number, both on the clear strip where a serial was prefixed to the frame number, and in the image area, where it could be reproduced in the print. Writing the number on the support side of the negative calls for a little practice, but very neat work can be done if the selected area is first prepared with amyl acetate which will accept the Indian or other ink used, with a fine brush, to write the number inside the frame. A retouching desk or light-box is useful for the purpose. The key to the negative files is in a card index which carries contact prints of each group of negatives. To make these contacts the "Eldia" is merely fed with perforated strips of positive paper instead of film.

The index of Leica contact prints is an excellent aid to memory. Often when passing through a factory I notice good and sometimes bad arrangements which one is apt to forget because the cursory glance does not at once reveal anything unusual. But if a photograph is made the record is there for all time. Sometimes it may be years before such a picture proves useful, but it bides its time. Some day it will be used to illustrate a lecture or an article; it may be just the thing to help in advising factory managements, or a colleague might wish to borrow it. The slight extra trouble is often amply repaid.

Since one cannot expect to remember the reasons for any and every picture made or the particular circumstances of a case, it is advisable to make notes at the time, on a card carried for the purpose with a pencil attached by string.

With complicated machinery it is not always possible to remember after the lapse of some weeks (and it takes at least as long to complete a tour of inspection before one sees the pictures) the direction in which the various parts rotate. Now it is precisely this that is often of great importance in accident reports and in the adoption of preventive measures. I generally chalk-mark an arrow on some static part of the machine to indicate the direction of rotation in the picture. It helps memory and saves the trouble of retouching the print.

Whenever possible I also make pictures of the injuries caused by machines or plant. These can be very gruesome photographs, but I have had occasion to use them in order to convince production managers, who cannot otherwise be persuaded of possible danger, that certain machines are prone to accident.

I also have occasion to use pictures and publications, drawings and sketches made by fellow-workers in other industries, or those collected by the public prosecutor's department. This means copying, so copying apparatus is necessary. Fortunately the Leica is also admirably suited to this work and there is a wide choice of equipment for it. These range from the fixed focus copying aids for standard paper sizes to the refinements of the Reprovit II. Since time does not usually press in such work the simpler devices will often suffice, but if there is much of it one experiences a growing need of the labor-saving apparatus.

For the accident inspector armed with a camera, illumination is of some importance. Pictures must be made on the spot under all possible conditions of light. To put off a picture until conditions are favorable, or because the sun is in the wrong section of the sky, is generally impossible. To avoid fogging the negative with flare from windows and the like, which cannot be excluded from the picture area, it is necessary always to use a sunshade on a coated lens. If the lens is uncoated flare will be inevitable.

In spite of stands and large relative apertures the existing factory illumination is often inadequate. Flash is indicated but naked powders must be ruled out because of fire risk, and expendable bulbs are expensive. Before the advent of speed lamps I used magnesium ribbon. It was a bit clumsy by modern standards and could be used only with stationary objects or moving parts rotating

Fig. 5: A machine-minder fixes the rip-cord to the empty drum...

Fig. 6: ... and by passing quickly under the strip of paper moving onto the web he severs each complete roll and starts another. Such quick movements are best photographed with speed lights.

in a single plane. It gave a good even light because the magnesium flare could be moved about during the exposure. But now that we have strobes, the very fast movements so necessary to an investigation of causes can be quite easily made visible on the Leica frame. The only regret is that the weight of the power pack is out of all proportion to the weight of the camera.

I have dealt here only with professional accident prevention in industry. But everything that has been said applies equally to those firms and production managers who wish to do their own good work. Such pictures could provide invaluable material for accident prevention on a national scale, particularly when on-the-spot pictures of accidents are reconstructed while events are still fresh in the memory of the workers. Such pictures made available through the medium of employers' organizations serve a wider purpose. Their immediate uses are also valuable. To post them up on a factory notice-board to be seen by every employee may be considered drastic by some — but it is as good a method as any of inculcating care.

Photomicrography of Metal Structure

by Dr.-Ing. Alfred Raible, Düsseldorf

WITH THE DEVELOPMENT of the miniature camera it was soon recognized[1,2] that there were many possible applications of miniature techniques in metallographic laboratories. Where formerly in the photomicrography of structure the question was whether to use photographic film or photographic plates, we now find that the problem has resolved itself down to one of magnification. In other words, upto what magnification, given the experience and skill of the technician entrusted with the task of photomicrography, will it be possible to use

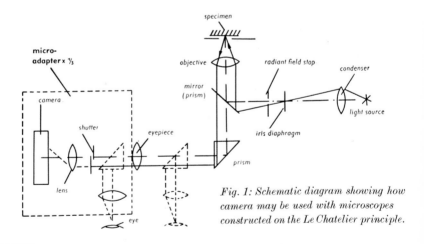

Fig. 1: Schematic diagram showing how camera may be used with microscopes constructed on the Le Chatelier principle.

[1] O. Bornhofen and A. Jack: *Zeitschrift für wissenschaftl. Mikroskopie und f. mikroskop. Technik* 1936, pp. 193–200.

[2] O. Bornhofen: *Die Leica in Beruf u. Wissenschaft*, Frankfurt 1941, p. 101, et seq.

miniature film and yet guarantee good results. The limits are set by the regularity or irregularity of the surface structures photographed. The greater the regularity the higher the power of the microscope objective that can be used. The image field of microscope systems for use with miniature film would not normally exceed a diameter of 72 mm.; and with photographic plates the diameter of the image would be extended up to a limit of about 130 mm.

Micro-apparatus available

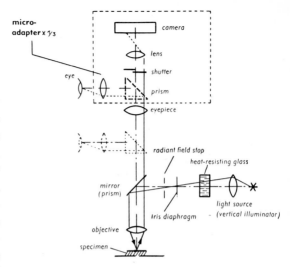

Fig. 2: Schematic diagram showing how the camera may be used with a Panphot microscope.

for miniature photomicrography — such as the earlier Leitz "Mifilmka", or the present model If Leica body screwed on the "Mikas" micro-adapter equipped with lateral eyepiece, deflecting prism, field lens and shutter release— fully permit the photomicrography of surface structures on miniature film, from which bromide prints or transparencies and lantern slides are easily made. The schematic diagrams of figs. 1 and 2 show the dispositions of the various pieces of miniature photographic equipment used on the microscope and will help explain the text.

A micro-adapter, screwed into the lens retaining ring, normally used for screwing in the interchangeable camera lenses (see diagrams), can be introduced into the image field of a microscope designed on the Le Chatelier principle (optical benches and the like, as shown in fig. 1), or can be inserted direct into the standard eyepiece holder of a vertical microscope (Panphot or Metallux as shown in fig. 2).

Instead of focusing by means of ground glass screens the microscope image is viewed and focused for the film plane by means of the deflecting prism at the position of the lateral eyepiece, which is part of the micro-adapter unit. The optical arrangement is such that an image sharply focused at the position of

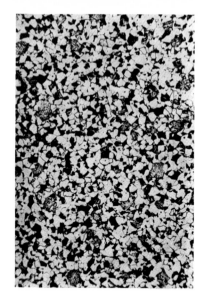

Fig. 3: Cr-Mo-Steel × *100.*

Fig. 4: Cr-Mo-Steel × *400.*

Fig. 5: Cr-Mo-Steel × *1000.*

Fig. 6: Pig-iron × *100.*

the prism will be rendered equally sharp in the film plane of the camera. Since the prism deflects part of the image-forming rays for viewing, a coupler-release is provided which swings it out of the path of these rays just prior to the release of the shutter, which is also incorporated in the micro-adapter. The field lens situated just above this shutter effects a ×3 linear reduction of the virtual image in the film plane which is, as a rule, compensated without loss of image quality by a corresponding ×3 enlargement of the negative when printing.

In most average work the sensitive material used would be a medium panchromatic film, 32...27°, such as Adox KB 17, Agfa Isopan F, Ilford F.P. 3 or Kodak Panatomic X. With such film and a green filter, specimens such as those illustrated in figs. 3—5 inclusive, would require an exposure of about $^1/_5$ sec. Positive prints are made on bromide or on chloro-bromide papers, the former allowing greater latitude in exposure. Experiments to increase contrast by using a slower film, 16...24°, of the type Ilford Pan F or Adox KB 14, have been quite satisfactory. Figs. 3, 4 & 5 were in fact made on such film. They illustrate the structure of a chrome-molybdenum steel type 13 Cr-Mo 44 showing the structure at increasing magnification over the range 100—1000 diameters.

Fig. 6 is a ×100 magnification illustrating the structure of a pig-iron specimen containing 4.2% carbon and 4.0% manganese.

The apparatus described is also very well suited to the exposure of color film in the camera should a color record be desired.

The use of the miniature camera for the production of photomicrographs of metallographic specimens has many decided advantages.

It is very quick in operation and there is also a considerable saving in the cost of sensitive materials.

Filing and storage space is reduced to an absolute minimum and there is appreciable reduction in the weight of the filmed records.

Forensic Photography with the Leica

by Professor G. Bohne

Director of the Scientific Department of Criminology in the University of Cologne

SINCE THE PUBLICATION of the basic text-books on forensic photography[1] there has been no doubt at all about the importance of the photograph as evidence in a court of law. The photograph is used both to record the material facts of a case and for the scientific examination of clues. Photography now plays an indispensable part in all criminal investigation conducted by the police, just as it has long been used in the more purely scientific applications of forensic medicine and for the establishment of scientific fact in crime laboratories. The speed with which photography was enlisted in the service of crime detection is in great contrast to the generally tardy or diffident attitude of the authorities when confronted with the proposed adoption of new methods. Photography has meanwhile amply justified its use by providing reliable and objective evidence. Today it can be observed that all advances in photographic means and applications are very quickly noted and put to use by police departments and the various laboratories engaged on research into crime.

This is not at all surprising when one considers that fixation by the photograph is the best and surest means of preserving a permanent record of clues and situations subject to change. Photography is also an invaluable aid in the examination of minute detail at the scene of a crime; of the traces on the instrument used by the perpetrator and of the other clues he may have left behind.

---

[1] Bertillon: *La photographie judiciaire*, 1890; Burinsky: *Photogr. judic.*, 1900; Hans Gross: *Handb. f. Untersuchungsrichter*, 1. Aufl. 1893, 7. Aufl. 1922, I 301 et seq., with other literature by the same author; Niceforo-Lindenau: *Die Kriminalpolizei und ihre Hilfswissenschaften*, 1909; Fr. Paul: *Handbuch der Krimin. Photogr.*, 1900; R. A. Reiss: *La photographie judiciaire*, 1903, and Urban: *Kompendium der gerichtlichen Photographie*, 1910.

180

These are the two principal applications of forensic photography. On the one hand its uses are descriptive: it amplifies, confirms or contradicts the verbal or written evidence of witnesses and, on the other, it supplements the evidence in respect of details not observed by the eye or inadequately described in verbal testimony. It provides an incontrovertible picture record which is often of particular importance in all those cases where it is not at first sight possible to tell which particular details of a scene, which will be disturbed, or what particular aspects of the subject or objects of a crime—also subject to disturbance or decay—will provide the all-important information leading to its solution. The uses of forensic photography are also explorative, and this applies in particular to the so-called scientific applications of the medium in various fields, such as balistics, the close scrutiny of indentations and their causes, the examination of blood and semen stains, the analysis of dust particles and the determination of the authenticity or otherwise of documents and handwriting.

To enumerate the uses of a miniature camera, and particularly the Leica, would be tantamount to listing all the applications of forensic photography.[2] The Leica can also be used to provide the identification photographs required for the completion of criminal records and it could replace some of the extremely costly apparatus hitherto used for this purpose. A camera such as the Leica has a decided technical and economic superiority, particularly in all those cases where cost would prohibit the use of the large quantities of plates and cut film required for the making of a long series of pictures.[3]

The modern ramifications of forensic photography sprang originally from the descriptive picture; descriptive on the one hand of persons—the identification picture in the "rogues' gallery"—and, on the other, of places—the scenes of their crimes. There can be no doubt that the Leica is theoretically capable of making the personal identification picture, as witness the use of Leica pictures in the recent identification and ultimate conviction of a murderer in England, to give but one specific instance. But in practice there are at the moment certain obstacles to the general use of the Leica camera for this purpose. For one thing, the three-part negative has been standardized in all police forces by

---

[2] cf. the recent survey by H. Tetzner: *Die Photographie in der Kriminalistik*. An introduction to the photographic methods used in natural science crime laboratories, Berlin, 1949.

[3] ibid. p. 13 et seq.

the international use of the Bertillon camera and there are no urgent reasons for a sudden change of procedure.

But quite other considerations apply to the photography of the scene of a crime or of an accident shortly after the event has occurred. Here it is necessary to record all the relevant details of the situation, especially in regard to the position of corpses in relation to the surroundings in which they are found; to photograph wounds inflicted on the bodies of living or dead persons and to record every trace, such as finger-prints, foot-prints and the like, left by the assailant. It may be necessary to photograph tire-marks, or the marks left by a housebreaker's tools; to trace the immediate causes and effects of arson, or of explosions; or to establish the precise manner in which a crash occurred, to list but a few of the applications in this field. It needs no special emphasis that the Leica camera, used when necessary on a stand which permits vertical photography up or down, is eminently suited to this type of work, because it provides a full range of interchangeable focal lengths and acceptance angles.

For work in confined spaces (attics, coal-cellars and the corners of sheds), as well as for maximum coverage in large rooms, the wide-angle lens is often a necessity. The wide-angle picture of rooms and of the scenes of accidents in the open presents to the eye a much wider coverage than the eye itself could take in at a glance. This has a particular virtue for the person or policeman assigned to the case because it often enables him to spot relevancies which might easily escape his notice when examining the scene himself and making his notes. The study of such wide-angle pictures is particularly rewarding in all those cases where the criminal has tried to re-arrange a situation and leave a set of dummy clues, as sometimes happens when attempts are made to make murder look like suicide. Often some minor point is overlooked and this the photograph reveals. Decades of crime investigation tend to confirm that the total view of such scenes of a crime, as taken with a wide-angle lens, or fitted together from several such photographs, can draw attention to anomalies or improbabilities which the perpetrator overlooked simply because his vision was restricted and his interest almost solely confined to the victim of his crime. It will be clear that there are many other types of case which would submit to similar treatment, for instance when establishing the effective area of an explosion or the radius over which clues are scattered during an assault, or the widely spread out traces of a traffic accident. In all such cases, and many others besides which can only be hinted at here, the wide-angle lens is often the best possible means of getting everything that is required into the picture.[4] Obviously, photographs can also be made with color film in all cases which warrant its use.

In these applications of forensic photography simple photogrammetry acquires considerable significance. Experience of hundreds of trials has confirmed that it is during the hearing of a case that certain measurements may be required for the first time: the size and dimensions of various objects, their positions in relation to each other and the distances between them, the angle made by an open door or casement window. All these may quite suddenly assume an importance which could not possibly have been foreseen when the investigation first began. Often it would be quite impossible to secure the necessary measurements by re-visiting the scene because vital changes may have taken place. Certain objects may be missing entirely or no longer be in their former positions; doors and windows might be closed or could have disappeared during the course of structural alterations undertaken before the trial began. Here it is only the photogrammetric record, made before anything at the scene of a crime was touched or moved, which will always provide the unexpected measurements sought. Specially constructed photographic apparatus is available for this purpose, such as the Stereometric Camera manufactured by Zeiss-Aerotopograph, to be used in conjunction with the Stereo-comparator supplied by the same firm. With the aid of automatic stereoplotting instruments such apparatus makes possible the construction of plan drawings to accurate scale from photographs of interiors and exteriors. But the equipment is costly, so it is hardly feasible for every regional criminal investigation department to be thus equipped. Fortunately there is an alternative method, at least for the photography of interiors, which is as simple as it is effective. As early as 1916 Robert Heindl proposed a photogrammetric system which did not depend on the use of special cameras; but in spite of its simplicity and reliability it has not found nearly so wide an application as it merits.[5] That this system can be used with miniature cameras such as the Leica, has been shown by exhaustive tests carried out at the Scientific Department of Criminology in the University of Cologne, so it can be expected that the method will be increasingly used by the appropriate law-enforcement officers.

The only additional equipment for the production of a photogrammetric

---

[4] ibid. p. 24 et seq.

[5] cf. Heindl in Vol. 65, p. 1 et seq. in the German Criminological Archives.

record is a square white board (plywood or zinc) of 20-inch side graduated in inches or centimeters along its base, which is the diameter of a semi-circle inscribed in the square. The semi-circle is graduated in degrees from 0—180 like a protractor. One diagonal of the square is also drawn in. This scale is introduced into the foreground of a room to be photographed so that it is included in the picture area. The board must lie horizontal and its base must be absolutely parallel to the lower edge of the photographic frame. The height of the camera above the board or its inclination upwards or downwards from the horizontal has no effect on the photogrammetric interpretation of the result.

Since a scale is included in the picture it is clear that the measurements of all lines that are horizontal or vertical to that edge of the photograph against which the scale is shown, can be read off direct; but it might not be so clear at first sight that measurements of angles or of lines that are neither parallel with, nor normal to, the datum line can also be found; measurements in fact which cannot be ascertained with the Bertillon system. The measurements are derived from the extension of the vertical sides of the photogrammetric square, i.e., of the vanishing lines at right-angles to the base of the square, till they meet in their so-called horizon or vanishing point. All other lines passing through this vanishing point and cutting the base line or its extension must be perpendicular to the base; and all lines parallel to the base and intercepted by any two vanishing lines must be of equal length, which can be read off directly on the datum line or its extension. To find the length of a line that does not run parallel to the datum line measurement proceeds as follows (see fig. 1):—

Let $A\ B\ C\ D$ be the photogrammetric square in a photograph. By extending the sides $A\ D$ and $B\ C$, the vanishing or horizon point H is found. To find, for example, the distance $X\ Y$ between two points joined by a line that is not parallel to the datum line, drop perpendiculars to the datum line or its extension through these points from H and let them cut the datum line at X^1 and Y^1. Through X and Y draw parallels to the datum line which cut the extension of the diagonal $A\ C$ in C^1 and C^2 respectively. From this construction we obtain the triangle $X\ Y\ E$ in which the length of the side $X\ E$ is known because it equals $X^1\ Y^1$, which can be read off direct from the datum line in the photograph. Similarly we know that the angle $Y\ E\ X$ is a right-angle since all lines through H cutting the datum line are perpendicular to it and so are perpendicular to all lines drawn parallel to the datum line. The length of the side $E\ Y = Y\ Y^1 — E\ Y^1$. Y is at a distance from the datum line exactly equal to

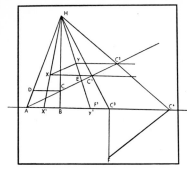

Fig. 1

the distance of C^2 from the same line; and the distance of E from the datum line is the same as that of C^1. But the distances of the points C^1 and C^2 from the datum line are given by the triangles $A\ C^2\ C^4$ and $A\ C^1\ C^3$, both of which are right-angled isosceles triangles since the angles at C^3 and C^4 are right-angles and the common angle at $A =$ 45°. It follows that $A\ C^3 = C^1\ C^3$ and that $A\ C^4 = C^4\ C^2$. Similarly $A\ C^4 - A\ C^3 = C^2 C^4 - C^1 C^3 = Y\ Y^1 - E\ Y^1 = Y\ E$. From C^3 drop a perpendicular $C^3\ F$ (corresponding to the right angle $Y\ E\ X$!) equal in length to $X^1\ Y^1 = X\ E$. Join C^4 to F to make the triangle $C^3\ C^4\ F = \triangle\ X\ Y\ E$. In this triangle $F\ C^4 = X\ Y$. The length of $F\ C^4$ can be read off at $F^1\ C^4$ along the extension of the datum line $A\ B$, which is the photogrammetric scale included in the picture.

To make such measurements it is clear that the Leica negative must be enlarged on a matt paper, but once the principle is understood it is unnecessary to make on the photograph the full construction given here. Fig. 2 illustrates such a photogrammetric scale, graduated in centimeters, included in a photograph taken with a 50 mm. lens. The accuracy of the result is obviously dependent on the accuracy of the draughtsman constructing the necessary figures, and also on the distance of the object to be measured, but results accurate to ± 1 cm. can be consistently obtained and this degree of accuracy suffices.[6]

We have already referred to the photography of clues left behind by a criminal at the scene of his crime, but particular mention should be made of the photography of blood-stains, from the size, shape and respective positions of which valuable deductions can be drawn, as also from the photography of wounds and injuries. It is self-evident that foot-marks and finger-prints, as well as other obvious traces, would be photographed as a matter of routine (figs. 3—5).

The Leica is also very useful in the service of traffic police because it enables them to fix permanently the exact conditions and often the causes of road

---

6 cf. Gadiot et van der Heyden: *Ann. de med. lég.*, 1924, p. 139 and the further suggestions made by Simonin: *Rev. intern. de Crim.*, 1930, p. 131. The process is capable of further development if a cube of 20-inch side graduated in inches or centimeters, is used instead of the flat plate.

Fig. 2: Interior with scale plate. By courtesy of the Department of Criminology, Cologne.

Fig. 3: Reproduction of a finger-print. Universal copying device. Leitz archives.

accidents. Such pictures of a traffic accident are an invaluable aid to the court in reaching a verdict and help also to sort out the insurance questions which inevitably arise (figs. 6 & 7).

Sometimes the use of color film is essential to bring out a point. Miniature color slides can be projected in court to illustrate an argument or a fact. The use of miniature color film permits the making of many more exposures than would be possible, for reasons of cost, with larger film sizes. This applies particularly to color negative processes and the making of color prints, which is a very expensive procedure. The cost of producing large

186

Fig. 4: Trail left by dragged corpse.
35 mm. Elmar at f/9, $^1/_3$ sec., by permission of the Berlin C.I.D.

Fig. 5: Detail from fig. 4.

200 mm. Telyt with intermediate collar at f/12, 3 secs., by permission of the Berlin C.I.D.

187

Fig. 6: Road Accident. Photo: Mayer, Luxembourg.

Fig. 7:
Detail from fig. 6.
Photo:
Mayer, Luxembourg.

numbers of comparative color sequences during the course of long-drawn-out criminal investigations is kept to a bare minimum by the use of miniature color film. Since it is almost grainless the miniature color frame can be enlarged almost indefinitely without loss of definition.

An important application of photography in forensic work lies in the various aspects of copying and the great enlargements possible, such as those used in the discovery of falsifications of all kinds, or in establishing the idiosyncrasies of typewriters and handwriting. Copying is also important in forensic medicine where it is applied to the photographic reproduction of human organs and their injuries, to the entry and exit points of bullets, to burns and other such phenomena. Here the Leica can be used either with a copying device fixed to the vertical column of an enlarger or, better still, with the universal copying apparatus Reprovit II, which permits ratios of reduction from 1:17 to 1:1 and ratios of magnification upto ×6.5. On the other hand, the Leica used with the mirror reflex housing is also suitable for close-ups, for macrophotography and even for photomicrography in conjunction with the Leitz microscope stand US 1, which permits the unimpeded examination and photography of large uneven surfaces, often necessary when investigating the authenticity of works of art, such as paintings. The Leitz sliding copier with ground glass screen is also particularly useful in all those cases where exact picture area and precise focusing are visually determined.

The Leica has proved to be particularly valuable in certain highly specialized forensic fields, such as in the analytical photomicrography of forged, mutilated and altered documents. Here the close optical examination of the specimen is just as important as the chemical analysis of inks and papers and the chemical determination of their age. White, black and colored inks, ordinary and indelible pencils, ball-point pens, black or colored rubber stamps, blue-prints, red-prints or multi-colored prints, can all be optically examined with the aid of different types of light source. Some experience is necessary to know whether the structure of the script will best be revealed by incident or by transmitted light, by infra-red or ultra-violet, by polarized or monochromatic sources, but it is certain that one or other of these will reveal what it is desired to know (figs. 8—10). It may be necessary to establish whether a particular portion of the script lies below, or is superimposed on, another portion; whether a steel pen or a fountain-pen was used; whether pencil or ball-point markings cross over or under ink markings and *vice versa*; whether signatures are original or traced.

189

 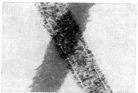 

Figs. 8—10: Line crossings illustrated from left to right are: (a) red ball-point over ink; (b) crayon pencil over ball-point, and (c) ink over ball-point. Photos: G. Bohne.

Where erasures have been made it is necessary to determine what was erased and whether it was written in ink, or in pencil or with a ball-point; and where attempts have been made to blot out what appeared on the original by over-laying ink or paints it will be necessary to reveal the obliterated text. In all such and many other similar cases the task is to find the light source and angle of illumination which will best reveal the structural peculiarities of a specimen under appropriate magnification; and when so revealed to the eye it is just as necessary to make a permanent record of the facts by photographing them. Since such records may consist of whole series of photomicrographs made to reveal the precise character and structure of a single word, and often of each of the individual letters which form it, some system must be adopted which will permit, at reasonable cost, the making of a long series of photomicro-graphs while guaranteeing complete uniformity of results under constant exposure conditions. These conditions are met by the miniature camera and specially by the Leica which, with its well-known micro-adapter, can be fixed to any microscope but particularly to the Panphot, which facilitates its use under widely different kinds of illumination. In a court of law, professional or expert opinion can be visually substantiated by the simple expedient of pro-jecting the photomicrographs during the hearing. This is easily done with a small portable projector and the thorough coverage possible with miniature film effectively forestalls objections or counter-arguments which could be devised by defending counsel if the evidence were supported only by one or two picture records. Apart from its uses in the investigation of forgeries it will be apparent that photomicrography has other forensic applications which can only be mentioned here. They include: the examination of all kinds of small marks or indentations and their causes, the matching of bullets and cartridge cases to the weapons from which they were fired, the confirmation of sperma-

190

tozoa in cases of rape, the revealing of minute traces of blood, the identification of organic and inorganic matter clingingto the clothing and shoes of a suspect, such as hairs, stearin traces, textile fibres, accretions under the finger-nails, among other similar clues. For the photography of such items it is often necessary to preserve the traces by coating surfaces with a layer of lacquer or collodion that acts as an artificial skin which is transparent and protects the clues from destruction or removal. Such a method has been described by Voigt in the magazine *Kriminalistik* (No. 12/1938, p. 265 et seq.), and Bohne has also suggested valuable methods of taking casts of the smallest traces left on bullets (*Arch. f. Krim.* 101, 1937, p. 111 et seq.). These methods have proved useful in detecting clues which are too small to be seen by the naked eye. The transparent skin permits photomicrography by incident or transmitted light and the traces so revealed provide evidence of an accuracy unrivaled by any other method. The applications of the Leica in criminal techniques are even further extended when the camera is used in conjunction with the Leitz Comparison Microscope.[7]

The present writer has made various successful tests using the Leica and micro-adapter not only with the ×10 eyepiece but also with every other microscope ocular in the Leitz range, and under the most varied conditions of illumination. Since the adapter is designed for use with the ×10 eyepiece slight adjustments must be made when using eyepieces of higher or lower power. But in all such analytical photomicrography where many straight and comparative sequences have to be made, particularly in cases of finger-print comparison (dactylography) and rifling marks (balistics), the Leica has proved eminently suitable for use in both incident and transmitted light, and its particular value lies in the fact that it is an easy matter to prepare long series of photomicrographs at a very

Fig. 11: Blood traces on the blade of a knife; preserved by protecting invisible clues with an artificial skin.

Ultropak × 50 with × 10 eyepiece, Photo: G. Bohne.

---

[7] cf. Bohne: Comparison microscope and miniature camera in Vol. 107 (1940) p. 109 et seq., and Vol. 108 (1941) p. 73 et seq. in the German Criminological Archives, also Tetzner: op. cit., p. 40 et seq.

Fig. 12: Falsification by erasure.
Universal copying device, magnification ×2, by normal illumination, Leitz archives.

Fig. 13: Falsification by erasure
Same apparatus and ratio of magnification but illumination by focusing spot-light from the side. Leitz archives.

Fig. 14: Forged signature in a passport.
Universal copying device, ratio of reduction 1:2.5, by normal illumination. Leitz archives.

Fig. 15: Forged signature in a passport.
As above, but erasure revealed by fluorescence. 35 mm. lens, exposure for 20 minutes to a quartz lamp screened by filter UG 1 with a Leitz fluorescence filter on the lens. Lamp/subject distance was 12 inches. Leitz archives.

rapid rate. These advantages of the miniature camera are further accentuated when color film is used for recording color comparisons either on reversal material or, even more so, on negative/positive color films which run up extremely high operating costs if a larger film size is used.

The advantages of using a miniature camera for on-the-spot criminal investigation and forensic use in the crime laboratory may be summed up under the following principal heads:

1. Much lower cost of sensitive materials.
2. Consequent ability to make many more exposures on long film strips and thus obtain a much clearer general impression of the circumstances of a case, including all clues or parts of clues, wounds inflicted, implements used, thorough microscopic analysis of specimens in long and exhaustive sequences, and the possibility of making any number of enlargements or transparencies of all the vital pictures.
3. The comparative ease of copying with the various copying aids made specially for the Leica and the instantaneous adaptation of this camera to photomicrography with a range of instruments specially designed for it.
4. The availability of high quality 35 mm. reversal and negative/positive color film, which is far and away the best demonstration material for the corroboration of evidence.
5. The simplicity of projecting 35 mm. slides during a hearing with very uncomplicated high-performance projection apparatus which does not require darkening of the court and is easily transportable.

But despite these conveniences of miniature methods there are sometimes occasions when the use of large plate negatives is essential for certain types of investigation and for the copying of very large matter. It is clear that there will also be occasions when specially sensitized high-contrast emulsions coated on plates may be needed, because they have qualities which miniature film exhibits only to a lesser degree.

The Leica in Mineralogy, Geology and the Mining Industry

by Professor E. Lehmann, Giessen

I. Photographic Surveys

THE SCIENCES of mineralogy and geology are principally concerned with phenomena dating back several million years. For this reason it is impossible to obtain direct evidence about origins. The existence of a single phenomenon does not entitle the worker to deduce general conclusions, but he must, in order to build up the evidence from which conclusions might be drawn, find corroboration in the existence of other similar phenomena, and as many of these as possible. The quest is fraught with difficulty because finds are distributed in irregular patterns over the faces of continents and are but rarely located in quantity in any one spot. The attentive observer will notice that promising sites, which in practice means virgin soil that is not built over, nor under cultivation, are few and far between. It will be apparent that those who are engaged in a study of the earth's crust must rely to a great extent on methods of comparison and combination made possible primarily by the record photograph. Such photographic documentary records allow the comparison and evaluation of objects remote in space and afford a means of reconstructing, step by step, the probable developments that led to their evolution.

There is another important respect in which photography is an indispensable aid to the mineralogist and geologist. The instructive deformations and discordances of exposed rock faces suffer the inevitable erosion of time: wind, rain, stonefall, growth of vegetation, mutilate or conceal the formations which are particularly prone to total destruction if the bare rock wall is unsheltered from weather. Many kinds of rock disintegrate very rapidly when exposed to the elements. Photography preserves the perishable and, not less important, it provides a reliable means of recording these phenomena at different stages of their existence.

Then there is the task of transmitting the recorded knowledge to others. Valuable though personal exploration in the field always is, there are limits to the ground that can be covered by any one man. The inevitable gaps are filled by the photographic transparency. Photographic sequences can now supply a comprehensive schematic survey where formerly the isolated picture served merely to enliven text. It is no longer necessary to labor the point that the photograph has acquired unrivaled prominence as a visual aid to instruction in all those faculties which rely primarily on the testimony of sight.

The pictorial photographer naturally seeks subjects which exhibit sufficient contrast for his artistic purposes, but things are different for the mineralogist or geologist who applies photography to his subject. Rocks but seldom offer effective contrasts of shape or color, hence the greatly increased importance of effective illumination by existing light. The modeling of light and shade must supply the lack of subject contrast in color; it must be used to emphasize shape and provide an impression of depth. In general, side illumination will provide suitable photographic conditions. Broken cloud in the sky can also be advantageous. Attention must be paid to accentuating stratification because the very slight color differences between strata cannot always be successfully recorded except in favorable illumination. Very often it will be necessary to demarcate strata with a line drawn along the boundary of two layers, but conditions will naturally vary and it may be found that sufficient differentiation will be possible if adjacent strata exhibit widely different surface textures.

Figs. 1 and 2 may help to explain what is meant. Fig. 1 illustrates an outcrop of basalt in the middle of a forest. The rock is a uniform dark gray, in fact almost black. The essential features are the typical pillar-like formation and the preponderantly pentagonal transverse section. Oblique illumination from the right (afternoon) accentuates these characteristics by bright illumination of the transverse sections and heavy shadow modeling of the column-shaped masses. Fig. 2 illustrates quite other conditions: open landscape, clear skies and strong morning sunlight. In the upper parts the white chalk has been carved into bizarre shapes by the action of wind and weather, but lower down it is still a homogeneous mass and contrasts well against the surrounding brown clayey soil. The necessary impression of depth is provided by the structures and trees behind. These objects, or the figures of the workmen on the right, give the scale.

The impression of depth in a photograph is often dependent on the quality

Fig. 1: Outcrop of basalt columns at Bieler Burg, near Wetzlar.
90 mm Elmar, f/8, $^1/_{40}$ sec.

Fig. 2: Weathered limestone at Niedergirmes, near Wetzlar. 135 mm Hektor, f/8, $^1/_{100}$ sec.

of the illumination, but it can be enhanced by including a strip of foreground, or bushes lying to one side of the main subject and positioned in front of or behind it, or by including the overhanging branch of a tree. For close-ups a few wild flowers or blades of grass can be used to similar effect.

II. The Photography of Individual Rock Specimens

Geologists and mineralogists unfortunately are unable to wait for suitable weather or ideal lighting conditions, especially when they go on excursions arranged during scientific congresses or on journeys abroad, when it is seldom possible to re-visit interesting spots. One of the more obvious methods of overcoming the difficulties presented by poor light is to use a fast lens, but there is another and perhaps surer method of photographing what one wants. This is to collect samples of rocks which exhibit in miniature the phenomenon displayed large in natural surroundings, such as, for example, the way in which strata are delineated and the manner of contact at the interfaces of two different types of adhering rock. Transverse sections or ground facets of such large or small specimens will often reveal considerably more detail than can be seen in the natural state, and photographic reproduction presents no problems.

The Leitz copying apparatus illustrated on p. 156 allows full control of light sources with rapid and sure operation. Large areas may call for the use of a wide-angle lens. The surface of the rock to be photographed should be positioned horizontally on the copying-board. Embedding specimens in a bowl which is then filled with water to cover the surface to be photographed is a good method of increasing subject contrast and often to be preferred to the preparation of surfaces with colorless lacquer. Whether lighting should be even or from one side only will depend in each case on the specimen.

Figs. 3 and 4 illustrate the type of photographic record that can be made. Fig. 3 shows how encroaching lava (dark) has dislodged bits of the limestone which drifted into the molten mass before the lava solidified. The specimen came from a small quarry which had been worked for years but, in spite of the pronounced difference in color, it was not possible to photograph in the natural state the join between the two types of rock. The second sample (fig. 4) is a mixture of several rock elements, the internal distribution of which can be made clearly visible *only* by grinding and polishing a facet. The seepage of molten lava has caused a fine pattern of streaks which are clearly differentiated from the black slate and also from the limestone which is in varying shades of gray according to purity. A comparison of these two pictures will also indicate the different methods used: fig. 4 is a ground facet whereas fig. 3 is a transverse section sawn through the living rock. The picture reveals the saw-marks even more clearly than they are visible to the eye when looking at the specimen.

III. Photomicrography

Good photomicrographs can only be made of mineral and petrological specimens which have first been cut into micro-sections. The even illumination of the specimen and the careful adjustment of the microscope are also important factors, and the objective used should be one which is as free as possible from bezel strain and field curvature.* Given these last conditions the others present little difficulty, but for high power work focusing adjustments should be made through magnifying eyepieces. A combination of low power objectives upto

---

* Since this text was written Leitz have announced the production of a new Flat Field microscope objective.

Fig. 3: Nature of the bond between lava and limestone, Vosges Mountains. Rock section enlarged to almost natural size.

P 3 with a Huygens eyepiece will be found satisfactory, but if objectives of higher power then P 3 are used a periplanatic eyepiece should replace the Huygens. For petrological microscopy only those special petrological microscope objectives should be used which are as free as possible from aberration, but some slight curvature of field is inevitable because it is impossible entirely to eradicate it[*]. But even at high magnification I have found it possible to use an 8 mm. apochromat with a $\times 8$ periplanatic eyepiece, or a P 6L $+\times 6$ or $\times 8$ periplanatic eyepieces (magnification $\times 300$—500), and obtain good results (fig. 5). Where the ultimate in resolution is unimportant any of the objectives P 1b, P 2, P 2b, P 3, and P 3b may be found adequate and parts of the negative can be enlarged as desired. For more general pictures at low magnification (1:1 upto $\times 25$) a long focus lens (Milars or Microsummars of focal lengths varying between 20 and 100 mm.) may be combined with mirror reflex housings and bellows.

When exposing through crossed nicol prisms attention should be paid to the

---

[*] See footnote on previous page.   199

Fig. 4: A complex formation from a seam in a mine at Aumenau. Ground and polished surface, half natural size.

avoidance of reflections in the image area from adjacent and strongly bire-fringent mineral crystals (calcite is an example). Such reflections can in general be avoided by adjusting the position of the micro-section. Slight rotation of the analyzer may often achieve the desired effect in this and other special cases where the specimen contains volcanic glass—a method which does not appear to be used as often as it could be. At times the use of polarizing filters might be preferable, but as with most applied uses of photography, various tests must be made to establish the best working conditions for the desired effect. Simi-larly, sub-stage iris diaphragms should be used in the same way as the stops of Leica lenses. The lower the requirements in regard to resolving power the smaller the iris diaphragm that can be used, and *vice versa*. In each case the principal aim will be to depict as clearly as possible only those essentials which it is desired to record.

The uses of the photomicrographs of petrological specimens for instruction and for publication are sufficiently well known. But it cannot be too strongly

Fig. 5: Lamellar systems in the mineral leucite. Micro-section between crossed nicol prisms, enlarged about ×300. 8 mm Apochromat with × 8 periplanatic eyepiece.

stressed that there is another most important application, namely, the use of the photomicrograph as an authentic documentary record. For such documentation preference will always be given to the film record rather than to the plate record for reasons which are sufficiently obvious and have been mentioned elsewhere in this book. It can be taken as a rule that any particular object is not an isolated phenomenon, but that every object is but one manifestation of a complex pattern and serves to illustrate a particular case. The choice of a particular photomicrograph for publication will depend on how typical it is of all the other cases in the complex pattern, though it will depend also on the photographic quality of the record. But all the other observations and records made in the same series are no less important for the evalution of the series as a whole. The systematic recording and classification of such evidence can have the very greatest documentary value. In other words, whenever we come across unusual variants, or when an observation is made for the very first time, or when certain factors indicate a reappraisal of existing knowledge, then the aim should be to record such phenomena in as many photomicrographs as possible and not rest content with but a few exposures. Film archives built up along these lines are invaluable sources of reference and provide fruitful avenues for further research. Every scientific department, institute or laboratory should strive to prepare material for such a film library. The cost in time is negligible since the photographic apparatus necessary is always ready for use once it has been installed.

IV. Color Photography

The color record is more emphatic than the monochrome. For this reason audience response to the color slide is much more immediate than to monochrome during projection at lectures and demonstrations. But it is only seldom that the color macro-record of a petrological specimen will present the same variety and saturation of hue that we find in landscape photography. With minerals and crystals things are different, but here color is only one point of recognition among several, and often the least important of these. Things are different again in micro-sections of rocks, where the same mineral constituent often recurs in many different individual specimens but is differently orientated. Under the microscope the minutest structures can be clearly discerned so that the optical study of micro-sections spreads into many fields other than color. It shows how color is dependent on crystallographic orientation, it measures the principal indices of refraction and fixes double refraction. Rotation apparatus such as the Leitz universal five-axes microscope stage is invaluable in establishing the optical constants of minerals and thus providing a ready means of classification. What more natural than that the color transparency illustrating such observations should be so highly valued in the study of mineralogy. At the microscope only one other person at a time can be given a demonstration, whereas the number of people who can view the projected transparency is limited only by the size of the lecture-room. There is no doubt that the color slide renders excellent service and can replace to a quite notable degree the micro-projection possible only with a cumbersome optical bench.

Every geologist will agree that the examples given in figs. 6—9 concede nothing in quality to the visually observed microscope image. This applies as much to the interference color effects when using an analyzer (crossed nicol prisms) as it does to the records made in polarized light without an analyzer.

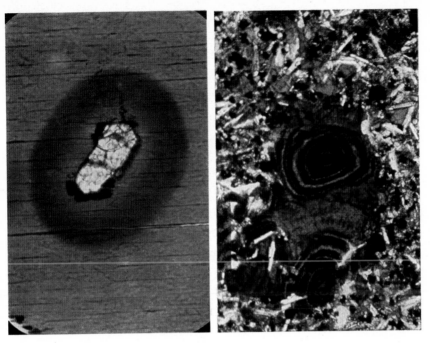

Fig. 6   Fig. 7

Fig. 6: Pleochroic rings surrounding the mineral zircon, in granite, Saxony. Micro-section of rock without analyzer. Magnification ×130.
On Kodachrome film with microscope objective No. 4 and × 6 Huygens eyepiece.

Fig. 7: Rhythmic precipitation of hematite. Basalt from the Westerwald. Micro-section without analyzer. Magnification ×60.
On Kodachrome film with microscope objective 2b and × 6 Huygens eyepiece.

Fairly high degrees of magnification are possible, given adequately corrected microscope objectives and some experience on the part of the person making the photomicrographs. The use of a mirror reflex housing in combination with a bellows extension facilitates exact delineation of the image in sharp focus and allows visual control of illumination, all factors demanding very careful attention for photomicrography in color.

Quite apart from the need for precise exposures, it will be found in the macrophotography of rocks that there are certain difficulties attendant on making, from negative color film, color prints which match the original colors

203

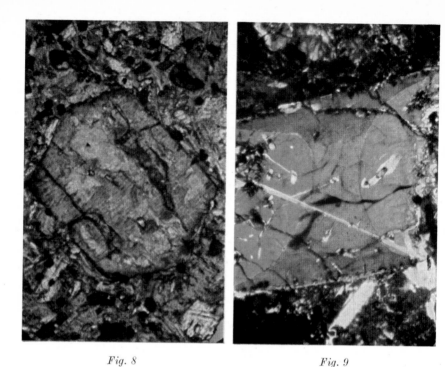

Fig. 8   *Fig. 9*

Fig. 8: Olivine partially transformed into iddingsite. Basalt from the Westerwald. Rock micro-section between crossed nicols at magnification ×60.
On Kodachrome film with microscope objective 2b and × 6 Huygens eyepiece.

Fig. 9: Augite shaped like an hour-glass. Basalt from the Vogelsberg. Rock micro-section between crossed nicols at magnification ×60.
On Kodachrome film with microscope objective 2b and × 6 Huygens eyepiece.

of the specimen. The evaluation of a color record presupposes a knowledge of the actual colors and this knowledge then conditions the choice of the right correction filters when making the print, but unfortunately it is just this knowledge which the photographic assistants in the darkroom lack. It is therefore advisable to include a reference color or test object somewhere in the exposed frame. Obviously a gray scale can also be included in record shots made in the field, but in general the aids are rather more primitive than this and such objects as a hammer or a foot-rule, both part of a field geologist's equipment, are used not merely to give scale but also to provide reference colors.

V. Photography in Mines

An important application of miniature photography which has hitherto received but scant attention remains to be mentioned. It concerns the varied uses of the miniature camera in the mining industry. A short account of some of these applications might not be out of place.

1. Lode-bearing veins below the surface of the earth are subject to constant change as work proceeds and this is particularly the case when mining for ore. To follow the development of a seam by means of pictures made at spaced intervals can provide valuable data in regard to the age and nature of the formation, and can serve as a basis for the calculation of its mass. The pictures also provide information about the state of galleries; they indicate where they may need strengthening and are a useful supplement to the proposed plan of excavation.

2. Movements of the earth strata due to the undermining of supporting masses cause shifts in the distribution of the total weight bearing on the galleries. Since the changes are gradual it is often difficult to detect them with the un-aided eye, but for reasons of safety it is important to maintain constant watch. Such control can be exercised by means of spaced series of photographs made from a constant camera position. By including control marks in the picture area changes can be much more accurately calculated than by physical measuring up.

3. In cases of mining accidents due to collapse there are many reasons why the accurate record of a situation before the collapse, while mining was in progress, and during the clearing operations, acquires significance. The growing recognition of the need for such information provides photography with a task it can perform in unexcelled fashion. The photographic record supplements eye-witness accounts and is often more reliable.

4. There is wide scope for the application of the photographic transparency in the instruction of new personnel entering a mine. Comparative pictures can illustrate correct and incorrect working methods and provide a visual aid to the recognition of danger spots within the mine. Dangerous areas can often be safely approached by a single individual where it would be inadvisable for groups of miners or trainees to progress in a body. Interest in such pictures is always great because they are of immediate concern to the day's routine.

A case can be made for the usefulness, to say nothing of the necessity, of

Fig. 10   *Fig. 11*

Fig. 10: Concrete replaces the older wooden pit-props. The gallery behind has been restricted by a fall. From the Königszug mine. 35 mm. Summaron at f/5.6 from a distance of 15 feet.

Fig. 11: A collapsing stretch from the same mine.
35 mm. Summaron at f/8 from a distance of 15 feet.

photography in the mining industry. Every mine should possess at least one simple and reliable camera that can be operated with the minimum of fuss. It should be of robust construction and capable of high performance, yet be able to withstand great ranges of temperature and humidity. It should be easily transportable and capable of free-hand operation, i.e., at fast shutter speeds, with provision for many exposures without reloading. In short, it must be a camera which has all the features that have proved so very valuable in the Leica. But there is yet another consideration: to ensure effortless operation at least one foreman in every mine should have some training in photographic technique.

Till quite recently photography in mines was a somewhat involved operation.

Fig. 12: Propping up a dangerous overhang.
35 mm. Summaron at f/5.6 from 20 feet.

The main difficulty was illumination but this problem has been resolved by the Leitz synchronized flash-guns for the f series and M 3 Leica cameras, which have well-protected internal synchronization for all shutter speeds and can be used with expendable bulbs or speed lamps. In general a single flash source will suffice but it is preferable to use two flash-heads for pictures to be used as visual aids, or which are intended for publication.

Fig. 10 compares part of a gallery supported by a concrete arch and having normal dimensions with the continuation which has partly caved in under the weight of the earth above and is supported by pit-props to allow just sufficient head room for a man of average height. The picture illustrates the effects of pressure on the galleries. In fig. 11 one whole section of pit-props is falling into disrepair and a further indication of the state of the wood is given by the presence of fungi on the old beams. In fig. 12 we see a section of a gallery the shape of which is dictated by the way the seam runs. The rock overhang at right top has been made temporarily safe by strong pit-props angled upwards from the left preparatory to extending the concrete tunnel which can be seen in the background. The pictures give a good general impression of the dangers of mining and how they are combated by the miner. They are also documentaries in that they illustrate historical developments in mining. It was but a few decades ago that wood was exclusively used for pit-props, but it was slowly replaced by steel supports which in turn were replaced by concrete tunnels in all galleries which have to be kept open for long periods, for instance as permanent lines of communication to the pit-head. Photography in the mining industry serves the dual purpose of instruction and control of safety measures.

It was not intended in this contribution to explain photographic technique. There is no dearth of reliable literature which will serve as an introduction to photographic method. A new and excellent little publication on the subject is Theo Kisselbach's *Pocket Leica Book*, which deals with such questions. Here it has been my intention only to outline some of the applications of photography in mineralogy, geology and mining; to indicate some fields in which the Leica has already been used with notable result, and to suggest others where it may also be applied with equal success.

Schlieren Photography with the Leica

by Dr. H. Jebsen-Marwedel and Theo Kisselbach

(N.B. The term "Schlieren" means, literally, "Striae", such as those found in glass, but is now also applied to the photography of optical retardations in transparent media, such as air, water and gas. Ed.)

In the examination of transparent media, liquids and glass in particular, it is difficult to record slight optical inhomogeneity on a photographic plate because contrasts are very small. To make it visible by means of photography it is often necessary to increase contrast existing between areas exhibiting very slight differences in refractive index. Thus detail can be photographed, for instance in the study of flow phenomena, which would otherwise be invisible to the eye.

The method employed is that of the Schlieren aperture[1] which in principle consists of a knife edge, a slit or a round aperture stop placed at the focal point of a condenser which collects the rays of a light source. Thus only a particular cross-section of parallel rays from the light source emerges through the slit. An image of the slit cast on a corresponding template of the same size as the slit would be uniformly bright or dark. But if a transparent medium to be examined is inserted in the path of these parallel rays, even slight refraction would prevent the deflected rays from striking the template. They would pass to one side and so become visible on a screen (for instance a ground glass screen), or be recorded on sensitive material, behind the template, as either a white or a black record in the image plane.

In the example here given the task was to record the spontaneous formation of characteristic patterns attributed to molecular forces acting inwards under

---

[1] H. Schardin: Die Schlierenverfahren und ihre Anwendung. *Ergebnisse der exakten Naturwissenschaften*, Vol. 20 (1942), Verlag Jul. Springer, Berlin.

surface tension when certain pairs of liquids rest one above the other with a common interface[2]. It was necessary to confine the phenomenon as nearly as possible to one plane, so the liquids were placed in a very narrow glass trough or cell (see diagram on page 212) to obtain, as it were, a cross-section of the kinetic forces which in reality are three dimensional.

This glass trough (8.5 × 10 cm.) was introduced into the optical arrangement described below in order to make such contrasts visible. One of the problems was that it was impossible to proceed as if making a kinematograph record. Once the forces had been set in motion they had to be photographed in stages separated by relatively small time intervals. The speed of operation of the Leica camera made it possible to produce a picture sequence in relatively quick succession. The contrast is all that

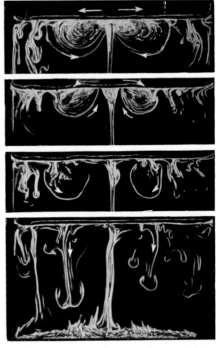

Spontaneous kinetic forces as revealed at the interface of certain pairs of liquids contained in a narrow vertical trough. This diffusion phenomenon was made visible by using the Schlieren method with the Leica camera.

could be desired and the observer obtains the impression that the photographs are stills from a motion picture record. He acquires good insight into the manner in which one liquid diffuses into another from the pattern of these spontaneous kinetic forces. The ratio of reduction was about 1:3 and the optical arrangement is given in the schematic diagram opposite:

[2] H. Jebsen-Marwedel: Das Schlierenwirbelphänomen an löslichen Flüssigkeitspaaren als Analogon zu Vorgängen an der Oberfläche von Glasschmelzen, die von Molekularkräften gesteuert werden und mitbestimmend sind für die Homogenisierung, *Sprechsaal*, Vol. 84, 1951, Nos. 1 & 2.

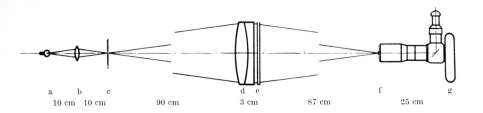

a   b   c   d   e   f   g

10 cm   10 cm   90 cm   3 cm   87 cm   25 cm

The low-voltage Leitz microscope lamp Monla (a) was almost a point source and its rays were brought to a focus at (c) by the condenser (b). At (c) there was a round aperture stop, of 2 mm. diameter, which cut off all extraneous light from the source. A 1:1 image of this aperture stop (c) was formed at a convenient distance by an achromat (d) of 45 cm. focal length. If a circular plate (f) of the same diameter as the aperture stop (c) is placed at the point shown it will intercept all these rays and screen the sensitive material behind

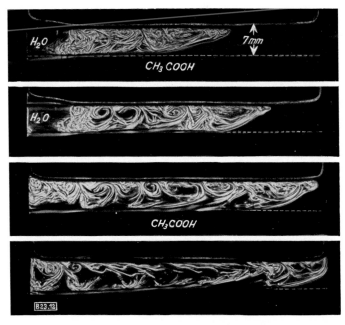

Spontaneous whirls with partial transition to barophoria or intertraction at the interface of certain pairs of liquids. Photograph made with the Leica and the Schlieren method.

it. But if a small trough is introduced into the pencil of rays at the point (e) any changes in refraction taking place in the transparent medium it contains will deflect emergent rays away from the normal point of convergence on the circular plate (f) so that they now pass beyond it and through the optical system of the camera (g) where they can be observed on the ground glass screen, sharply focused and exposed. The kinetic phenomena here reproduced all took place in the trough (e). A 60 mm. extension tube was used with the 200 mm. Telyt lens and fine focus adjustments were made with the lens focusing mount. The whole system was erected on an optical bench. The arrangement and the approximate intervals are as shown in the diagram.

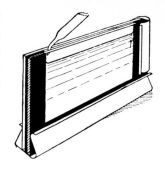

The Leica in the Science of Zoology

by Professor W. E. Ankel, Giessen

AFTER TWENTY-FIVE YEARS of experience with the Leica the zoologist could write a book about it. His moral might be that an instrument which combines so much appeal with such incisive performance will give of itself only as much as is coaxed out of it. The operator develops himself on the Leica while the camera itself remains the subject of interrupted development in the factory of its birth. An end to this development is not yet in sight.

From a fund of experience and knowledge acquired with the Leica only that much can be set out here which will indicate its applied uses over the field embraced by the work of the zoologist. This field is of quite exceptional breadth, extending as it does from the morphology and behavior of large mammals to the minutest peculiarities of sub-microscopic protozoa. It ranges from field work to laboratory research; from investigation to instruction.

To photograph characteristic specimens on the low beaches of Heligoland, covered at high tide and accessible only down forbidding overhangs, was field work with a vengeance. Balancing precariously on slime and slippery algae, buffeted by the wind and fingers clammy with salt spray, I worked there in the spring of 1933. I used the 50 mm. Elmar with intermediate collars and the extensible four-pod "Beeho" and thus obtained the first pictures that really satisfied me—they can still be shown in any company.

Three years later, while attached to the Swedish zoological station at Kristineberg[1], I had more experience but continued to work with four-pods, this time with supplementary front lenses because of their greater depth of field. I had not yet acquired a ground glass focusing screen. With such apparatus

---

[1] Founded in 1877, the Zoological Station of Kristineberg lies on an island due south of Lysekil on the West Coast of Sweden, near the little town of Fiskebäcksil.

pictures of barnacles and limpets were made on the rocky coast (fig. 1). To photograph mollusca clinging to the steep rock between sea level and the surge line is difficult because boats cannot approach. I stood in water upto my chest with the Leica held above my head. There on the steep rock faces worn smooth by glacial action were colonies of limpets all thrown upto about the same height by the action of the waves. To catch such a wave at the right instant required a shutter speed of $1/_{200}$ sec., and the object was to give a good idea of the fringe distribution of the mollusks. Hence large depth of field at a small stop, at least f/9. The sun was low and its rays glanced off the shining rocks. My sunshade had been left on dry land so the lens was shielded with the hand. With body braced against the surge, each wave was anticipated, and as it reached the right height against the rock the shutter was released, but in the next instant the crest broke against the rock wall, submerging the mollusks and kicking back spray on zoologist and camera. This happened five, six, seven times with slight variation in wave levels to make sure of getting at least one

Fig. 1: Limpet (Patella) surrounded by barnacles (Balanus) on a rocky section of the Swedish West Coast. Photo: W. E. Ankel, with Beooy and No. 3 front lens at f/18, 3 secs.

Fig. 2: Limpets (Patella) between sea level and surge line on steep rock (West Coast of Sweden). Photo: W. E. Ankel.

picture that was right. Then back to *terra firma* over the wet and slippery rocks. That was how fig. 2 was made.

The young Swedish zoologists with whom I was working were quite fascinated by this approach to field work with a camera. The Leica was not a very well-known camera at the time and it provided many another surprise for those who were still unaware of its wide range of applied uses. I had a micro-adapter with me, and returning one day from such an outing in the field I entered the laboratory, unscrewed the lens and, screwing on the micro-adapter, went on to photomicrography. Sometimes the session at the microscope would be interrupted because a flight of eider-duck was observed to alight near by. When the films were developed in our little makeshift darkroom, frames like those of the mollusks would be adjacent to others showing thousandfold magnifications. The quality was excellent throughout the film strip and many of those pictures and photomicrographs were later used to illustrate books.

When we first began to collect our Leica experiences the aids were very simple and many a photographic note had to be made from the three-and-a-half foot mark—the closest camera/subject distance that the rangefinder permits. Many such exposures were made free hand during instructional visits to shoals off-shore or to island bird sanctuaries, and proved to be quite satisfactory (fig. 6).

Meanwhile the possibilities for that type of work have been much extended. The optical near-focusing device Nooky has been developed and with its aid focusing is automatic to within $17\frac{1}{2}$ inches of the object (measured from the film plane) and corresponds to a ratio of reduction of 1:6.5. For the 90 mm. Elmar there is another device which permits fixed focus close-ups at a reduction ratio of 1:4. With such accessories many useful pictures can be made which would never be taken with the sliding copier or reflex housing because of the time factor and the need for a stand.

Fig. 3: Larva of the lancelet fish (Amphioxus). Photomicrographs of a living specimen at three different magnifications. Top: lateral view of the antero-posterior axis. Center: Notochord with dorsal nerve cord along which are visible the rudimentary eye spots (black pigment spots). On the ventral side of the notochord are shown the archenteron or primitive gut and the attached liver diverticulum. The muscle segments attached to the notochord can also be seen. Below: detail of the notochord and nerve system.
Micro-adapter, objectives 1, 3 & 6a with × 10 eyepiece and Monla lamp. Photos: W. E. Ankel.

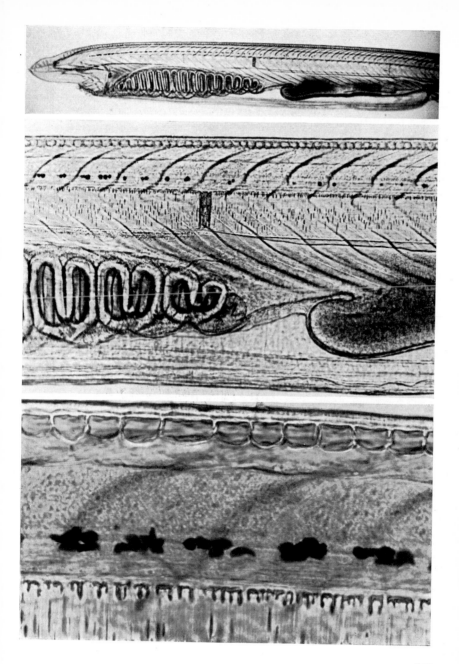

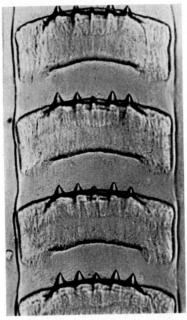

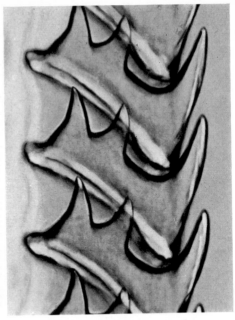

Fig. 4: The radula of a gastropod (Neptunea). These are typical of the Phylum Mollusca and show (left) the center and (right) the edge serrations.

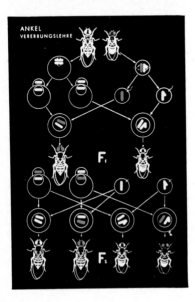

Fig. 5: Schematic diagram as an aid to the study of heredity (From the Ankel Collection of Transparencies on the Study of Heredity). Photo: W. E. Ankel.

Rapidity and ease of operation are expected by the zoologist who uses his camera as a note-book. These facilities are the most important qualities of the miniature camera for zoological and microscope work. I have made hundreds of exposures which I would never have decided upon had I been using plates. The great value of the rapid sequence becomes apparent when assessing results, and since I made this discovery I have always had my Leica with me in the field and in the laboratory, and used it consequently as a photographic note-book. The natural scientist soon learns not to hope for another chance: he almost never witnesses an identical repeat performance. A specimen or a preparation can be photographed while it is under observation and the record is a reliable aid to memory. It is as well to include a scale in the picture area or to photograph a micrometer scale, using the same objective, on an adjacent frame. Let it not be thought, however, that the zoologist will never find it necessary to draw.

Here is an example which may serve to illustrate the value of such "notes". One September night the currents were favorable and carried an extraordinarily rich harvest of animal plankton right into the little harbor of the Kristineberg zoological station. In this single night the haul was so large that I am forever thankful I spent it photographing and drawing the specimens, which included the larvae of mollusks, sea-urchins *(Echinoidea),* amphioxus, fish, small jelly-fish (medusans) and unicellular flagellates. I made photomicrographs of living amphioxus larva at various magnifications and these pictures (fig. 3) suggest drawn illustrations from a text-book and are clearer by far in regard to structure. Those in the know will appreciate their worth; to me they are invaluable as a visual aid when lecturing. Much the same applies to pictures I was also able to make at that time from freshly prepared microscope slides of the tongue-like appendages of the gastropod *Neptunea,* showing the characteristic rows of teeth which capture minute floating particles of food (fig. 4).

Not all such photographic records are of the same quality but they are all indispensable, particularly when writing up the day's work. In photomicrography exact exposure might occasion certain difficulties because most exposure meters are unsuitable for this type of work. The Ilford S.E.I. photometer will be found most useful for precise exposure determination both for microscope work in the laboratory and for photography in the field. Failing this it is advisable in photomicrography to prepare test strips and note exposures for given objectives under constant conditions of illumination. In passing it might be mentioned that the Leica mounted on a microscope (there are micro-adapters for $^1/_2$ and $^1/_3$rd linear reduction of the microscope image) requires considerably less camera exposure than do plate cameras used in the same way. With the Leica it is possible to make instantaneous exposures to microscope images and thus record in sequence the various phases of movement in living specimens; also to extend the possibilities of photomicrography by dark field illumination with its resultant loss of intensity. I prefer to use the Leica focal plane shutter rather than the built-in blade shutter of the micro-adapter. I have found this procedure to be simpler and less likely to lead to errors of manipulation, because the blade shutter is left in the open position.

With advances in modern emulsion manufacture the resolving power of film is high enough to stand extreme enlargement provided the recommended development procedure is carefully maintained. Using film rated at 6...20° and a $^1/_{12}$th fluorite oil-immersion objective I have enlarged Leica negatives to microscope magnification and compared the prints with contacts from a 9×12 cm. plate camera. They were indistinguishable. The great advantage of this is that it becomes unnecessary to carry plates when on expeditions, even though much of the work may be at high magnifications. Moreover, it is quite nonsensical to carry about breakable glass-plate records that might well be irreplaceable. The examples already given will have served to show that the Leica is indispensable apparatus for the zoologist when on expedition or in the field, and my experiences with it were confirmed and amplified in later years when working at marine biological stations in the Bay of Biscay, in

Naples and the Straits of Messina. But it is at home, in the well-equipped laboratory of the Institute of Zoology, that the Leica first reveals the whole breadth of its range. Used in conjunction with the Ortholux, the Panphot, the Panopak, the polarizing microscope and the phase contrast condenser, the Leica makes possible the photomicrography of microscope slides at all magnifications, either by transmitted or by incident light.

Fig. 6: Cast of a marine worm (Arenicola) among two successive ripple patterns left by ebbing tides.

It is used to photograph rareties worthy of preservation in a museum; it is used for making transparencies of the entire collection of photographs in the Institute archives; it is used to copy documents and technical literature, an application which has acquired increasing importance since the war and which has been greatly simplified by the special Leitz copying aids.

During the war I gave courses in marine biology to members of the armed forces at St. Jean de Luz in the Bay of Biscay, and there it was that I first used the sliding copier with magnifying eyepiece for ground glass focusing (fig. 7) and, also for the first time, color film. They have both greatly widened the zoological applications of the Leica camera. For field work we used the sliding copier on a wooden stand with a ball

Fig. 7: Leitz portable copying equipment with adjustable U-base stand for use on uneven ground.

and socket head, and switched to the folding U-shaped stand for work in the laboratory. We photographed in color the animal and vegetable life left on the drift line and in the puddles as the tide receded, and these pictures still live up to the memory of those variegated hues. Since then Leitz have introduced bellows adjustment for the sliding copier and the mirror reflex housing. With this refinement focusing is continuous from infinity down to natural size reproduction. Whether in the field or in the laboratory, there are virtually no limits to the applications of the Leica in the service of the zoologist. Of the many possibilities we can here note but a few.

The zoologist studying the colors of animals can document his findings with color photographs made with the Leica and any one of a number of available optical and mechanical aids. Examples are protective coloration and warning colors (figs. 8 & 9), ability to change color and also the color-sense of animals.

Fig. 8: A variable species but most probably the caterpillar of the Ground Lackey moth (Malacosoma castrensis).

Fig. 9: One of the owlet moths (Diphtera alpium) at rest on the lichen-covered bark of a tree. Notice the good camouflage.

The introduction of certain pigments into living animal tissue permits the observation of internal physiological processes. Every stage in the observation of these extremely delicate changes can be recorded by photomicrography in color.

Hitherto it was necessary to enlist the aid of a painter or sketcher to depict living creatures in the natural color of their characteristic surroundings; but the subjectivity of the artist, desirable in other fields, can introduce unwanted complications which color film avoids.

Zoologists with a flair for painting (and painters with a flair for zoology) have indeed produced color illustrations of animals and parts of living creatures—in some cases the illustrations are hundreds of years old—which are of surprising quality and completeness of detail. Private collections and others difficult of access in lapsed editions of old books, often contain valuable hand-colored drawings, copper engravings and lithographs. These can be copied on color film for the benefit of our pupils. It was only by copying such rare specimens that I was able to deliver a lecture on "The History and Technique of Zoological Illustration".

Many Departments of Zoology are building up collections of transparencies— the harvest of zoological notes made with the Leica on every field day and every voyage of exploration and discovery. The negative record is sometimes regarded as tied-up capital until the time comes to use it for scientific purposes, but with the direct reversal transparency in color every picture made can immediately be used for lectures and demonstrations, and there is no end to repeated display. The possibility of duplicating Kodachromes makes unique material available to ever-widening audiences. In the winter months, when I give my lectures on entomology, I use the color slides made during the previous summer (figs. 8 & 9). It is possible to obtain very striking color effects with a polarizing microscope which reveals minute changes taking place in a structure and fine detail observable only by polarized light. For the first time in the history of zoology, color film has made it possible to record in brilliant reproduction phenomena revealed only by the polarizing microscope, and this material is always ready for use when illustrating a lecture.

Much of the zoologist's knowledge is acquired from stained microscope slides. To display these to large audiences would require micro-projection, but the procedure is cumbersome and valuable originals are exposed to the danger of damage by light and heat. In many instances the projection of the color photomicrograph of original specimens is just as effective and is being increasingly adopted, certainly in all those cases where microscope magnification is not extreme.

Colored wall illustrations, particularly schematic diagrams (fig. 5) are useful visual aids in lecture rooms. They are effortlessly copied in full color with the Leica and reversal color film. The entire collection of hand-colored wall illustrations acquired over decades by the Zoological Institutes of Giessen and Darmstadt were destroyed by fire during the war. This wealth of accurate detail was, however, not totally lost because the precaution had been taken to copy every single one in color reversal material with the Leica camera. After the war the work of replacing these murals was begun with the aid of these Leica color transparencies.

The reproduction of color transparencies for publication in books by means of four-color printing processes is seldom possible in limited editions because of the high initial cost. But fortunately black and white reproductions are easily made from color transparencies and the quality is excellent because the color film is virtually grainless.

The developments that have taken place in photography with the Leica of larger animals in their natural surroundings can be merely mentioned here. Elsewhere in this book there is a chapter on the subject. Here it remains to note the great advances made possible by the introduction of speed lamps and synchronized flash, both of which permit very short exposures outdoors at night or in dark spots. To cite an example, let me tell how a pupil of mine, using a speed light, was able to photograph a wren feeding young at the nest, which was in deep shadow under the typical overhang so favored by these birds. The very short duration of speed flash also freezes the movements of birds in full flight, something that is not possible even with the fastest shutter speed.

Finally, let us return to the considerations with which this chapter opened. Behind the construction of a camera like the Leica there is a vast accumulation of knowledge and experience. To the superficial user the instrument gives unwillingly of the work that has been put into it. The whole range of possibilities open to such apparatus can be spanned only if the operator is himself a willing and knowledgeable student. Here, as elsewhere in technical fields, the personality of the user determines the quality of the end product. Personal effort and ability alone will elevate status from that of serving a highly developed machine to one of being served by it.

Color Photography in Entomological Research and Instruction

by Dr. J. Franz, Darmstadt

(with 8 color pictures by the author)

COLOR PHOTOGRAPHY of insects usually evokes images of brilliantly marked lepidoptera or the sheen and color of tropical beetles. Tempting though this is, it is not the intention here to expand on the aesthetics of insect photography, but rather to confine attention to the practical applications of color photography in the science of entomology.

The subject is perhaps best introduced by a few remarks on photographic method. Since insects are usually very small creatures equipment for macro-photography is indicated in order to permit little or no reduction in the size of the image on the film, or even to allow some magnification of the specimen. The present writer has used the Leica IIIf, and latterly the Leica M 3, in conjunction with the Leitz mirror reflex housing and has found this equipment very satisfactory for the purpose. Lens extension tubes or bellows extension are also necessary for use with a lens of standard 50 mm. focal length and with a long focus 135 mm. lens. With such apparatus one is armed for any eventuality and all ratios of reduction. The slow shutter speeds of the Leica IIIf or M 3 are a very necessary feature because it is often essential to give exposures longer than $1/_{25}$ sec. in close-up work. Any good *reversal* color film, such as Ilford Color Film, Kodachrome or Agfacolor, is preferable to negative color material for insect photography because prints from the latter are made at processing stations by darkroom workers who have no idea of the color rendering that should be aimed at. The reversal transparency can be evaluated by the photographer himself, who has seen the specimen and knows how it should appear in reproduction. Exposure readings should be made with an accurate exposure meter capable of selective readings, like those made with the Ilford S.E.I. photometer. With reflected light meters the reading is not so accurate, but if

Fig. 1   *Fig. 2*

Fig. 1: Web hibernaculum of the caterpillar of one of the Tortricids (Cacoecia histrionana) showing depredation. The color picture clearly indicates the healthy needles, those that have been newly attacked (paleness) and those that have wilted (brown). Fig. 2 is a comparative illustration in monochrome.

such a meter is used after calibration it will be found that a good result is generally assured if the usual bracketed exposures are made with varying lens stops.

The meaning of color photography in the study of insects may perhaps be summarized as follows: with its help the entomologist is now able to record

Fig. 3: Leaf gall of the willow sawfly (Pontania viminalis).

Fig. 4: Typical transverse breeding tunnels of the lesser pine-shoot beetle (Blastophagus minor) on Scotch fir.

Fig. 5: The carnivorous sundew (Drosera) showing tentacles at left bending towards the center to digest prey (a small beetle) trapped by mucilage, while on the right tentacles discard the remains of a digested gnat.

Fig. 6: Host caterpillar of the Figure-of-eight moth (Episema caeruleocephala) bearing a cluster of cocoons of an ichneumon fly (Apanteles). These developed inside the host.

226

3

4

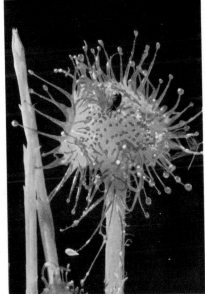

5

6

quickly and accurately the colors of transitory phenomena. This is also largely true of every other scientific application of color photography. But, as the following examples will indicate, it is particularly in the study of the world of insects, where the presence of color is so widespread and subject to such rapid change, that the advent of color photography must be regarded as a definite advance beyond the laborious and only other accurate recording medium—the free-hand drawing.

When insects feed on plants or suck their sap the plant tissue often becomes characteristically discolored. The ability accurately to record the feeding pattern and nature of the damage is a great help to the plant pathologist because various insect pests can be readily identified by the pattern they leave behind. In the case of green plants the change of color in the foliage to yellow or brown is symptomatic of depredation. For the identification of the insect responsible, and thus for the adoption of the appropriate counter measures, the monochrome photograph is soon found to be inadequate. Figs. 1 and 2 are comparative photographs in color and monochrome of the depredations of a caterpillar *(Cacoecia histrionana)* on pine needles, and will illustrate the point. The typical color changes caused by this depredation—the paleness of the freshly attacked needles and the reddish-brown of those that have already wilted—are clearly visible only in the color picture. In spite of advances in modern methods it is still not possible to preserve such sprigs of pine-needles in a satisfactory manner. The needles tend to fall off or—if they are stuck on again—some inevitable damage is done to the vegetable tissue. In such cases the color picture provides the only satisfactory method of preserving the record if one is short of time, or insufficiently gifted, to make a colored drawing.

A striking picture of a pathological condition in plants is provided by the hypertrophy or gall on willow leaf caused by the willow sawfly, *Pontania viminalis*, (fig. 3). The knowledge of the various kinds of leaf and twig galls is a science on its own. Shape and color play a predominant part in determining the many hundreds of types of galls and their causal agencies: mainly sawflies, gall midges, gall wasps of the order hymenoptera. But available specimens for study have hitherto consisted entirely of dried up and uninteresting looking galls. Color photography offers the possibility of filling the much-felt gaps by the collection of color photographs of galls in the natural state.

In applied entomology growing importance is attached to the surveillance of insect populations. Let us assume that a new type of pest has been introduced

228

into a country or that a certain indigenous type of bark-boring beetle (fig. 4) is increasing rapidly in numbers. It is now possible when fighting these pests to instruct all helpers in what to expect and what to look for by showing them projected pictures of the offending types. The entomologist who uses photography as a visual aid would, of course, strive to make his pictures as typical as possible of the destruction caused. The business of instructing the layman is much simplified if good color slides are used because they have a fascination transcending their strictly functional purpose.

In the life cycle of insects there are many chanting situations which exhibit an extraordinary variety of color. It is often necessary to point out these changes to comparatively large numbers of observers, but anyone who has experienced the difficulty of demonstrating intimate biological processes to a wide circle of interested people in the field, will appreciate the simplification

 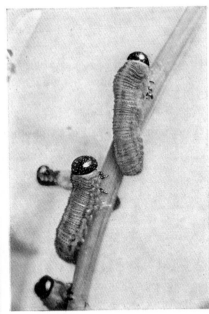

Fig. 7: Assassin bug (Rhinocoris annulatus) sucking out the larva of a European pine sawfly (Neodiprion sertifer).

Fig. 8: Young larvae of a European pine sawfly (Neodiprion sertifer) attacked by a virus disease. Symptom: change of color.

of method which the color photograph permits. For photography in the field it is advisable to be prepared for low magnification work by taking along equipment which will allow three to four times magnification of the object. The insectivorous sundews *(Drosera)* thus reveal more detail in the illustration (fig. 5) than is visible to the unaided eye, and the record is there for all time to demonstrate at short notice the mechanism of capture, digestion and discard.

Fig. 6 illustrates yet another incident from the vast range of this subject (cocoons of the ichneumon fly, *Apanteles*, developing on the body of the living caterpillar of the Figure-of-eight moth, *Episema caeruleocephala*). Our knowledge of the nature and color of insect larvae and pupae is disgracefully limited, simply because most of them cannot be dried and mounted like the imago. Color photography is the ideal complement to methods of preserving larvae in alcohol or other media, particularly when there is little time to devote to tedious preparation (as when on research expeditions). Naturally enough, it is not always easy to make good, sharp pictures of moving insects and their larvae; but such photography will present fewer difficulties if specimens are sought, or collected specimens are photographed, in the early morning, when it is still cool. The activity of insects decreases with decreasing temperature, but in addition to restricting their movements in this way they then can be photographed by the favorable reddish illumination of morning sunlight. It is, however, necessary to know something about the vitality of specimens in various degrees of cold, else one will find that the "star turn" might decide to draw in his extremities, relapse into torpor, or behave in other ways unfavorable to photography of a *typical* condition. One should not try to make a beginning in entomological photography by chasing butterflies as they flit from flower to flower. It is less discouraging to start with more static specimens providing easier conditions for the photographer (fig. 7).

Three other photographic pitfalls should perhaps be mentioned: heavy shadow, reflections and wind. In oblique sunlight it will generally be found possible to work with the camera horizontal and the sun almost directly at one's back, but should conditions be such that a heavy shadow is thrown to one or other side of the insect it is advisable to brighten it up with a reflector —a piece of white cloth will often serve the purpose. It should be unnecessary to stress that the photographer would not choose to wear a bright red pullover when bending over to photograph a white butterfly, and green reflections from trees can also be troublesome when working in a wood. In such unfavorable conditions for good color photography, or when there is a breeze, it is advisable to remove the specimen, complete with the foliage or twig on which it rests, to a more favorable spot, providing always that the insect is one that cannot fly away when disturbed. But such complications need not be dealt with here, since it is natural to suppose that only the patient entomologist, hardened to disappointment, would venture on such quests.

Finally, a word or two about color pictures of *pathological discoloration*. An insect attacked by a virus or a parasite will often suffer characteristic changes in the coloration of its body. Fig. 8 illustrates the condition of young larvae of the European pine sawfly *(Neodiprion sertifer)* attacked by a virus disease. The healthy larvae of this species are yellow-green in color whereas the diseased larvae are brown, tinged with violet. This color change, together with the shrunken bodies and their attitudes on the needle, are as typical as they are transitory. Fig. 9 illustrates similar discoloration caused by the presence of a parasite. In this case the fully grown larvae and females of a species of scale bug *(Gossyparia ulmi)* are shown on the branch of an elm tree. In spite of some loss in reproduction (the projected transparency illustrates the condition admirably) it will be observed that many of these creatures are a light brown color and that these are also somewhat smaller than the other females. Such variation in color and size is often caused by parasitical attack, in this case by a minute parasitic fly of the genus *Coccophagus*, which develops inside the body of the host. In such cases the color picture gives a fairly accurate indication of the degree to which parasitism has progressed and is a useful documentary record of a transient state.

Fig. 9: Fully-grown larvae and females of a scale bug species (Gossyparia ulmi) found on elm trees. The females which appear reddish are the hosts of a parasite fly (Coccophagus).

231

Such examples could be multiplied indefinitely but it is our task here merely to indicate the applications of color photography in the study of insects (cf. article by the same author in *Die Umschau* No. 1/1950). The collection of specimens and the free-hand drawing are not rendered superfluous, but the color photograph is an additional aid to securing fuller color records of insect ife than have hit hertobeen possible, and making these records available to others.

Leica Photography in the Service of Microbiology

by Dr. Erwin Burcik, Hohenheim

It WAS ABOUT seventy-five years ago that Robert Koch drew attention to the photomicrography of micro-organisms by pointing out how difficult it was to sketch them satisfactorily. The difficulties rose to insurmountable proportions when bacteria were cultured in colonies or their behavior observed in liquid media. It was only very occasionally that a gifted hand could represent with pencil or brush the exact conditions obtaining during microscopic observation. Photography was the only possible answer.

The following comments may serve to demonstrate the important place that must be accorded to miniature film in microbiology. It is not the intention of the writer to demonstrate everything that can be done with the Leica in this field but rather to indicate applications where its use is of definite advantage. The personal experiences retold here, in company with the observations of other authors contributing to this book, may provide suggestions useful to wider circles in this and in other fields.

The science of microbiology is concerned with short-lived and sensitive micro-organisms, if we discount the stained and reasonably permanent preparations. Certain very delicate organisms, such as protozoa, can succumb within a very few minutes to the influence of the microscope lamp. Many micro-organisms are themselves in motion or else subject to the *Brownian movement* of molecules in liquid preparations. Such organisms cannot be satisfactorily photographed with the old and well-tried plate microscope cameras. Quickness of operation and the ability to observe the specimen right upto the moment of exposure, and indeed during the exposure itself, are essential. The Leica and the Leitz micro-adapter "Mikas" are an ideal combination for such difficult photomicrography. Like an ordinary microscope eyepiece, this combination of camera and micro-adapter is merely placed in the draw-tube of the micro-

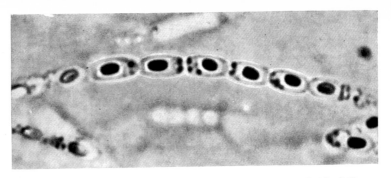

Fig. 1: Bacillus mycoides with spores. Unstained living preparation. Bright field.
Leica micro-adapter with 1 × conical tube, apochromat × 90, N.A. 1.30, enlarged approximately × 3000.

scope and fastened there by means of a thumb-screw. The ability to focus and observe the microscope image right upto the moment of the exposure is particularly important for all microbiological specimens under cover glasses, because movement or change in the distribution of the bacteria is more or less prevalent in all such preparations. With unstained preparations the very minute differences in refractive index and the very small size of the micro-organisms dictate that focus must be set for one particular optical plane in order to obtain a photographic record exhibiting sufficient contrast (fig. 1). Here the telescopic focusing eyepiece of the Leitz micro-adapter has proved much superior to ground glass focusing, as many comparative tests have revealed.

The conical tubes supplied with the "Mikas" micro-adapter vary the choice of magnification between $\frac{1}{3}$, $\frac{1}{2}$ and full microscope magnification. This allows selection of the most suitable image field and also takes in account the conditions governing optimum total magnification. This is of considerable importance when transparencies are to be made from the negative. The projected picture appears to each observer to be of different magnification according to his distance from the screen. In the photography of micro-organisms, which contain fine detail lying at the limits of microscope resolving power, it is necessary to adhere strictly to Abbe's Laws. Only those projected pictures whose magnification on the screen lies within the limits of useful microscope magnification will be found satisfactory. Abbe's Laws governing the resolving power of microscopes and the limits beyond which magnification is "empty" can thus be taken in consideration before the picture is exposed, by a simple choice of the right conical tube for the micro-adapter. This is a much more thorough method than the expedient of merely changing the eyepiece for one of different magnification.

The gain in intensity of image-forming light (square law), and the consequent reduction in exposure times with the conical tube allowing the least magnification, is of particular value when using dark field illumination or a phase contrast condenser. Compared with photomicrography on 6×9 or 9×12 cm. plates the much shorter "camera extension" of the Leica with its micro-adapter —actually the shorter traverse of image rays to the film plane—brings with it so great an increase in the intensity of image-forming light that even a small microscope arc lamp will easily permit instantaneous exposure of microorganisms with phase contrast procedure (fig. 2).

Now what is the position in regard to the photomicrography of stained specimens with the Leica? The opinion is often advanced that here the photographic plate is definitely superior to the miniature film, and this in spite of the fact that the technical literature contains many illustrations which show that the Leica format is well able to produce results on a par with plate exposures. In our experience the failures are attributable not to the miniature film but almost always to incorrect illumination of the specimen. The relatively coarser structure and coloring of an histological microtome section are much less susceptible to small errors in the positioning of the light source than the very

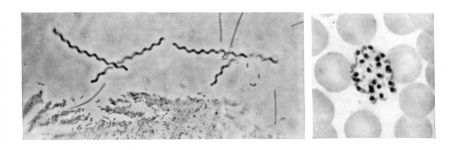

Fig. 2   Fig. 3

Fig. 2: Spirochetes from sewage. Instantaneous exposure of living specimens with phase contrast. Apochromat Pv 40/0.70; Leica micro-adapter with $^1/_3 \times$ conical tube; arc lamp; 80...31° film, $^1/_{50}$ sec, enlarged approximately $\times$ 1500.

Fig. 3: Plasmodium vivax. Giemsa stain. Leica micro-adapter with 1 $\times$ conical tube. Achromat, $\times$ 100, N.A. 1.30; yellow-green filter, enlarged approximately $\times$ 2000.

delicately stained and extremely fine details of a microbiological specimen placed against a completely clear viewing field. Moreover, the high orders of magnification necessary for most microbiological preparations require particularly careful adjustment of the microscope lamp in order to avoid the formation of diffraction patterns round outlines and unevenness of field, both of which impair the quality of the image. The iris diaphragm on the sub-stage condenser should not be closed more than is absolutely necessary and the Köhler principle of illumination should be scrupulously maintained. Figs. 3 and 4 are photomicrographs of specimens delicately stained by the Giemsa method, which often presents particular difficulty in satisfactory reproduction. For both these records the Berek sub-stage condenser with two iris diaphragms was used. This arrangement leads almost automatically to correct Köhler illumination.

Side by side with correct (or critical) illumination of stained micro-organisms the choice of the right filter is also important to the results. Where monochromatic specimens are to be rendered in as high contrast as possible, such as bacteria with an intense stain, a strong contrast filter would be used: for a fuchsin stain

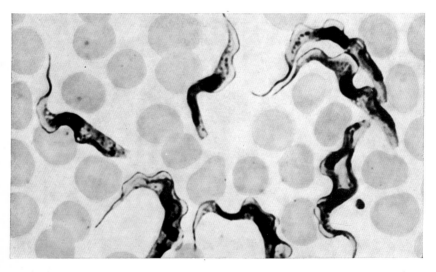

Fig. 4: Trypanosoma brucei. Giemsa stain.
Leica with mirror reflex housing. Apochromat × 90, N.A. 1.32; yellow-green filter, enlarged approximately × 2500.

a dark blue-green filter, for a methylene-blue stain a strong orange filter, and so on. Optimal results under the most difficult conditions can be obtained with the large Leitz Monochromator with its high light transmission. It allows the selective emphasis or suppression of even the most minute details provided only that the detail required is differentially stained from the unwanted detail. If micro-organisms are to be photographed in natural color the Leica with its micro-adapter is an ideal equipment for the purpose, but it should be remembered that the elimination of color cast from a delicately stained image of micro-organisms, usually seen against a predominantly white field, is considerably more difficult than when photographing the bolder stain of an histological specimen. Even the faint green color of the glass object stage can cause a shift towards the green not only in the clear white field but naturally also in, for instance, the light blue of plasma stained by the Giemsa method. The load of the microscope lamp and the age of the bulb also play a part in determining color response at high magnification.

It is outside the scope of this short article to deal with the technics of color photomicrography in microbiology. Here we can only stress that the photographic reproduction of micro-organisms on color film is no more difficult than making the monochrome photomicrograph once the necessary basic principles have been grasped and some practical experience obtained in the use of reversal color materials. In addition to the color photomicrography of stained specimens by bright field illumination, fluorescence micrography and the Hoffmann method (fig. 5) can also be applied. Using these two latter methods the gain in the intensity of illumination is of particular importance.

It was mentioned above that drawing or painting colonies of bacteria was as good as impossible. Experience shows that the photography of similar objects is not without its own difficulties. Even low power magnifications of the photographic image have their own peculiar laws.

In such cases the use of miniature film is a decided advantage. Since the small negatives are always enlarged, a double camera extension will permit a print magnification of from three to eight diameters. Should it be necessary to have greater magnifications of colonies of micro-organisms which can be seen with the naked eye, special miniature lenses like the Microsummars or the Milars can be used without a microscope; or the camera itself can be fitted to a microscope draw-tube for the photography of objects too small to be seen in any other way.

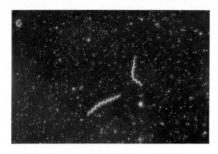

Fig. 5   Fig. 6

Fig. 5: Treponema pallidum. Dark field illumination using the Hoffmann method, which has since been supplanted by the Heine system based on Zernike.

Leitz micro-adapter with 1 × conical tube, apochromat × 60 with iris diaphragm and dark field condenser D 1.20 A. Agfacolor daylight film, enlarged approximately × 1200.

Fig. 6: Mirror-like colonies of Bacterium ozaenae on Endo's fuchsin agar.

Leica revolving stage, 50 mm Elmar f/3.5 at f/8, Agfacolor daylight reversal film to daylight. About half natural size.

For most low power work the standard 50 mm. Elmar f/3.5 will be found suitable. The necessary lens extensions are provided by extension tubes or the long extension bellows, and focusing is on ground glass either with the sliding copier or the Visoflex housing.

Illumination is just as important in macrophotography, but no rules of thumb can be given because of the varying nature of specimens. Because of the restricted diameter of the image field, the Leitz microscope lamp "Monla" is useful. It can be focused to a spot, and angled from one side it throws detail into relief (fig. 7). For work by transmitted light a light-box, or a sheet of plate glass arranged so that light or dark backgrounds can be inserted below it, can be used. Black velvet gives a dead black background without reflections.

For the color photography of colonies of micro-organisms daylight illumination is to be preferred, because tungsten tends to falsify the gray and yellow tones which are fairly prevalent in such subjects.

Reflections from the specimen can be eliminated by using a polarizing filter but in our own practice we dispense with it because the peculiarities of the surface are often an essential character of the colony. Fig. 6 illustrates a fuchsin-stained colony in which the reflections of the cross-bars of a window are to be discerned, clearly illustrating the shiny surface of the mirror-like bacteria which have multiplied in the broth.

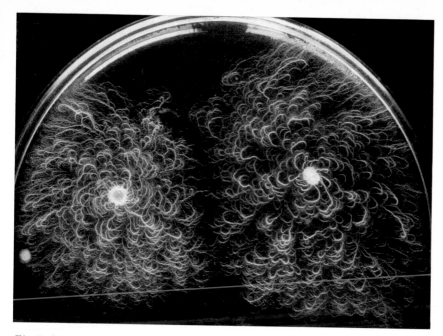

Fig. 7: Colonies of Bacillus mycoides on an Agar plate.
Leica revolving stage, 50 mm Elmar f/3.5 at f/8. Oblique Monla lamp illumination.

It is often stressed that color film should not be reserved only for scenes or specimens exhibiting great variety of hue. Figs. 8 and 9 again illustrate the point in this special field. The difference between the flat grayish colonies of *Bacterium coli* in fig. 9, and the smaller cream-colored colonies of *Corynebacterium bifidum* could not have been recognized in a monochrome reproduction, but color brings out such slight differences in hue. In such work, of course, great care must be taken to prevent color cast.

The choice of suitable sensitive materials is as important in microbiology as in any other photographic field. For photomicrography experience has taught us to use a slow orthochromatic film. Panchromatic emulsions would only be used in isolated instances whenever it is essential to preserve a correct tone scale. Resolving power is of primary importance and, almost equally so, good protection against halation. It is apt to be forgotten that micrography by transmitted light—the illumination most often used—presents in acute form all the problems of backlit exposures.

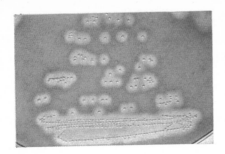
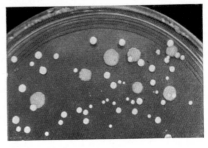

Fig. 8   Fig. 9

Fig. 8: Colonies of hemolytic streptococci on blood agar.
Data as for fig. 6.

Fig. 9: Colonies of Corynebacterium bifidum and Bacterium coli on a special agar plate.
Data as for fig. 6.

In cases where fast emulsion speeds are essential, such as for instantaneous exposures at high magnification, in phase contrast work, by dark-field illumination, in fluorescence micrography and the like, a very fast film might occasionally be used as an extraordinary measure.

In all cases the aim should be to produce fine-grained negatives. Gradation will be dependent on the contrasts of the specimen. Intensively stained preparations—fuchsin or Gram stains—will yield good pictures when development is hard, emphasizing the characteristic shapes of micro-organisms. For colonies, delicate Giemsa stain, and similar subjects with a long tone scale, development should aim at preserving gradation on a long gray scale for optimum natural effect. For color work in our own laboratories we have decided, after numerous tests, to use only reversal color materials. Our experience—and it has been confirmed by colleagues elsewhere—is that negative color film is less suitable for the production of photomicrographs for use in research and instruction. It might be found satisfactory for the coarser coloration of histological specimens, but there is not much to be said for the use of negative color materials when accurate color response to delicate hues is required. To obtain a satisfactory positive print is fraught with difficulty because the printers in the processing stations have no idea of the color balance to be aimed at. They must make countless test prints, referring back all the while to the client, before they can produce a satisfactory enlargement. The cost in time and money rules this out of court.

Tests with Kodachrome reversal film all, unfortunately, showed the same fault—a tendency to exaggerate color. With this material it proved impossible to obtain the same delicacy of pastel, and particularly blue, rendition exhibited by Agfacolor reversal film. Anscocolor reversal film, on the other hand, yielded excellent transparencies, but it is still difficult to obtain this material in Europe.

Below we mention some of the films and developers used by us and name their applications but no claim is made that the list is comprehensive.

Film:	Applications:
Agfa Agepe Document film Ilford Microneg	With and without contrast filter for all photomicrography where the aim is to obtain maximum resolution and good contrast.
Agfa Isopan FF Adox KB 14 Ilford Pan F Agfa Isopan F Adox KB 17	For macrophotography and photomicrography in accurate tone scale reproduction. Photographs of colonies of bacteria would usually be made on medium pans, 32...27°, because the gradation of the film is less steep.
Agfa Isopan ISS Ilford HP3 Adox KB 21	For instantaneous or short time exposures under light of poor photographic quality.
Agfacolor Reversal film (Daylight)	For all color exposures to daylight, in fluorescence micrography and to fluorescing screen images.
Agfacolor Reversal film (Tungsten)	For photomicrography and macro-work by tungsten illuminant. The low-voltage Leitz Monla lamp is rheostat controlled for light of the right color temperature.

Developers:	Applications:
Fabofin Ilford I.D. 11 Johnsons Fine Grain	Fine grain developer. Excellent compensation and very fine grain. Suitable for all types of film but the recommended times of development for each must be rigidly maintained.
W. 665 Atomal Ultrafin SF Ilford I.D. 48 Johnsons Meritol	Developers yielding maximum resolving power for use with negatives which must be greatly enlarged (murals for lecture rooms, etc.).
Negutan Johnsons Azol (at low dilution)	Energetic developer for use in cases of known under-exposure to obtain maximum negative densities, but with relatively coarse grain.

It might seem curious that so little has been said about equipment. The reason is simple and of particular interest to the practical worker: the apparatus already mentioned, namely, the Leica with the standard 50 mm. Elmar lens, a device for close-ups (sliding copier or bellows) and the micro-adapter "Mikas", span the entire range of photographic applications in microbiology. For very critical work some might prefer to use the Aristophot and the Ortholux microscope with its universal applications, but with a little experience it is relatively simple to produce comparable pictures with the apparatus already named.

The simplicity of apparatus is a deciding factor in microbiology. It should always be ready for use on the spot, and the simpler the equipment the easier it is to maintain fully hygienic working conditions. In our experience the use of the Leica allows the photography of living slide cultures under conditions which present no difficulty in maintaining absolute sterility. This is very important because colonies of micro-organisms must often be photographed *before* a sample is extracted with a hollow platinum needle—a process which, of course, destroys the specimens.

The quality of microscope objectives and the ease of manipulation of the instrument are important considerations in micrography. This is particularly so in regard to illumination. For normal microscope stands the microscope lamp "Monla", and especially the modified version "Monlafix", can be thoroughly recommended, but optimum conditions of illumination are, of course, more easily ensured by apparatus equipped with built-in illumination such as the Ortholux or Dialux microscopes. The monotubes supplied for monocular or binocular vision (or both) make for ease of operation. In a single movement they allow the change over from visual observation to photographic recording. Regarding microscope optics it will be found that achromatic or fluorite objectives are quite satisfactory for most photographic applications in microbiology, and especially for stained preparations exposed through a strong filter. It is only for difficult subjects at high magnification that apochromats will be definitely superior. This is particularly true of photomicrography in color. The purity of color rendition possible with an apochromat is often unobtainable with achromatic objectives, least of all at high magnification.

This short article on the applications of the Leica in microbiology would be incomplete were we not briefly to consider the miniature camera as a direct instrument of research. The advantages of miniature photography in other spheres apply equally to this one. The saving in time and money allows the preparation of photographic records on a scale which is out of the question when using the "small" 6×9 cm. format. We have long since converted to recording and filing the results of our research work on miniature film. Time and again we have found that photography supplies a much clearer account of the work done than the longest of detailed written descriptions. Many of these photographic records are put straight into the files and remain there pending the time when they may be required for enlargement.

The examination and photography of living micro-organisms often calls for quickness because the rapid growth and multiplication of individual cells can bring about a quite different stage in their existence within a few hours. When sequence studies are made it is often impossible to keep pace with developments without assistants who write down everything observed. In many such cases the Leica has rendered excellent service. Recently in the course of two days we were able with it to follow the development of nearly 200 different unicellular yeast cultures, one after the other, without taking any notes save the occasional jotting down of a figure. The development of these cultures, starting in each case from a single cell, was recorded in several hundred miniature photomicrographs.

The Leica can also be used to advantage for the measurement and counting of micro-organisms. For determining the number of individual cells present a counting chamber or a netmicrometer may be used in the following way. For studying the rate of increase the counting chamber is filled and an exposure made. The chamber is then cleaned, refilled and another exposure made, and so on. Within an hour or so the count can begin on the photographic prints, made on a matt paper so that each cell can be struck off with a soft pencil as counted. Though this may seem complicated it will be found in practice that it is time-saving and more accurate than a visual count under the microscope; moreover, each count is thus documented.

Those who have measured micro-organisms will know the difficulties inherent in the method of using the stage and eyepiece micrometers for direct measurement under the microscope. The detour *via* the miniature negative greatly simplifies things and the results are of greater accuracy. The first step is to photograph the divisions of the stage micrometer through every combination of microscope objective, eyepiece and micro-adapter conical extension which it is intended to use for measurement. These records once made and annotated are preserved for use whenever required. Next, the specimen to be measured is photographed through the microscope and a positive print at ×1000 or ×2000 magnification, as necessary, is made. On this print, while still on the enlarger baseboard, the stage micrometer photographed through the same combination of microscope optics and conical extension is printed superimposed at the same magnification, namely, ×1000 or ×2000, in a convenient position on the paper.

The required measurements are then conveniently made with the help of a magnifying glass on the finished print; the measured cells are marked and those of any particular diameter to be counted are suitably indicated. But it is important that the print should be in normal gradation. Prints that are too hard or too soft, in the photographic sense, can be a source of error because of the minute dimensions of the objects to be measured. Our experience has shown that long series of measurements can thus be carried out with great economy of time and without the rapid tiring of the worker who measures directly through the microscope.

We are very conscious that these few examples of the applications of the Leica in microbiology leave much of the field uncovered, but they may suffice to show how this miniature camera through its optical and mechanical precision, its versatility and handiness, has rapidly acquired a usefulness in microbiology which makes it an indispensable aid to instruction, to research and to the applied aspects of this science.

Color Photomicrography
in Polarized Light as Applied to Plant Cytology

by Dr. H. Ziegenspeck, Augsburg

and Dr. Hans H. Pfeiffer, Bremen

WITH POLARIZED LIGHT we are able to reveal structural differences in plants and animals to a degree not often possible by methods of artificial staining. With the Leitz "Biopol" or with a polarizing microscope the cells and tissues of plants can be separated into color patterns with an effect that is at once instructive and surprisingly beautiful. Using a gypsum compensator Red I it will be found that photomicrography in color of specimens and their backgrounds provides material of considerable scientific value and sometimes of high aesthetic quality. In the language of chemistry the term "optical staining" is now employed to describe these methods, which reveal the minutest differences in structure under the microscope and indicate changes of state in leptonic or ultra-microscopic particles (beyond the resolving power of the microscope).

It thus becomes the business of research not merely to observe but also to *record such phenomena in natural color*. Although the tendency today is still to rely on monochrome to record structural differences where possible, the time is not far off when conversion to color processes will be inevitable despite their cost. In many cases the change over has already been made. As things are the Leica system is the obvious choice for color work, particularly since it is now possible to produce from the Leica transparency any number of excellent color prints,[1] which can be used in epidiascopes instead of micro-projection of the original slide. Since the Leica micro-adapter can be used with any standard microscope there is no qualitative or quantitative application of polarization

[1] W. Raths, *Z. angew. Photogr., Wiss. Techn. 4*, 92 (1942).

microscopy[2] to which it cannot also be applied, although there are certain aspects of research, dealing primarily with macroscopic orders of magnification or reduction, where the mirror reflex housing might be preferred. For successful application of the Leica to photomicrography by polarized light it is, of course, essential that the microscopist should be as familiar with the laws of photomicrography[3] as he is with his specimens so that he may recognize the limits of photomicrographical evaluation. It need not be stressed that such experience cannot be had without cost, and even the most experienced must reckon with some failures or near misses. But to help keep them to a minimum it might be as well to outline briefly some *fundamentals of technique*, though some experience will be necessary to apply them. The *sensitive material* is Agfacolor negative film (Leverkusen), rated at 16...24°, which does not exhibit any serious color aberration even when slightly under-exposed. The *light source* should correspond in color temperature to the photoflood illumination for which the film is balanced, so a low-voltage lamp such as the Leitz Monla 6V, 5A with a radiant field stop and a transformer and rheostat for mains voltage stabilization is ideal. Another very good light source for accurate color rendition is a gas discharge tube made by Osram[4]. Because of the limited exposure latitude of the film some difficulty may be experienced in accurate measurement of exposure times. It is well known that over-exposure is coupled with an increase of brightness (burning out), loss of saturation and a shift in hue towards the color of the layer that has received the least exposure and is thus most intensely dyed, whereas slight under-exposure increases saturation. If under-exposure is excessive saturation again decreases, shadows are "clogged", and there is a shift of hue towards the colors of the two emulsion layers that have received the strongest exposure and are thus more intensely dyed[5]. Those who by experience have acquired the ability to judge correct exposure on monochrome negatives may attempt to derive the correct exposure time for color by first making a monochrome test strip, but this method can be full of surprises and is not really critical enough for determining correct exposure. Others may be prepared to accept the high

---

[2] Hans H. Pfeiffer, Polarisationsoptische Untersuchungsmethoden in Biologie und Medizin, in: *Siegeszug der Mikroskopie, Festschr. z. 60. Geburtstag v. W. J. Schmidt* (Frankfurt a..M. 1944); — *Das Polarisationsmikroskop als Messinstrument in Biologie und Medizin* (Braunschweig 1949).

[3] E. v. Angerer, *Wissenschaftliche Photographie, eine Einführung in Theorie und Praxis*, 3. Aufl. (Leipzig 1943); — K. Michel, *Grundzüge der Mikrophotographie*, 3. Aufl. (Jena 1949).

[4] A. v. Larzio, *Kinotechn. 25*, 60 (1943).

[5] A. Grabner, *Photogr. Rdsch. Mitt. 78*, 247 (1941).

additional cost of bracketed exposures, that is, making three exposures of each subject on the color film: one at the estimated correct exposure, one at half this exposure and a third at double the estimated value. Intermediate exposures between these values could also be made but cost is the limiting factor. By keeping records of successful exposures a measure of accuracy is provided for future work. It should also be mentioned that color shifts due to slight variation in exposure are proportionately less

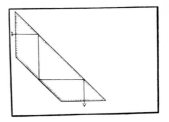

Fig. 1: Sectional view of the Berek Compensator (E. Leitz Wetzlar).

if the exposure is a long one and correspondingly greater if the exposure is short.

Some commercially available exposure meters are adaptable to photomicrography. They include the Ilford S.E.I. photometer (see Ilford Technical Information Sheet U 308) and the Tempophot[6]. Other suitable aids to the determination of exposure are actinometers and extinction photometers,[7] but both of these are inferior to systems, like the Ilford S.E.I., where subject brightness is measured against a standard incorporated light source.

For photomicrography in *polarized light* it will be necessary to use a polarizing microscope meant for the purpose, but other microscopes can be used if provision has been made for the acceptance of nicol prisms or two polarizing filters (the polarizer is placed between the light source and the sub-stage condenser while the analyzer is usually at the position of the eyepiece). For most research microscopes, such as those used in medicine and biology, Leitz have introduced, for work by polarized light, the new "Biopol", which freely permits the use of other ancillary equipment. All such polarizing instruments are entirely suitable for photomicrography, both for normal orthoscopic observation and for axial (conoscopic) images through a magnifier. With a prism known as the Berek compensator (fig. 1) even very small optical retardations (anisotropic effects) can be successfully recorded by polarized light in the photomicrograph.

For photomicrography in color often only apochromatic objectives with com-

[6] M. Wieland, *Anleitung zur Bestimmung der Belichtungszeit für die mikrofotografische Aufnahme mit dem elektrischen Belichtungsmesser* (Wetzlar 1916); — Br. Lange, *Photoelements and their application* (New York 1938).

[7] H. Wessel, *Bl. Unters.- u. Forsch.-Instr. 17*, 4 (1943).

pensating or periplanatic eyepieces which flatten the field are used, but well-corrected achromats, such as those for which the "Biopol" is designed, will exhibit no chromatic aberration even at high orders of magnification. The color photomicrographs reproduced here were made with a three-lens condenser of numerical aperture 1.0, but there is less chance of chromatic aberration if an achromatic condenser of numerical aperture 1.4, or an achromatic-aplanatic condenser of N.A. 1.0, is used.

What is the *procedure* for making color photomicrographs with the Leica ? With the Leica fixed to the microscope stand the image is viewed for definition and correct field through a telescopic eyepiece while fine focus adjustments are made with the microscope controls. The light source is positioned about 12 inches from the microscope plano-mirror and centered exactly in its middle. The sub-stage condenser is racked out almost as far as it will go and the preparation is placed on the stage and sharply focused, using at first a low magnification objective (about ×10) and then successively higher powers. The definition of the image, which is cast on a ground glass screen resting on the tube from which the eyepiece has been removed, is controlled by means of a magnifier. The *exact centering* of the optical system is of the greatest importance, but with vertical microscopes beginners might here experience some slight initial difficulty. By adjusting the sub-stage iris diaphragm and the angle of the microscope plano-mirror an even disk of light must be obtained along the axis of the microscope tube and in the center of the ground glass screen resting on it. When this condition has been fulfilled open the radiant field stop on the light source to a diameter of 10—15 mm. and the sub-stage condenser iris diaphragm as wide as it can be. With subjects of low contrast it might be necessary to close the sub-stage diaphragm a little. When using lowpower objectives for polarization microscopy some people prefer to interpose a field lens between the light source and the microscope mirror or to clip a small aspherical collector lens to the polarizing member of the nicol prisms.

The few examples reproduced here may serve to illustrate what can be done by photomicrography in polarized light. Of these figs. 2 and 3 are respectively a transverse section and a radial cut through fir wood. The transverse section shows that the wood of this typical gymnosperm consists entirely of tracheids (imperforate cells with continuous primary walls), which in the spring have wide lumina and thin walls. The lumina get narrower and the walls thicker as the tracheids are formed later in the year towards the fall. The picture clearly

248

indicates wide tracheids gradually narrowing until they widen abruptly again in the following spring and so trace the seasons, leaving an annual ring in the wood. But above and beyond this the use of polarized light here permits the study of the micelles of the cell wall, which are beyond the resolving power of the microscope. The two rays, ordinary and extraordinary, into which the polarizer splits transmitted light, proceed at different wave velocities. One of these rays is retarded and it is given a further relative retardation by the analyzer which brings it into the same plane of vibration as the other ray so that a phase difference becomes apparent, this difference of phase varying for each of the component colors, i.e., visible wavelengths, of white light. For certain wavelengths this interference causes a reinforced wave while for others the wavelengths are mutually destructive, so that instead of white light the so-called interference colors or fringes are formed. If a double refracting (anisotropic) specimen is placed in the paths of these rays it will influence their behavior in a definite way, producing certain effects which will be "additive" if the vibration plane of the specimen is parallel with the vibration plane of the polarizer, and "subtractive" if these two planes are crossed. By using a gypsum compensator Red I, with direction of vibration as shown by the horizontal arrow at fig. 2, the background appears red to magenta in color (instead of dark), and all the cell walls running parallel to this direction appear blue or green (in the addition colors, see Table), while those at right angles to this direction appear yellow or white (subtraction colors).

When—as in the case of the cellulose walls of plant cells—the type of birefringency and its dependence on the orientation of the ultra-microscopic micelles or chainlike cellulose molecules which build up the cell wall, is known, it is possible to infer the manner in which a coherent system of such molecular aggregations[8] exist in the cell walls (or, as in fig. 2, in the intercellular substance surrounding each cell). Similarly, the radial section (fig. 3) shows adjacent tracheids and their numerous bordered pits on the surface of the section, but the use of a gypsum compensator further reveals that a pair of quadrants running tangentially to the circumferences of the bordered pits appears in the addition colors blue to pale yellow, and a second pair of quadrants, at right angles to the first pair, and also tangential to the bordered pits, in the subtraction colors yellow

---

[8] H. Ziegenspeck, *Mikroskopie* (Vienna) *3*, 372 (1948); — Der submikroskopische Bau des Holzes, in: H. Freund, *Handb. d. Mikroskopie in der Technik*, *5/I*, 371 (Frankfurt a. M. 1951).

to black—i.e., the micelles are arranged tangentially to the circumferences of the bordered pits.

Table of interference colors with and without gypsum compensators (red) of the first and second orders.

mμ	without gypsum plates	Addition colors	Subtraction colors	Addition colors	Subtraction colors
		with gypsum compensator Red I		with gypsum compensator Red II	
158	Gray-blue I	Blue II	Yellow I	Blue III	Yellow II
259	White I	Green II	White I	Green III	Green II
332	Yellow I	Yellow II	Gray-blue I	Yellow III	Blue II
505	Orange I	Orange II	Gray I	Orange III	Indigo II
536	Red I	Red II	Black	Red III	Red I
589	Indigo II	Violet III	Gray I	Violet IV	Orange I

Roman numerals indicate the first and higher order spectra clearly defined when using gypsum plates of the type mentioned.

Even deeper investigation is possible and further knowledge can be derived if, for instance, the *metachromatism* and *dichroism* of these crystalline structures are studied. Here, again, photomicrography with the Leica is an invaluable aid to research.

Fig. 4 is a tangential view of the wood of a deciduous tree, namely, the linden or lime tree, and it should be noted that the direction of vibration of the gypsum compensator Red I is horizontal, as shown by the arrow. Again we have an additive blue and a subtractive yellow coloring of the cell walls. From existing knowledge of the chemical composition of the cell walls and the nature of their double refraction we are able to deduce the fact that the arrangement of the micelles must be pericellular.

Figs. 2—4: Color photomicrographs of wood in polarized light. Fig. 2: transverse section, and Fig. 3: radial cut through fir; Fig. 4: tangential view of linden or lime tree wood. Objective 00, × 10 periplanatic eyepiece with ¹/₃ adapter and Leica using gypsum compensator Red I, Monla Lamp, 3 secs.

Fig. 5: Color photomicrograph of the petiolus of Nuphar advena showing the inner hair cells with projecting crystals of calcium oxalate embedded in the walls. Objective × 4, × 10 periplanatic eyepiece with ¹/₃ adapter and Leica using gypsum compensator Red I, Monla Lamp, 3 secs.

250

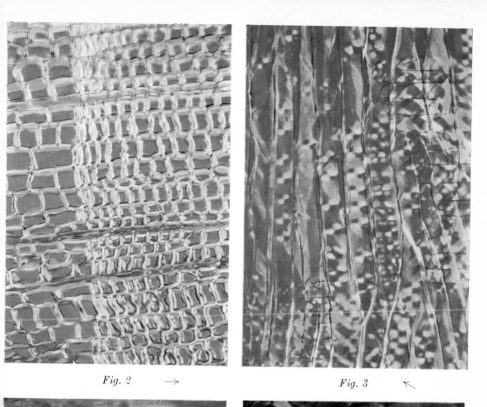

Fig. 2   →

Fig. 3   ←

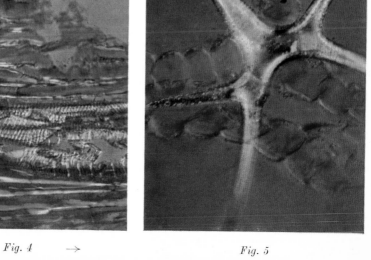

Fig. 4   →

Fig. 5

Lastly, let us consider a rather more easily made microscope preparation as photographed in color between crossed nicols. Various examples could be given, such as the starch grains of the common potato or the easily detachable epidermis of a leaf, revealing its stomates and their guard cells, but in fig. 5 we shall consider a preparation easily cut with the hands, namely, the petiole or leaf-stalk of water-lilies *(Nymphaea)* and more specifically of the species *Nuphar advena*. In the intercellular spaces visible to the unaided eye star-shaped hairs are found at low magnification. These were discovered and described by *H. Mohl*, but about seventy years ago there was a lively controversy between *H. Schenk* on the one hand, and *Friedrich G. Kohl* and *H. Molisch* on the other, over the question whether these hairs were embedded in the cell walls or merely stored in the cell. These hairs are orientated inwards and reveal a very fine granularity consisting of monoclinic crystals of calcium oxalate, a substance which disperses light strongly even when the crystals are very thin.

Notice how the addition and subtraction colors delineate certain definite parts of the hairs. A closer examination of the individual crystals can, and indeed does, provide certain basic information about their optical characteristics. Crystals lying along their *clino-axes* appear dark between crossed nicols, and in the subtraction colors with a gypsum compensator Red I if the clino-pinacoid faces are parallel with one of the vibration planes of the nicols. But if these faces of the crystals make an angle of 45° with the vibration planes of the nicols—i.e., the vibration planes of the crystals are parallel with their clino-pinacoid faces and with a plane at right angles to these—then the specimen appears very strongly colored (in addition colors with a gypsum compensator). But crystals which lie along their *clino-pinacoid faces* exhibit double refraction even more strongly; they are dark between nicols if the clino-axis is parallel with the nicol vibration planes—i.e., if the vibration planes of the crystals are parallel with their clino- and ortho-axes.

Such examples could be multiplied and extended to qualitative and quantitative investigation of the dye dichroism of biological and medical objects.[9] But the short account above should suffice to illustrate the value of being able *to record in color* the "optical staining" which preparations can be made to exhibit. In the realisation of this aim there is no doubt that it would be difficult to over-estimate the importance of Leica technique.

Hans H. Pfeiffer, *Expt. Cell Res. 7*, 169 (1954).

The Importance of Color Photography in the Study of Botany

by Professor Werner Rauh,

Botanical Department of the University of Heidelberg

AFTER NEARLY twenty years of continuous development in color materials it seems a bit late to write about the importance of color photography to botany. For many years now the color photograph has been an essential visual aid in the study of botany both in schools and in universities. In no other branch of natural history does color, as compared with shape, play so predominant a part. The greens, reds, yellows, blues and violets of plant life are but very inadequately represented in the monochrome print, so it is hardly surprising to find that the entire botanical faculty converted to color photography within a very few years. From the wealth of available material only a few examples can be given here.

Color photography has the greatest significance in the taxonomy or classification both of the lower (cryptogamic) and higher (phanerogamic) plants: among the cryptogamia there are many organisms, such as the colored bacteria (*Bacterium prodigiosum*, Sarcinae), the brown bacteria and the red bacteria which can only be exhibited to a large circle of students by means of the color photograph. The differences between the various kinds of algae, the red, green and brown algae, are much better brought out by good color pictures than by mere description. Most kinds of fungi, the lower as well as the higher orders, can often only be recognized because of color differences. Consider a book on edible and poisonous fungi illustrated only with black and white prints—it is as useless to the uninitiated as if there were no illustrations at all!

The classification of the higher plants centers mainly on the usually conspicuously colored flower organs. These organs are too small to be exhibited in their natural size to a lecture room full of people, but they can be greatly magni-

 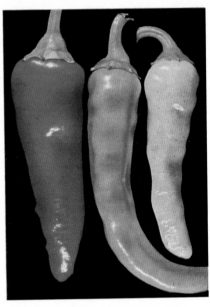

Fig. 1: Fly Agaric (Amanita muscaria).
f/12.5, ¹/₁₀ sec., on negative color film.

Fig. 2: Capsicum pods. f/12.5, ¹/₁₀ sec., with
copying aid on tungsten type Agfacolor reversal film.

fied by means of the color photograph. This enables the lecturer to explain
clearly and with few words the structure of flowers. It will be found that the
systematic use of projected color transparencies for this purpose will also tend
to rid this subject of its notorious dryness.

Color photography is also an inestimably valuable aid in explaining certain
questions concerning the morphology of plants. Consider, for example, the
bracts of some of the higher plants. By bracts are meant those leaf-like organs
which are in the immediate vicinity of the bloom and which generally differ
from foliage leaves only in that they have a simpler structure or are less developed. In such cases the monochrome print might be quite suitable for demonstrating the transition from foliage leaves to the simpler structure of the bracts;
but there are plants, of which a spurge *(Euphorbia pulcherrima)* may serve as
an example, where the bracts do not differ from the foliage leaves in any respect

Fig. 3: Oriental Poppy (Papaver orientalis). f/9, ¹/₂₀ sec., on Agfacolor reversal film.

254

save color. Only the color photograph can bring out the difference. Similarly, color photography may be used to notable effect in plant physiology. If, for instance, in a series of lectures held during the summer, it is necessary to discuss the dye formations which give leaves their blazing fall coloring, no suitable demonstration material is available at that time of year. The color transparency is a substitute that is entirely satisfactory.

In questions concerning heredity and, in particular, the existence of hybrids, the color photograph once again renders splendid service.

In plant ecology no difficulty is now experienced in studying the variety and color of whole plant societies or the individual physical factors of a single specimen, because we are able to demonstrate in color both the type of vegetation indigenous to an area immediately accessible as well as plant life from different habitats scattered over the face of the earth.

In applied botany color photography has been used for some years with success. The pathology of plants and the physiology of parasitism are much more emphatically demonstrated in color than in monochrome.

These few references to the uses of color photography in botany do not exhaust its applications. They should be regarded merely as pointers to other uses. To summarize: we have attempted to show how color photography has supplanted monochrome work in botanical instruction during the past few years, but it should not be thought that a color transparency can completely replace the actual living specimen. Some happy mean must always be struck between the demonstration of living specimens and the showing of colored reproductions.

Hints on the Color Photography of Plants

Since the first edition of this book appeared many new Leica accessories have become available which are ideally suited to the color photography of flowers and plants. The most important of these is the universal focusing bellows for use with the Visoflex housing and the 135 mm. Hektor lens. The Leica becomes a bellows camera, with all that that means in speed and accuracy of operation. With the long focus lens it is possible to pick out detail from a distance, a factor which is important when photographing mountain flora because the use of a

Fig. 4: Tropical Orchids (Dendrochilum saccolabium).
f/9, $^1/_{10}$ sec., on Agfacolor reversal film in back light.   →

stand is essential and could cause trouble on difficult ground. The uninterrupted focusing range of the bellows extends right down to natural size reproduction of small objects. If magnifications are desired ($\times 2$ or greater upto $\times 6.5$) a Leica lens of shorter focal length can be used with the bellows, or those who prefer it might try the Reprovit II with a 24 mm. Microsummar lens and extension tubes. For general views and parts of a plant the 50 mm. and 90 mm. Elmar lenses will be found most suitable.

Particular attention should be paid to backgrounds, because they are more prominent in color than in monochrome. Background colors should not be assertive, but rather neutral or quiet. In applied photography good contrasts are often desirable. Colors appear more brilliant if they are seen against the very dark background of black velvet. It will seldom be possible to make pictures that are both scientifically valuable and aesthetically beautiful unless a little deft arranging is done which excludes superfluous items.

As far as possible daylight should be used for the exposures. Although there is a greater risk of exposure error, it is to be preferred to the more constant illumination of tungsten. For daylight work the diffuse light from a haze-covered sun is preferable to direct sunlight, because shadows are softer. Despite the rules about frontal illumination for color film it will be found that flowers can be photographed in direct back light, which increases the brilliance of color and adds modeling to shape. It should be added for the sake of completeness that ultra-violet light sources may be used for certain types of object which fluoresce. Color film is very suitable material for recording the fluorescence of chlorophyll, of aesculin, of eosin and fluorescein.

And now a word or two about the most suitable color materials for the photography of plants.

The colors of Kodachrome are very brilliant but somewhat too fierce in the greens. Moderate over-exposure will often yield fairly good results. More subdued and perhaps even more accurate renderings of color are possible with Agfacolor and Anscocolor reversal films. The latter of these is very difficult to acquire in Europe. Quite good results can now be obtained with negative color processes. Color negative films have certain advantages over reversal materials: color casts or hue shifts to which the latter are sometimes prone can be eliminated by appropriate filtration of the color negative when making the print. Any number of positive color transparencies can be made from a good color negative, which can also be used in the normal way in the enlarger for the purpose of making monochrome prints. Lastly, when using color negative materials in the camera, one is largely independent of the prevailing weather conditions and the nature of existing light. Well-saturated and accurate color response is assured even under dull or rainy skies.

Finally, let us touch upon a point which really deserves the much fuller treatment of a separate discussion. All makes of color film suffer from an inability to record accurately the pure blues of certain flowers, such as the cornflower or the gentianella. In the color record there is a shift towards the magenta which can to some extent be prevented by under-exposure. This peculiarity is not due to any fault of the color material but is traceable to the optical peculiarities of the petals of such flowers. Seybold established that the petals of all flowers, including blue flowers, exhibit a fairly strong red reflectance which is not noticeable to the eye but which is nevertheless recorded by the "physically objective" response of color films. So we obtain a red image as well as a blue one and the two together cause an apparent hue shift towards the magenta. One could try to suppress this tendency by using filters which exclude the red, but it is almost inevitable that the effects of such filtration would be noticeable in the modified response of the film to the remaining colors of the record.

Photography in the Service of Somatology and Psychology

by Dr. Hans Fricke, Wetzlar

IT IS UNFORTUNATE that photographic methods are all too seldom employed in psychology and phenomenology. This is particularly true of the applied aspects of these sciences, so it might be of some value to report here on the more useful applications of photography to these fields, in which the present writer has been occupied for several decades and taken the opportunity to collect photographic material running into several tens of thousand exposures.

But first a few basic comments: notable advances in photography have made available apparatus and materials with which it is possible to record all and more than the eye can see. However, it is necessary first to see in order to be able to record, while the recording is a matter of accomplished photographic technique. This should be stressed at the outset in considering the fields under review. Trained observation can never be replaced by the photographic print, but the print makes it possible faithfully to record what is observed at the essential moments of its occurrence. To do this successfully requires suitable exposure technique and practised mastery of apparatus.

To suit the requirements of each case it will be necessary to photograph either the whole body or parts of it in a completely satisfactory and objective manner. The first essential in the photography of the whole body is that the picture must be entirely free from the distortions which might falsify relative sizes and measurements in the print. It will, accordingly, be necessary to make the exposures from increased distances and to ensure that the taking apparatus

Figs. 1 and 1a: Somatic exposures, with scales.
The entire body: photographed from a distance of 16 feet with a lens of 135 mm. focal length and mirror reflex housing. Two vertical strip lights were the main illumination.

Figs. 2 and 2a: Pictures of a head.
(Only frontal and sagittal views together reveal all the details of face and skull)

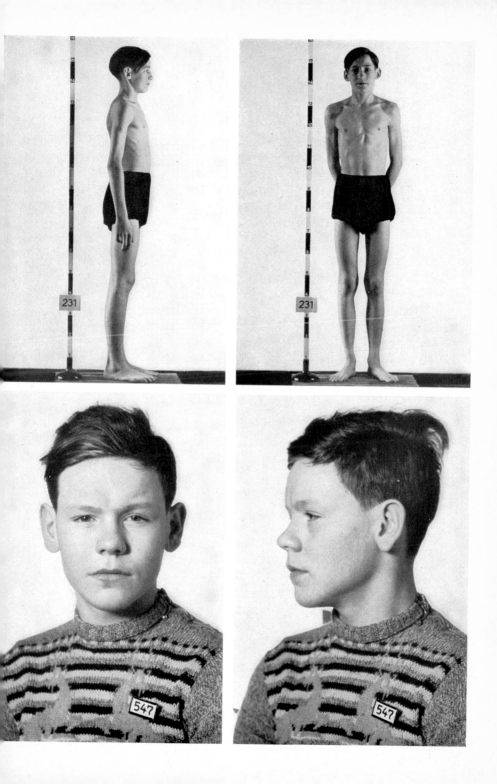

is absolutely level. A long focus lens permitting a minimum camera/subject distance of 13 feet and uninterrupted ground glass observation of the subject would be the only satisfactory equipment. It is the ability to observe the ground glass image right upto the instant the exposure is made, which permits the necessary control of subject definition and illumination. In order to extract measurements from the prints a suitable scale should be included in the picture area and positioned in the same plane as the subject.

Illumination deserves attention. Lights should emphasize the body contours and throw the surface structure (musculation) into readily discernible relief. I have found vertical strip lighting (fluorescence tubes) very satisfactory. Positioned slightly to one side (oblique illumination) it sheds an even light over the whole subject and throws the surface structure into ideal relief. If so-called daylight fluorescence or strip lighting with a bluish emission is used it will be found that flesh tones and skin gradations are particularly good. Moreover, the photographic (actinic) efficiency of such lighting is so good that two 40 W. tubes positioned side by side will, in a room with light walls, permit an exposure of $^1/_5$ sec., at f/4.5 on medium speed films, 32...27°, without the use of any other light source. Backgrounds should preferably be white. If the strip lighting is correctly positioned it will, as a rule, be unnecessary to employ any other special lighting. To brighten up shadows on the far side a white reflector is ample, though an additional light can be used if desired. To obtain the outline of the entire body against the background it will be advisable to make the subject stand on a small pedestal to which the height scale is also fixed.

When making pictures of the whole body for use in somatology it should be borne in mind that posture is very largely conditioned by the psychics of the subject. The natural tonicity of the body, peculiarities of posture and individual

Fig. 3: Frontal view of a boy's head.
Face with a strong intellectual cast. Picture was made with a long focus lens during an excursion. It was necessary to guide this particular situation in order to obtain a picture of the individual "repose" attitude.

Fig. 4: Well-defined features of a boy from section of a negative. Sagittal view of a face with strong features; made during an outing.
135 mm. Hektor.

Fig. 5: Mimetic behavior. Subject was in rapid movement under poor existing light.
35 mm. lens with very fast film.

Fig. 6: Long focus lens and artificial light. The head was in movement.

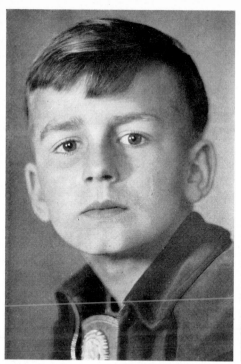
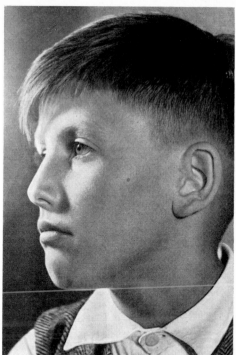

4

6

deformities can only be recorded under "natural" exposure conditions. In such cases the subject is best put at ease by informality of approach: the business of exposure is treated as a mere incidental and no attempt should be made to correct the bearing of the subject before the exposure is made. It will, of course, be self-evident that in certain special cases it may be necessary to induce the reverse conditions: it may, for example, be desired to photograph the manifestations of an emotional state in which the subject can hardly be said to be at ease.

For distortion-free records it is essential to use a rigid stand the height of which can be quickly adjusted so that the optical axis of the lens is always horizontal at exactly half the subject's height. If the lens axis is tilted from the horizontal there will be unavoidable proportional distortion of the image.

On the other hand, when photographing only certain parts of the body or its structural formation, it may be necessary and even desirable to tilt the camera— i.e., to select an oblique viewpoint from above or below. In some cases pronounced back light may be necessary to throw up fine details of surface configuration or bring out certain outlines more clearly. For such work the bundled beam of a spot-light is sometimes useful. In these cases I use a clear 100—250 W. projection lamp with a concave mirror to direct the beam.

Particular interest attaches to the photography of the face. It may be that the structure and shape of the head and face are required or, in addition to this, the individual cast of feature conditioned by peculiarities of musculature and fleshy parts; or yet again it may be desired to record fleeting emotional responses in cases of mimetic behavior.

For such work strip lighting can be used only for general illumination because its reflections or "catch-lights" in the eyes would be elongated and appear unnatural. For this purpose I therefore prefer to use two diffused tungsten sources of which one is the main light angled from the left and above while the second is positioned directly in front of, and at a greater distance from, the subject in order to brighten up shadow. Illumination from both sides may perhaps yield pictures having greater "effect", but it should be avoided in the interests of objective clarity in the record of shape detail. In some cases it may be necessary to disregard these rules and even, in certain circumstances, to use a spot-light from behind the subject. In the photography of the face, with its strong power of expressing emotion, care should be taken to ensure that each picture records some momentary psychological reaction in addition to showing

Fig. 7: Group of young spectators on a playing field. Chance shots with a long focus lens can have great value in the assessment and description of individual qualities.
400 mm. Telyt.

the purely physical outlines of individual features. It is the responsibility of the specialist to play on the emotions of the patient and so guide them that the clearly defined responses desired are in fact momentarily exhibited at just those times when all the other conditions required in the record are satisfied. Time and again it has been confirmed in practice that, in all such cases, it is not photography which is the main purpose but rather the establishment of *rapport* with the personality with whom one is confronted. To make a record of one's observations calls for some adroitness in the manipulation of the camera. For head studies I always try to avoid the use of strong lights.

The most suitable photographic equipment for the purpose is again, in my view, a long focus lens of sufficiently large relative aperture used in conjunction with a mirror reflex housing. Satisfactory results can also be had with a standard lens but it is always better not to have the camera in the immediate vicinity of the patient unless this is absolutely necessary. Even in cases where facial detail is required, such as the expression of a mouth or the imitative play of features, it will be found impossible to obtain a satisfactory record without a long focus lens and ground glass control of the image. For purely scientific purposes the background should again be preferably white, though toned or dark backgrounds often improve the plasticity of the record print.

In passing it should be mentioned that special exposure technique might be necessary for certain scientific aspects of this work. By the use of colored light or, in certain cases, of invisible radiation (ultra-violet, infra-red), pecularities of the skin blood vessels and of the arrangement of veins and arteries may be made visible in the photograph. By projecting a squared graticule onto the skin it is possible to measure form details or displacements of the body surface. Stereoscopic evaluation is also possible by using the Leica stereo-attachment. For all such special cases the investigator would develop his own methods or would seek competent advice.

For the applications described above, an interior room suitably equipped will be found most satisfactory, but this would not, of course, apply to the large number of action pictures of body movements which are best made in the open. A systematic kinetographic record of individual peculiarities of movement could also be made indoors now that we have flash and speed lights permitting very short exposures under poor conditions of existing light, but in general it will be preferable to do this kind of work out-of-doors.

The technique of open air photography need only be touched on in this connexion because it corresponds closely with the normal use of the camera. Correct exposure and focus settings, together with a thorough knowledge of negative techniques, will be the only essentials. In most instances the standard (50 mm.) focal length should prove satisfactory, though I prefer the use of long and very long focal lengths even for this work, in order to be able to operate from a distance, more or less unobserved, and thus unlikely to disturb natural situations. The biggest problem is to obtain satisfactory definition of body movements since these are often unexpected and very quick. Greater field depth is always possible since the long focus lens can be stopped down, but the resulting increase in exposure time might sometimes cause image blur. To hit the right compromise between aperture and shutter speed is something of an art and it may often be found necessary to use the fastest available film in order to over-

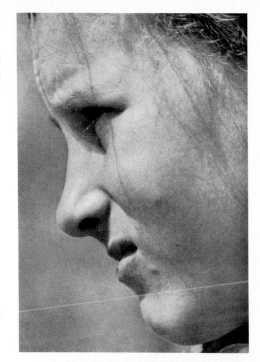

Fig. 8: From section of a negative.
The head was photographed from a great
distance with a 400 mm. lens to illustrate a
mimetic peculiarity conditioned by the sub-
ject's psychological make-up.

Fig. 9: Picture of neck and throat.
A good example of quality in the reproduction of skin
details (in this case blastocysts) exposed to grazing
sidelight (daylight) with a 50 mm. lens and optical
near-focusing device.

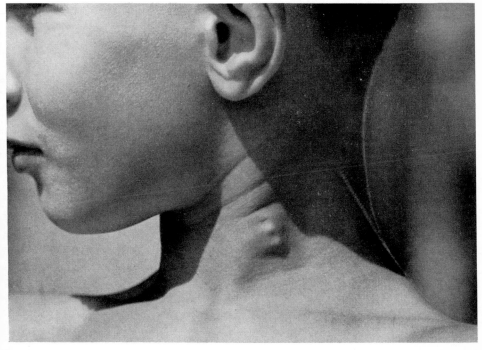

come all the difficulties. Many of my best pictures of imitative impulses, peculiarities of posture in given conditions and of kinetic sequences have only been made possible by shooting with the very longest focal length from considerable distances.

There are some occasions when long distance photography is difficult. In a narrow lane, for instance, or in the quadrangles of school premises often only close-ups are possible. In such cases I use a wide-angle lens of shortest possible focal length with a waist-level viewfinder which permits aiming of the Leica without resort to the obvious action of holding it upto the eye. Since situations are fluid and it is necessary to operate quickly and unobtrusively, exact focus settings cannot be made. Distance must be guessed, but this is easy when using a wide-angle lens with enormous field depth which compensates for errors of judgment. The large acceptance angle is also most welcome since accurate "aiming" of the camera is not always assured, as experience has shown, when interesting situations suddenly develop during the course of play. But with a sufficiently large acceptance angle such items will always be on the negative and correct positioning of the subject in the positive is merely a matter of enlarging part of the negative or cropping the print.

In all such cases it is recommended that a fine-grained, medium speed film, 32...27°, with good gradation and permitting big enlargements without sign of graininess, should be used. Any branded fine grain developer solution in a Correx tank will be suitable for processing. Such a developer will also yield good results if fast film has occasionally to be employed in exceptional circumstances.

The making of prints and transparencies is no different from the customary methods, but particular attention should be paid to correct tonal gradation of the print. There will be no loss of tones if the negative exposure is related to a normal grade of paper, or at least to a grade that is not too hard. Perfect reproduction of fine skin tones and delicate shadows requires as much careful manipulation and mastery of the art of printing as it does care in the making of the negative.

Good photographic documentary records are not merely of value to the specialist—they are indispensable to his practice. It is true that many details of the human body can be quite accurately described by reference to types, but it is more difficult to define an individual cast of features or to describe peculiar imitative behavior. Many gaps will be found in such written accounts whenever

Fig. 10: Boys wrestling. Typical example of body control in the intuitive years of development.

400 mm. Telyt from a distance of about 100 yards Section of negative.

Fig. 11: Musculature.
Photograph made with a long focus lens while observing the flow of movement and the tensioning of all the body muscles.

Taken from a very great distance with the longest available telephoto lens. Exposure was $^1/_{1000}$ sec. on very fast film.

diagnosis and observation have failed to reveal, or could not anticipate, later aspects which develop and have a bearing on the case. It is then more than merely useful to be able to turn up the earlier photographic record in order to trace the original symptoms. The various aspects of growth and development can only be satisfactorily recorded by means of photographs which permit a study of detail. Therefore: there should be no examination of patients and no diagnosis of their conditions without photographic documentation at each stage. In some cases, it is true, there will be room for discussion about the scientific value of the photographic record but it must be remembered, as already expressly pointed out, that photography as applied to psychology is limited to the tangibles of a situation—i.e., it is not absolute. A photograph which is not clearly documented in regard to the circumstances of a particular case can be misleading and has, indeed, been so in the past. It is here that the responsibility of the investigator is greatest because his specialist knowledge and trained observation of a case can never be replaced by "automatic" photography.

It will be self-evident that such photographic material must be classified and filed. Miniature photography permits the collection of comprehensive records, requiring the most varied exposure technique, at relatively small cost. And when such records have fulfilled the private purposes of the investigator they still retain their value as a source of material for instruction. Many typical details can be exhibited in convincing pictures requiring little or no explanation.

However, such suitable picture material will be found only in large collections. Every specialist knows that, of the wealth of phenomena met in practice, the special cases suitable for instructional purposes are few and far between. It should, moreover, be made quite clear that inadequate photographic apparatus and slipshod photographic techniques are bound to yield unsatisfactory results. It is essential to acquire mastery of equipment and a good technique—both of which are indispensable to modern scientific work.

A whole series of scientific publications by well-known authors, particularly in the medical field, has clearly demonstrated the inestimable value of the good illustration. Regrettably, psychology has as yet scarcely found the way to graphic depiction of typical or interesting phenomena although practical work in this field offers ample material for the purpose. It is hard to understand why it has not yet been recognized that the diagnostically very important processes of child growth should be kept in picture record by school examining and advisory bodies on further education and employment. This in spite of the fact that the publications of Zeller* contain much valuable guidance on the point. The staggering changes that can take place in the cast of features during the process of development and growth can be more informative, even to a layman, than the dreary reports turned out by our schools.

---

* Zeller, Wilfried, Doctor of Medicine. Publications : *Der erste Gestaltwandel des Kindes*, Leipzig 1936. *Entwicklungsdiagnose im Jugendalter*, Leipzig 1938. *Konstitution und Entwicklung*, Göttingen 1952.

The Leica in Medicine

With Particular Regard to Dermatology, Pathology, Bacteriology and Experimental Medicine

by Dr. Walther Schultze, Professor of Medicine in the University of Giessen

Color Photography in Medicine

W H E N , I N 1926, I first turned to the Leica for applied scientific use it was not to make medical photographs but in connexion with climatological work in the basin of the Upper Inn. The reason for the choice was the reduced weight of the camera as compared with plate apparatus: a great advantage in territory that was not opened up and most difficult of access. The very favorable impression that the Leica made on me at that time prompted the attempt to use this camera also for medical photography.

I have very pleasant memories of these early, I almost said youthful, years of the Leica and of the fruitful co-operation with its inventor, Oskar Barnack. The development of the first Leica aids to scientific photography dates from this time. One had merely to discuss a question with Barnack, to point out a difficulty experienced with the miniature in the close-up photography of the living human being either in regard to accurate picture framing or in establishing field depth, for him to tackle the problem at once. It was typical of this very able and obliging man that on the next occasion he would produce not drawings or plans but an entirely new piece of apparatus for further test. I am very conscious how much I owe Barnack and it fills me with pride—and with regret—that during these early days of scientific development in miniature photography I owned Leica No. 1000—until the Americans came in 1945!

By means of supplementary front lenses and other aids to close-up work it became possible to reproduce small objects at predetermined ratios of reduction and so it came about that we were able to depict diseases of the skin in a manner not hitherto possible with large cameras. Meanwhile sensitive materials had been so improved that the grain problems subsided and good enlargements could be made. With the advent of fine grain development we witnessed a step-by-step improvement in miniature techniques as applied to scientific uses in dermatology until, in 1931, we felt able to dispense altogether with the large camera in our particular field. Within a short period of development spanned by five years the Leica had firmly established itself in our clinical work. But we had the advantage of knowing that Oskar Barnack was within easy reach. Many a problem was solved with his aid and we are indebted to him and to other members of the Leitz organization for their co-operation and unstinted help. I could not embark on a description of the applied uses of Leica technique in this field without acknowledging the debt, and adding that never once did we experience any set-backs or disappointments due to the camera.

The most important requirement of medical photography is that pictures must be critically sharp in depth and reveal good surface structure in correct tonal gradation. From color materials we expect that pathogenic symptoms and adjacent healthy tissue should be rendered in their natural colors.

By 1932 we had so standardized our camera technique and the processing of our Leica films that I was able, in an article which appeared in the *Münchner Medizinischen Wochenschrift*, to take up a quite unequivocal position in a discussion that was then raging: Large format or miniature film in scientific photography ?

At first I tended to confine the uses of the Leica to the recording of more or less typical pathological conditions, but we soon realized that for lecture purposes the monochrome record was not an entirely satisfactory substitute for direct visual examination of the patient. Monochrome exposures were made in the following cases: for recording visible pathological conditions and for supplementing written records both for medical and for forensic purposes. Documents supported by good Leica pictures often convey much more than is possible with words alone. Patients who suffer from protuberances, tumors or swellings, that is, all probable cases of carcinoma, are photographed as a matter of routine before treatment begins in order to have an objective record of the success or failure of the treatment at later examinations. Similarly, all manifestations of tuberculosis of the skin are always photographically recorded to provide for the possibility of control, at some later date, of the efficacy of the prescribed treatment. Such pictures are also of value to the patient who can be shown what improvement or deterioration has taken place. Many sufferers from tuberculosis of the skin are glad to have a set of such pictures in order themselves to control their progress. In cases where the course of an illness or disease is rapid the photographic sequence records each stage. We also use the Leica to document rare complaints and others where some doubt exists as to the nature of the disease. One of the widest applications of miniature photography is to record and compare the relative progress made under different types of treatment. In all cases of radiation therapy, which is not without its later consequences for the patient, it is a rule that the nidus of a pathogenic organism and the area of skin treated, the so-called "treatment fields" and their eventual sub-divisions, must be clearly recorded on the photographic print. This is a method that was developed in 1935-6 for Grenz ray (borderline ray) treatment and was described by A. Kreiner in *Strahlentherapie* 1937, Vol. 60, p. 619. The photographic record of treatment fields is a permanent record which may be referred to years later to establish the response to treatment of a nidus subjected to a certain type of radiation therapy, and it facilitates a study of the relative effectiveness of various different kinds of radiation, such as deep X-rays, radium bombs and Grenz ray. Thus one is able to evaluate results—a most important factor in the whole field of radiation therapy—and exercise the strongest self-criticism of treatments prescribed because it is from the errors one makes that most is learned. Our own efforts over the years to investigate the mechanism of the serious after-effects of deep X-ray and radium therapy, as applied to tuberculosis of the skin, have in part failed since even in well-run departments of radiology records of the treatment fields on the skin are not made with sufficient care and exactitude. In my view it is quite useless to record in writing on the patient's dossier that, for example: "Deep X-ray—stating the dose—was given on such-and-such a day on the left cheek", or that "Radiation therapy of the right foot was repeated under the following conditions..." We should demand that the treatment fields should be drawn on the skin and then photographed so that an exact record is at all times available. A photograph is of great help to the radiologist in re-applying radiation therapy always to the same spot should later treatments be necessary. If this small extra care protects the patient from radiation damage to healthy tissue it will have been well worth while.

Photography as applied to science, and especially to medicine, must be very careful and precise if it is to have convincing documentary worth. I must therefore treat of detail rather more thoroughly than was perhaps considered necessary by other contributors to this book. In the medical field it is becoming increasingly apparent that technical duties—and medical photography is numbered among them—are carried out by medically qualified men and women assistants and laboratory staff whose photographic training is problematic, to say the least. Many medical training centers for male and female medical staff lack modern apparatus and the instructors are themselves only good amateur photographers or at best professionals who are not fully acquainted with the requirements of medical and scientific photography. There is a much-felt need for really good training centers. It often happens that doctors who lack basic photographic knowledge assign various photographic tasks to their medically trained assistants or staff—a state of affairs that I, at least, have found to obtain in more than thirty years' experience in this field.

Illumination and Exposure

Illumination and exposure are decisive factors in the macrophotography of pathological conditions. With color film, which is playing an ever greater part in medical work, only those light sources should be used for which the film is balanced. The best color response is obtained with daylight type color film exposed to sunlight under light haze or when there is much white cumulus in the sky. With the sun low on the horizon the spectral composition of sunlight is predominantly of longer wavelength and the color response of the film is accordingly more ruddy, exhibiting a hue shift towards the long-wave red. Account must also be taken of reflected sky light. With the sun at its zenith there is a shift in spectral composition so that, for instance in winter at noon, an exposure to a snowscape would reveal a strong blue cast. Sun behind light haze gives a peculiarly soft illumination. Heavy shadows should be avoided in scientific photography and should they exist they must be brightened up by means of reflectors. The maximum luminance range that can be successfully accommodated on color film is of the order 1:30 and there are some who consider even that ratio too high (figs. 1 and 1a).

Color response is dependent both on direct incident light and on light reflected from the surroundings. The latter can cause quite serious shifts of hue. A green or a cream wall reflecting direct sunlight or sky light onto a subject can so alter

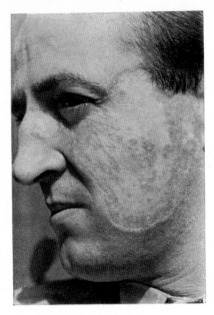
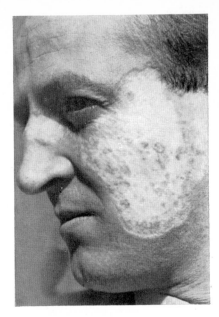

Fig. 1: Erythema.   *Fig. 1a*

Fig. 1: Agfacolor negative film Type T, on 7/9/48 in full midday sunlight. Monobar bellows with 135 mm. Hektor at f/6.3, $^1/_{20}$ sec. Ratio of reduction 0.18, enlarged to 2×3 in. (approx.).

Fig. 1a: Monochrome enlargement from the same Agfacolor negative film.

the color values of the image that there can be no question of correct color response on color film. Color is best photographed when the surroundings are a neutral gray or the backdrop is black. To brighten the shadow side of the image only pure white reflectors should be used, so that no falsifying hue is introduced into the reflections. A good method of obtaining even lighting of the subject is to use pronounced frontal illumination. Fill-in side light or a reflector may be necessary to brighten any shadows cast. In diffused light color photographs of parts of the human body appear somewhat flat, particularly if the film has received slight over-exposure. Under such illumination it is advisable to under-expose about one-quarter to one-half of a lens stop. Since daylight (sunshine and sky light) is subject to both diurnal and seasonal change, it is advisable to use a good photo-electric exposure meter for reflected light and incident light readings. The Sixtomat J made by Gossen has proved very suitable. The photo-electric cells of such meters should not be exposed to light for long periods because they tend to lose their light sensitivity when so treated. The meter should be protected from jars and jolts to the delicately poised mechanism. When in doubt about the correct exposure for a subject make highlight and shadow readings and average them out for the exposure. In general it will be found that color reversal materials, both for daylight and for tungsten, have less exposure latitude than color negative materials. Most of my color exposures have been made on Agfacolor film of both types, but I have also used the products of Kodak, Ansco and Gevaert.

Light Sources

For scientific work it is desirable to keep the lighting as constant as possible so it will always be preferable to use artificial light sources under the control of the operator. Mixed lighting should be avoided. By mixed lighting is meant the use of tungsten sources of varying color temperatures or a combination of daylight and tungsten. For good color work the color temperature of all the light sources used should be the same and correspond exactly with the color temperature for which the color film is balanced. Color temperature meters are available for measuring the color temperature of light sources. Gossen manufactures the Kelvilux and has also produced the Sixtomat $\times$ 3, which is not, however, so accurate as the former though it does give good approximations. Further, the light sources used for color photography should have continuous spectra. Certain types of gas discharge tube have discontinuous spectra with limited applications to color work. Overrun tungsten sources, such as photofloods with a color temperature of about 3400° K, are most suitable. Ordinary carbon arc should not be used. Carbon arc sources should be of the *white flame* type, such as those used for motion picture color film. It is always well to remember that color photography is a chemical process which is dependent on certain well-defined physical factors if it is to be successful. Subjective impressions, such as those received by the human eye with its good power of accommodation, cannot be subjectively interpreted by color processes, which are essentially objective. Because it is objective, color photography is an eminently suitable aid to scientific and medical work. But results obtained with color film will only then be satisfactory if the man who applies color photography to his own special field is aware of the physical and also of the physiological factors

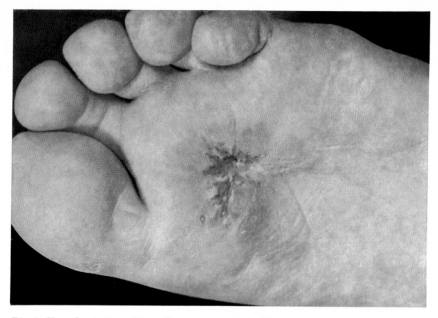

Fig. 2: Hyperkeratosis and deep X-ray damage to healthy tissue.
Agfacolor negative film Type K, 2 500 W Nitraphot lamps Type B each at a distance of $3^1/_2$ feet, with 135 mm Hektor at f/6.3, $^1/_2$ sec. Ratio of reduction 0.3, enlarged to $3^1/_8 \times 4^1/_2$ in. (approx.).

which condition the quality of the record. Accordingly, it might be as well to list here the color temperatures of certain important artificial and natural light sources used in color photography:

Direct Sunlight	5000—6000° Kelvin
Sunlight under clear blue sky	5500—6600° K
Domestic Tungsten lamp—60 W	2700° K
Nitraphot B and S	3000—3300° K
Photoflood (G.E.C., Philips)	3400° K
Magnesium ribbon	3400° K
Expendable flash bulbs (according to type)	3800—4700° K
White Flame Carbon arc	5500° K
Electronic flash (according to type)	6000—7000° K

From this table it can be seen which types of color film are suitable for the various light sources listed.

Agfacolor negative film Type K is balanced for a color temperature of 3200° K while Type T is balanced for medium sunlight at 5500° K. The rated speed is 16...24°. Agfacolor reversal films for tungsten and daylight are similarly balanced but the rated speed is lower at 8...21°. This is also the rated speed of Kodachrome but tungsten type films of this make are balanced for a color temperature of 3400° K. Variations of ± 100° K in the color temperature of the light source are permissible for reversal materials whereas negative color films have a somewhat larger tolerance in this respect.

For color work generally, I have had great success with electronic flash speed lamps. I use a Mannesmann pack with a flash duration of $^1/_{3000}$ sec. This eliminates the danger of subject movement. The normal breathing of the patient or tremblings and twitchings of the muscles do not cause loss of definition through blur. The Mannesmann multiflash unit is perfectly synchronized with the Leica IIIf or M 3 cameras for shutter speeds of $^1/_{30}$ and $^1/_{50}$ sec. Since flash tubes have a very constant performance it is an easy matter to create working conditions which allow exactly repeatable results. Standard quality is important in documentary work of this nature. As compared with half-watt and carbon arc illumination, speed flash has the further advantage of generating little heat. The patient suffers a minimum of discomfort and cultures and preparations remain unaffected. Wherever photography is applied to science good electronic equipment is indispensable. There are some firms, such as Langham in England, who specialize in the manufacture of high performance apparatus for professional use in medicine, ophthalmology and intraoral photography.

Color films for use with electronic flash should be balanced for daylight. If negative color materials are used a slight prolongation of the time of development will improve gradation and brilliance of color rendering. With reversal color films, which are always developed to gammas greater than unity, this is unnecessary. The high blue emission of electronic flash can be quite adequately compensated by switching on a domestic tungsten lamp, which has a high red emission, and seating the patient near that light. This is one of the few occasions where mixed lighting does not, in our experience, adversely affect the result. Similarly, poor existing daylight can be supplemented by using electronic flash. "Daylight" fluorescent tube lighting, provided a sufficient number of tubes is available, can also be used with color film since the emission corresponds closely to that of diffused daylight. Because of the low wattage, however, exposures will be relatively much longer than to electronic flash, which is sure to find increasing application to scientific photography, particularly since prices have fallen. Taking the long view, electronic flash is cheaper than expendable bulbs for most photographic work and decidedly safer and more convenient than naked flash or magnesium ribbon.

As already mentioned, mixed daylight and tungsten should be avoided for scientific photography in natural color. This applies equally to the so-called "daylight tungsten lamps" that are used in consulting rooms and operating theaters. Their emission is balanced neither for daylight nor artificial type color films. Films exposed to such sources suffer from blue or green color casts. Though color casts can be largely eradicated in the printing of Agfacolor negative film by the choice of suitable positive filtration it is better not to introduce such errors into the camera exposure. Such errors of illumination often discourage beginners in color photography. There is a tendency to blame the processing station or the manufacturer of the film or paper for errors which could have been avoided at the time the exposure was made. The use of light filters on the camera lens is often recommended to balance the spectral composition of unsuitable light sources to the spectral response of the film, but it is not always easy to choose the right filter. Filter factors must also be applied which, of course, entails an increased exposure which might not always be desirable (but see Windisch: *Die Farbfotografie*, Heering-Verlag, 1952, p. 71, or the monograph by Dr. Heinz Berger: *Agfacolor*, Verlag Giradet, 1951). For scientific purposes color photography by artificial light is most successful if it is conducted in a room which is screened from daylight and equipped only with photoflood illumination of the required color temperature for the film in use. The light sources should be positioned to either side and slightly behind the camera position so that they can be directed to cover the whole subject. Although flare is reduced by modern lens coatings it is nevertheless imperative to prevent scattered light striking the front element of the lens obliquely. Always use a lens shade to prevent this or, better still, the reciprocating bellows of the Monobar bellows focusing device, to be described later, because the increase so obtained in the brilliance of color rendering is a very definite gain. The long reciprocating bellows attachment is a most efficient lens shade, protecting the lens from stray light even when it is necessary to use additional light sources from behind or to one side of the subject. In cases where slight differences of structure must be recorded a side light, of the same color temperature as the main lights and thus balanced for the film, can be positioned to give good surface modeling without in any way affecting color rendition through flare if the reciprocating bellows is used to protect the lens. If light is angled from one direction only, for instance from directly in front of the subject, slight surface differences are not so clearly recorded. For the color photography of what might be termed texture it is always best to err on the side of slight underexposure rather than the other way. The light source for a texture shot should not be positioned too close to the subject. If it is, the intensity of light might kill delicate differences of color tone and structure. For such work it is essential that the camera should be on a rigid stand. The slightest camera shake would ruin the picture.

In medical photography, as for the photography of other living specimens, one must relate the shortest possible exposure time which will guarantee a good color result from a carefully lit subject to the time interval during which living subjects can remain perfectly still. Since 24×36 mm. miniature film must always be enlarged in projection or on paper, both in monochrome and color, satisfactory results will be obtained only if this condition is fulfilled. If exposure times are too long it will never be possible to obtain really sharp pictures of subjects who for one reason or another, such as old age, weakness following an illness or even fear, suffer from slight trembling or rapid breathing which they cannot control. The slowest shutter speed that can be successfully used on a normal, healthy person is about half-a-second. With children, old folk and sick people the shutter must be speeded up to at least one-eighth or one-tenth of a second. Often it may be necessary to expose at $^1/_{20}$ sec., or even faster. The faster the shutter speed the larger the lens stop that must be selected, with consequent reduction in depth of field. Hence the conditions of exposure must always be suited to the requirements of a case. If the depth of field required in the record is small, a large aperture may be used with a fast shutter speed, but if the required depth of field is great one must perforce stop the lens down and use a slow shutter speed. The difficulty with which one is faced in the latter event can be overcome only by using brighter illumination. In such cases, two, three or even more additional light sources may be needed if expendable flash bulbs or a speed lamp with an output of 200—400 joules is not available. The latter are very efficient, and with some experience of their use it is possible to obtain good, clean illumination of the type that one has every right to expect in a scientific documentary photograph.

The care and positioning of patients is important. It is a basic requirement that invalids and persons who are suffering must be made quite comfortable so that they are in a completely relaxed condition while the exposures are made. If the muscles are in any way tensed there will always be a slight tremor in the subject. The larger the ratio of the image to the object photographed the greater is the danger from blur due to heartbeat, breathing or tenseness. Patients should be invited to sit on a chair that is somewhat lower than normal so that the soles of the feet rest firmly on the floor. If a higher chair is used a foot-rest should be provided. The patient's arms should rest on broad arm-rests and the back should be supported by a cushion that must not be too soft. For photographs of the head a neck-rest should be provided, and it should be one which fits the patient comfortably. With an adjustable neck-rest the patient's head can be positioned in any desired manner. Photography of the breast and back is also easier if the head is properly supported in an appropriate position. A patient who lacks this support can grow restless. Photography of the extremities also calls for special positioning, and for this purpose sand-filled bolsters may be used to steady the extremities. Photographs of hands and fingers are best made from above. I have found that the very stable Leitz Aristophot stand is best suited to such vertical work. It has a prismatic bar to which the bellows focusing device with mirror reflex housing and other ancillary apparatus can be fixed. The extremity to be photographed rests quite steady on the base of this stand and the conditions of work are comfortable both for the patient and for the operator. Since the base of the stand is a broad one supporting a single vertical prismatic bar there is no impedimenta, such as tripod legs, to cast awkward shadows or become entangled with the patient or the photographer. Illumination is from above, directed onto the subject, and does not reduce the brilliance of the image on the ground glass screen by scattered light. The base of the stand is covered with a black cloth which serves as a good background for maximum color contrast and helps to cover up parts of the equipment which would otherwise appear in the record. For Agfacolor negative film the gray scale that should be included in the picture area—or separately photographed with bracketed exposures to the same light sources—is also best rested on a black background.

In the medical photography of living subjects at large ratios of reduction the conditions of exposure and focus must be carefully watched. As in X-ray work, it is advisable to make the exposure at the instant when the breath is completely exhaled. The subject is under constant observation on the ground glass screen

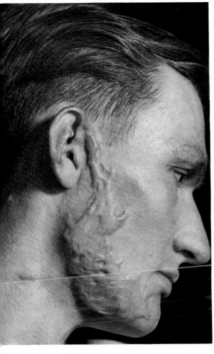
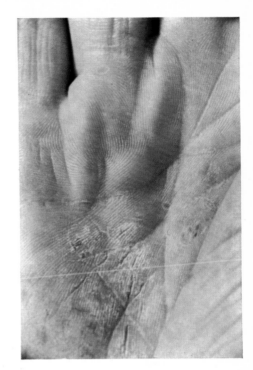

Fig. 3   *Fig. 4*

Fig. 3: Hyperplastic scar (after a burn).
Agfacolor negative film Type T, 2 250 W Nitraphot lamps from a distance of $3^1/_2$ feet with one speed light from the side and also at a distance of $3^1/_2$ feet. Monobar bellows with 135 mm. Hektor at f/6.3, $^1/_{3000}$ sec. (duration of flash). Ratio of reduction 0.1, enlarged to $2^1/_2 \times 3^1/_2$ in. (approx.). The use of tungsten counteracts the high blue of electronic flash

Fig. 4: Eczema of the palm.
Agfacolor negative film Type K, 2 500 W Nitraphot lamps Type B each at a distance of 20 inches, with monobar bellows and 135 mm. Hektor at f/8, $^1/_4$ sec. Ratio of reduction 0.35, enlarged to $2^1/_2 \times 3^1/_2$ in. (approx.)

of the mirror reflex housing and can be controlled for best effect right upto the instant of pressing the release which trips the shutter and fires the synchronized speed lamp. Accurate focus and good illumination of the subject are, of course, simultaneously controlled via the ground glass screen. The control of speed light illumination is easier if the apparatus has a built-in tungsten pilot light, like those fitted to some of the Langham models.

The Monobar Bellows

Camera adjustments and focusing have been made so much easier since Leitz introduced the Monobar Focusing Bellows—some years ago now—that the large ratios of reduction and even of magnification so necessary in scientific work can be made without any additional effort. The use of the very finely color corrected 135 mm. Hektor lens permits a large and therefore most convenient camera/subject distance while retaining excellent perspective, good plastic modeling and accurate color rendition even when subjects are so small that they have hitherto presented some considerable difficulty to the photographer. Transparencies made with a long focus lens gain considerably in plasticity when they are projected through a projection lens of comparable focal length. With a long focus taking lens it is so very easy to emphasize the essential parts of a subject and to exclude everything that does not contribute to the record. This very fine construction solves a series of problems. It consists of a bellows operated by means of a rack and pinion on a monobar which also accepts a mirror reflex housing; thus relieving us of the somewhat inconvenient and time-consuming camera adjustments necessary with earlier aids, such as supplementary front lenses, fixed focus intermediate collars or extension tubes and subject-framing four-pods. During the last five years I have not made a single macro-record without using the bellows and I believe that anyone who has once used this apparatus would never turn to any other.

This bellows equipment can also be adapted for use with standard and short focus lenses like the 50 mm. Elmar and 35 mm. Summaron if the Leitz sliding copier is mounted on the monobar platform instead of the mirror reflex housing. Whereas with the 135 mm. Hektor focusing is continuous from ∞ down to 1:1 reproduction, the 50 mm. Elmar extends this range to a magnification of $\times 2.5$ and with the 35 mm. Summaron magnifications may be increased to $\times 6.5$. The ratios of reduction or magnification, corresponding to internationally accepted scales, are engraved beside the monobar rack together with the exposure prolongation factors appropriate to each extension of the bellows. To fit the 135 mm. Hektor lens, the mount holding the lens elements is unscrewed from the neck of the barrel just behind the aperture setting ring and screwed into a short adapter which in turn screws into the lens panel on the front end of the bellows. The mirror reflex housing fits flush into a light-tight recess in the rear panel of the bellows and is held in position by a retaining screw on the monobar platform. Model f and earlier Leica cameras screw onto the rear of the standard reflex housing but a specially enlarged reflex housing with bayonet fastening is available for the Leica M 3. The hinged, surface-silvered mirror in the housing deflects the image-forming rays through a right-angle onto a very fine-grained ground glass screen for visual observation and control of framing and focus by means of a $\times 5$ magnifying eyepiece through which an erect image is seen, which is also laterally correct if the magnifying eyepiece used is of the pentaprism kind known by the code word Peego. The image so seen is extremely bright and dead accurate focus can be set by racking the bellows to and fro on the beautifully firm and smooth movement of the rack and pinion. If desired a $\times 30$ eyepiece can be used to focus the aerial image in the clear glass center section of the ground glass screen, but this is a refinement which is not entirely necessary so it is not a standard feature of the equipment. The most important advantage of this apparatus is that it permits observation of the ground glass image right upto the instant the exposure is made. A twin coupler-release swings the mirror—quite vibration free—out of the path of the image-forming rays a fraction of a second before the shutter is tripped. The rays thus reach the film plane instead of the eye and there they form an image as sharp as the one observed. With an image size of 0.1—i.e., a reduction ratio of $1:10$—the available depth of field at an aperture of f/8 is as much as 23 inches and the camera/subject distance, measured from the film plane, is well over 5 feet. For a natural size $(1:1)$ image, field depth at f/8 is 1.1 mm. and camera/subject distance is rather more than 21 inches. For further details see table on next page where, to avoid awkward fractions, measurements are given in the metric system.

We referred earlier to the need for a sunshade; on the lens side of the monobar arrangement, described above, a very neat, detachable reciprocating bellows is provided with a slip-on collar which fits the front of the lens mount in exactly the same way as a sunshade, and is similarly fastened there with a thumb-screw. This bellows has a much longer extension than a normal sunshade and it reciprocates with the focusing bellows as the latter is racked in or out. It can be manually lengthened or shortened at will to provide maximum protection of the coated outer lens surface, which it completely surrounds. The image is thus seen on the ground glass screen in its correct brilliance and contrast, and so provides a measure of accuracy in estimating exposure. It is well known that most photo-electric meters do not function as they ought in artificial light. One

Image size: ratios of reduction and magnification	Coverage of lens	Field Depth at Stops given				Subject distance from film plane	
		5.6	8	11	16	135 mm lens & Reflex Housing	50 mm lens & Sliding Copier
	mm	mm	mm	mm	mm	cm	cm
0.05 (1:20)	480 ×720	156.8	224	308	448	297.9	113
0.1 (1:10)	240 ×360	41.1	58.7	80.7	117.3	163.6	62.5
0.2 (1: 5)	120 ×180	11.2	16	22	32	97.5	37.2
0.5 (1: 2)	48 × 72	2.2	3.2	4.4	6.4	61	23.3
1 : 1	24 × 36	0.7	1.1	1.5	2.1	54.3	20.7
2.5 : 1	9.6× 14.4	0.2	0.3	0.4	0.6	—	25.4

of the few exceptions is the Ilford S.E.I. photometer, already referred to elsewhere in this book. If a record of exposures is kept it will be found that failures are reduced to a minimum when using the monobar bellows.

Record Keeping and Special Techniques

The exposure data for the best records made should be noted down in tabular form so that whenever the same illumination is used the exposure can be accurately repeated. It will be necessary to keep records of the following: subject recorded, light source used (type, distance from and angle to subject, and perhaps the color temperature), photographic equipment used, lens (focal length), ratio of reduction, lens stop and shutter speed. By noting the ratio of reduction the camera/subject distance is automatically given when using the monobar bellows. Further points to note are: type of film (with emulsion number if Agfacolor negative film is used), how developed and how printed. An index of subjects and patients' names, together with the date of the exposure and a serial number, makes it an easy matter to trace any negative or its print. When a particular set of working conditions is seen to produce consistently good results it is important to stick to them whenever possible. This helps to standardize procedure and reduce errors to a bare minimum. Past errors can be avoided not only in the photography of living subjects but, more important still, in the satisfactory exposure of medical preparations, organs and parts of

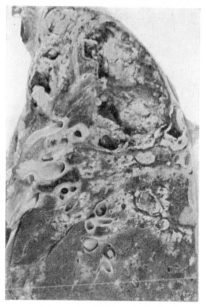

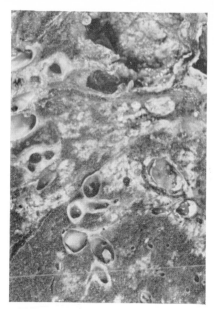

Fig. 5

Fig. 6

Fig. 5: Pulmonary tuberculosis (formation of cavities); Kaiserling method.

Agfacolor negative film Type K, 2 500 W Nitraphot lamps Type B, each at a distance of 24 inches, with monobar bellows and 135 mm. Hektor at f/6.3, $^1/_2$ sec. Ratio of reduction 0.2 enlarged × $2^1/_2$.

Fig. 6: This monochrome enlargement from the same color negative illustrates the difficulties presented by the absence of color.

Fig. 7: Pulmonary tuberculosis. Section of negative.

Agfacolor negative film Type K, 2 500 W Nitraphot lamps at distances of 20 and 28 inches with monobar bellows and 135 mm. Hektor at f/9, $^1/_4$ sec. Ratio of reduction 0.4, enlarged × $2^1/_2$.

287

organs. In medical work the photography of cultures, organs and special preparations is conditioned by exactly the same factors governing the photography of living subjects described above. The same applies also to photography undertaken during surgical operations. In none of these cases should there be any variation from the correct spectral quality of the light sources used. In color work field depth must encompass the entire dimensions of an object otherwise there is a very real danger of giving false impressions. During surgery the inevitable movements of the patient, such as the rhythmic throb of exposed blood vessels, movements of the intestine and the like, will not affect the clarity of the result if high tension flash discharge provides the illumination. The available intensity of such speed lights is sufficient to allow adequate stopping down of the lens.

Preserved organs and cultures present some difficulty to the photographer because of reflections from the glass receptacles in which they are stored, for instance in cases where anatomical or pathological specimens are preserved in a manner, such as the Kaiserling method, which prevents alteration of their colors. Reflections from glass surfaces can often be reduced to a minimum or even entirely avoided by careful placing of the lights. Polarizing filters may also be used for the same purpose, but their efficiency is greater in daylight than it is under artificial illumination. To use such a polarizing filter the object to be photographed is visually examined through it while the polarizing filter is rotated. During rotation it will be observed that reflections are reduced to a minimum at some definite angle of turn which can be read off from the engraved figures on the metal mount. The polarizing filter is then placed on the lens with the appropriate figure uppermost. Good color records of plate cultures can be made if the shallow dish containing the culture is placed over a hole of the same size cut in a box which, in effect, provides a deep black background which reduces reflections of the light source to a minimum. Slant cultures are easily photographed if the tube is appropriately inclined but the operation must be carried out quickly because, if light sources with great heat output are used, condensation on the inside of the tube can obscure the culture. Similarly, cultures that are still warm should not be taken straight from the breeding cabinets into a colder atmosphere. It is better to wait until there is no difference of temperature between the culture and the surroundings in which it is to be photographed.

With the Leitz monobar bellows I have found that such close-up work, even for verticals, is easily carried out provided a sufficiently rigid stand is used. For years I have been using a Bilora stand with a pan and tilt head which permits verticals, but an essential point is that the stand must have a center-post which can be racked up and down to vary camera/subject distance, as required, in order to avoid the tedious business of having to realign the legs of the tripod, which should be permanently positioned on non-slip pads on the floor of the clinic.

The prismatic bar of the Leitz Aristophot stand with its dove-tailed drive is a particularly convenient method of mounting the monobar bellows for the vertical photography of extremities, of cultures, of small organs and of parasites. This method permits direct magnifications on the film when using 50 mm. or 35 mm. focal lengths and enables the worker to sit down to his task with the magnifier and ground glass screen of the reflex housing at eye level, which is a great convenience because vision is normal, i.e., in the horizontal plane, and control of all the factors governing the exposure can be carried out with the minimum of inconvenience or discomfort. Thus, for instance, the capillary system of the skin can be quite easily photographed. As Frerksen has shown, the larger capillary vessels of the skin are best revealed in monochrome by exposure to the infra-red. But for colored reproduction of the capillaries the present writer has found the following method most suitable: the capillaries of the nail-fold, or of any other part of the body, are photographed in color by means of the capillary microscope. The Leitz microscope lamp Monla is firmly attached to the capillary microscope and is slightly over-run at 5.4 amps. The speed lamp used is positioned 4 to 8 inches, according to output, from the subject so that the reflector sheds a concentrated beam onto the area of the skin to be investigated. The observation of the image field, prior to the syn-chronized release of shutter and flash, can be made via the telescopic eye-piece of the Mikas or via the eyepiece of the reflex housing, depending on which apparatus is being used.

Herrnring, Küchmeister and Pirtkien described a similar method using the Ultropak, but apparently only for monochrome work (*Kli. Wo.*, H. 37, 38, 1952, p. 897). Regarding sensitive materials it should perhaps be mentioned that there can be no doubt that skin tones in monochrome are best rendered on an orthochromatic emulsion, but these, unfortunately, have been almost entirely replaced by panchromatic film. In medical work very fast panchroma-tic materials rated at 64...30° or faster, are not really suitable emulsions and one would, in general, prefer medium speed films rated at 32...27°. To develop such films without grain troubles is no great feat if one follows the recommendations of H. Stöckler set out in the opening chapter of this book.

For all average work he recommends Rodinal, Perinal or other such highly concentrated p-aminophenol/caustic developers, such as Johnson's Azol. These concentrated solutions have a long storage life and are used at high dilution only, usually 1:50 or thereabouts according to strength. The normal development time would be 8—10 minutes at 65° F. for a film rated at 32...27°. (See also relevant manufacturers' recommendations.)

Films may be divided into three groups according to speed:

steep gradation	6...20° to 16...24°
normal gradation	20...25° to 40...28°
soft gradation	64...30° to 128...33°

Development can be carried out in the darkroom or in daylight loading tanks such as the Agfa-Leitz Rondinax. If very fine grain is desired use a hard or steep gradation emulsion and develop it in a special fine grain developer such as Atomal, W. 665, Ultrafin, I.D. 48 or Johnson's Meritol, but with such developers there is always some loss of emulsion speed so exposure must be increased, usually by a whole lens stop. Recently this disadvantage of fine grain development has been overcome by the introduction of Neodyn-blue developer, by Tetenal of Hamburg, and so far from loss of speed there is an actual gain of about one whole stop. This developer is most suited to slow, hard gradation films, particularly when subject contrast is great, and there is a tendency to use such films increasingly with this type of development for all normal miniature photography. At the time of writing the new method showed much promise.

Formerly stereo-photography played, not without justification, an important part in scientific work, but it tended to be neglected with the advent of the miniature camera principally because there was no entirely satisfactory exposure technique. Some even thought that the stereoscopic images could be entirely dispensed with because the enlarged miniature film possessed greater plasticity than the contact print from the large negative. The principle of stereo-projection is well understood and 3-D apparatus for the purpose is now available for the Leica since the recent introduction of the Leitz Stemar stereoscopic attachments and the 3-D projection lenses devised for use with standard Leitz projectors. Scientific interest today is centering more and more on the colored paper print and on stereograms in color. The variable interocular distance of the Leitz Stemar attachments is an ingenious approach to the problem of stereoscopic close-ups and should greatly simplify this technique. At present this apparatus is being manufactured only by the Canada branch of the Leitz factory.

There is no doubt about the importance of color in scientific and medical photography, as already indicated by the present writer in the very first issue of *Leica Fotografie*: No. 1/1949, pp. 25—28. There is every likelihood that color will displace monochrome. With reversal materials a direct color transparency is obtained, but since 1949 Agfa Leverkusen have marketed Agfacolor negative film, which has certain very definite advantages. Any number of colored prints can be made on paper, or any number of transparencies can be produced from the negative which can, moreover, be printed in monochrome on ordinary bromide papers if desired. The colors of the positive print can be controlled by means of suitable filtration of the enlarger light source, thus making possible the elimination of undesirable color casts. The negative image appears in colors complementary to those of the subject. The film is suitable both for macrophotography and photomicrography and little difficulty should be experienced in its use if the instructions are carefully followed. A further advantage is that the film can be processed by the user and color prints can also be made in one's own darkroom. Details of the process are available in text-books on color processing and printing, or may be obtained from the manufacturer. If desired, the films can be returned to processing stations for development and printing in the manner already customary with reversal materials.

Projection

In addition to the method of viewing photographic records in monochrome or color on a paper surface there is the possibility of projecting the transparency. This latter is the preferred method for the lecturing scientist. Excellent projection apparatus, equipped with long focus lenses, is available for use in large lecture rooms and image quality is of a brilliance far transcending the paper record. There are various makes of projection screen but one of the best is a dead white P.V.C. plastic surface obtainable from some manufacturers. The 2-inch square Leica transparency is now standard throughout the world and represents a great saving in weight, in bulk and in cost.

Transparencies for scientific use should be securely mounted in a dust-free manner between cover glasses. Cardboard ready-mounts and some types of quick-framing glass mounts are not entirely satisfactory. Monochrome transparencies should be made on 2-inch square lantern slides. By varying the gradation of the slides consistent quality can be obtained from negatives which vary between hard and soft gradation. Film strip projection should be avoided because of the inevitable damage the strips must suffer even in the best of projection apparatus. It is self-evident that transparencies must be properly filed in dust-proof containers and suitably indexed for easy reference.

Photomicrography in Medicine

The Leica is now being used increasingly for photomicrography, particularly since the advent of color film. Plate cameras in the sizes 6×9 or 9×12 cm. had their earlier justification because the sensitive material lay flat in a single plane, ensuring maximum definition. But a well-constructed miniature, such as the Leica camera, ensures an equally flat film plane and modern thin-coated emulsions guarantee excellent resolving power. The smaller 24×36 mm. format, when used with a point source low-voltage lamp, such as the Monla microscope lamp, receives even, and much brighter, illumination over the whole of the film plane, permitting exposure times to be reduced and thus lessening the danger of shake or vibration. To this must be added the fact that miniature sensitive materials are much cheaper and therefore permit the production of additional serial exposures with varying exposure times, if need be, to ensure good results.

Specimens and preparations for photomicrography must be clean, thin and well stained. The microscope objectives should be either apochromats or fluorite objectives. If objectives used exhibit any chromatic aberration color fringes will be inevitable in the record, particularly towards the edges of the photomicrograph. Only those microscope eyepieces should be used which compensate for field curvature* of the image. Such an eyepiece, which has been used with great success, is the $\times 10$ periplanatic. Preparations on the microscope stage must be critically illuminated. Uneven illumination of the specimen will ruin the record, particularly if it is in color. Telescopic eyepieces allow excellent control of the focusing of the specimen, but the estimation of exposure is more difficult than with a ground glass image.

292

---

* Since this text was written Leitz have announced the production of a new Flat Field microscope objective.

Leitz make a reflex housing with interchangeable ground glass and clear glass screens. The magnifying eyepiece enables accurate focus of the aerial image on the clear glass screen in cases where subject contrast and detail are poor. A ×20 or ×30 magnifier eyepiece might be necessary for exact focusing on a bacteria slide or when microscope magnifications are high. By changing over to the ground glass screen the evenness of illumination can also be controlled and the slide adjusted to bring only the required parts into the picture.

It is essential to keep exposure records in photomicrography. Note particularly the load at which the low voltage lamp is run, the distance of the light source from the microscope mirror in cases where it is not a built-in light source, such as those supplied with the Ortholux and Panphot microscopes; note also the type of lamp used, the type of condenser, the setting of the iris diaphragm, the microscope objective and eyepiece used, the tube length and the microscope magnification, also the filters (if any), the type of film and the exposure time. If notes are also made about the type of development such records will provide accurate data for subsequent consistent work.

Light sources: Tungsten sources are generally used in photomicrography. Compared with carbon arc the light is steadier and more even. Since tungsten has a continuous spectrum it is most suitable for color work. A Philips 6V,5A projector lamp F/26 Type 6106M, slightly over-run at 5.4 amps., has a color temperature for which tungsten type color film is balanced. Used in the Monla lamp with the Leitz transformer the current supply can be accurately controlled. If the lamp is considerably over-run the blue emission will be too high, brightness will be very great and the life of the bulb very short. If the lamp is run below rated amperage the red emission is too high for good color work. Given the quality of the light source, the next step is to ensure proper illumination of the specimen. Illumination is controlled by means of the Köhler principle: the radiant field stop covering the light source is brought to a focus, by means of the sub-stage condenser, at the position of the microscope slide on the stage. With the sub-stage iris diaphragm well stopped down and using a microscope objective of low power, this condition is easily brought about. The Berek condenser, with twin iris diaphragms, makes this operation even easier and the markings enable these diaphragm settings to be accurately repeated. It is, of course, most important that the light source should itself be accurately directed at the center of the microscope mirror. Only a correctly centered light source will permit even illumination of the image field. Even illumination can

Fig. 8   Fig. 9

Fig. 8: Skin capillaries of the nail-fold (frost-bite).
Agfacolor negative film Type T, Monla lamp 6 amp., and 1 speed flash from a distance of about 5 inches using Mikas micro-attachment with $^1/_3 \times$ adapter and reflex housing with a $\times$ 10 periplanatic eyepiece and objective 2, N.A. 0.18, with Leitz capillary microscope. Primary magnification $\times$ 25 subsequently enlarged to about $\times$ 100.

Fig. 9: Skin texture on the back of a hand
Agfacolor negative film Type T, 2 250 W Nitraphot lamps Type S, each from a distance of 12 inches and a speed lamp from a distance of 6 inches. Monobar bellows with wide-angle 35 mm. Summaron at f/12. Ratio of reduction 0.9, enlarged to $2^1/_4 \times 3^1/_4$ in. (approx.).

be controlled by means of a piece of ground glass resting on the microscope tube, from which the eyepiece has been removed. If the lamp is not correctly centered there will be a loss of brightness on the ground glass image. The image of the radiant field stop should appear as a bright disk of light in the center of the microscope tube. These adjustments should be made with the lamp running below rated load. A regulator on the Leitz transformer permits this, the reason being that the brightness would otherwise be too great for the human eye although maximum brightness is required for the photographic exposure. If no potentiometer is available neutral density filters may be interposed between the

294

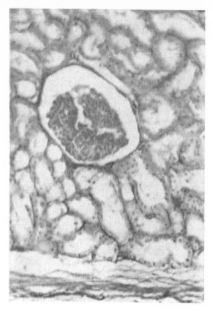
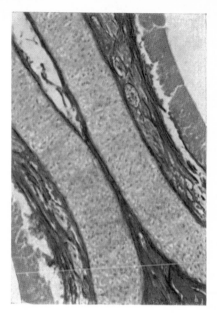

Fig. 10   *Fig. 11*

Fig. 10: Kidney (van Gieson's stain).

Kodachrome Type A film, Monla lamp at 5.2 amps., with Mikas micro-attachment and $^1/_2$ × adapter, reflex housing, × 10 periplanatic eyepiece, 16 mm. apochromatic objective, exposure time $^1/_{100}$ sec. Primary magnification × 60. Enlarged × 2. Total magnification × 120.

Fig. 11: Posterior nares of the rhinopharynx (Azo stain).

Kodachrome Type A film. Monla lamp at 5.2 amps., with Mikas and $^1/_2$ × adapter, reflex housing, × 10 periplanatic eyepiece, 16 mm. apochromatic objective, exposure time $^1/_{60}$ sec. Primary magnification × 60. Enlarged × 2. Total magnification × 120.

light source and the microscope mirror. For dark field illumination it is, of course, essential that maximum light output must be used, especially if the specimens are living; and for dark field illumination it is even more important that the light source and condensers should be critically centered. For dark field microscopy the reader is referred to the manufacturer's literature on the subject.

For photomicrography in monochrome the use of colored filters is often an advantage. They are used to control the spectral composition of light reaching the emulsion through the various colors of the microscope slide. The emulsion responds most to the colors that are least retarded. Choice of filter will depend on the spectral sensitivity of the emulsion used, or on the particular colors of the specimen which it is desired to record. The transmission of such filters is dependent on their density and thickness. For details of transmission reference should be made to filter catalogues. A color-blind (unsensitized) emulsion responds only to blue light and the effect is that of using a blue filter on a panchromatic film. Orthochromatic emulsions are additionally sensitized to the yellow-green. With such emulsions a yellow-green filter would give the best results. Panchromatic emulsions are sensitized for the whole of the visible spectrum and they respond in different ways according to the color of the filter used.

A frequent cause of error is to use too high a microscope magnification—i.e., higher than the magnification necessary to see what is wanted. This error is most often made in photomicrography in color. The color transparency is subsequently enlarged in projection or paper enlargements are made if Agfacolor negative material is used. No matter how great this subsequent enlargement, the image will only reveal detail within the resolving power of the numerical aperture of the microscope objective used. Useful subsequent enlargement of the photomicrograph will be possible only if the enlarger magnification lies somewhere between 500 and 1000 times the value of the numerical aperture of the microscope objective used. If the enlarger magnification is smaller than the lower value given the eye will not be able, from normal viewing distance, to pick out detail in the print. If the enlarger magnification is within the values given the eye will be able to pick out every detail from a normal viewing distance. Should the enlarger magnification be greater than the higher value given the details of image structure would not be clearly distinguishable. These are basic principles which must always be borne in mind in photomicrography. Since there is a limit to the resolving power of microscope objectives, the enlargement of the final print should not exceed the higher, nor be less than the lower, value given. Further, there is a risk of diffraction patterns becoming visible if the sub-stage iris diaphragm is stopped down too far.

Sharp photomicrographs can be expected only if the microscope and camera rest on a completely vibration-free support. The traffic on our streets can cause sufficient vibration indoors to warrant some method of counteracting its effects. A special spring-loaded bench may be used for the purpose, or, if one is not available, an underlay of sorbo rubber or even of tennis balls will provide sufficient protection. In my own work I use the Aristophot stand. The microscope rests on a rigid base plate which in turn rests on a sorbo underlay. The photographic equipment is fixed to the prismatic bar of the stand and can be easily raised and lowered onto the microscope. The Aristophot stand is in series production and is supplied by Leitz for the Ortholux microscope. It can also be used with any other microscope of normal dimensions.

A series of stepped exposures is by far the best means of establishing the correct exposure. Exposure time is dependent on the color or stain of the specimen as well as on the spectral sensitivity of the film used. In photomicrography there is little point in using very fast monochrome films because of their disturbing grain, even when developed in fine grain developers. Much better are the slow, thin-coated emulsions of fairly steep gradation with speed ratings between 6...20° and 12...23°. I have found Agfa Isopan FF to be a very suitable material with high resolving power.

Even the best of lenses and the most painstaking enlargement will not improve a negative that is unsharp, but if the negative is a good one, carefully enlarged on the right grade of paper, there will be no apparent difference between this enlarged print from a 35 mm. frame and a contact print from a plate negative. The resolving power of microscope objectives and the resolving power of the sensitive materials determine the quality of the print. Limiting the size of the final enlargement to a value between 500 and 1000 times the N.A. of the microscope objective (Abbe's useful magnification) will forestall failure. When enlarging miniature photomicrographs the print magnification should always be given. It is easily calculated from the initial magnification of the microscope objective and the secondary magnification of the eyepiece, but reductions in the magnification of the negative image due to the use of field lenses, micro-adapters and the like must also be taken into account. As an alternative method, the ultimate magnification on the print is also quite easily determined by recording the stage micrometer.

For low magnification work the monobar bellows should be used with a 50 mm. or 35 mm. camera lens. Magnifications up to ×6.5 are possible. These lenses will be found specially useful for work by reflected light, such as close-ups of the skin and direct magnification of parasites. They can also be used to give an entire view of long cuts or incisions. Since camera/subject distance is fairly large by comparison with micrography, powerful light sources such as speed flash may be preferred. Many preparations which are translucent are often photographed by a combination of reflected and transmitted light in order to bring out structure to best advantage. Since Leica lenses are excellently corrected for color such records can also be made on color film if desired.

By using the Leitz Ultropak (after Heine) for reflected light microscopy it is possible to record both surface texture and internal structure in small translucent living specimens. Unfortunately, this piece of apparatus, which is in effect a ring illuminant surrounding the microscope objective to permit observation and photography by reflected light or a combination of reflected and transmitted light, has not found the applications it deserves in medicine. The same applies also to polarization microscopy. With the advent of color photography this position will doubtless soon be remedied. The possibilities of fluorescence micrography can be mentioned only in passing.

With the Leitz phase contrast condenser (after Heine) the transition from bright field illumination to the actual phase contrast and dark field illumination of Zernike is possible in a continuous manner. This permits the examination and photography of thin preparations in the unfixed and unstained natural state, which reveals living cells and tissue structures which it was not hitherto possible to see or to record. This youngest branch of research microscopy holds much promise for photomicrography.

Photomicrography in Color

To take account of the growing importance of color in medical photomicrography it has been decided to reprint here an extract from the introduction to the use of Agfacolor negative materials in photomicrography, published by W. Schultze and E. Reckziegel in *Röntgenblättern*, 1951, Issue No. 5, p. 269.

There are many instances in which the monochrome record of a microscopical subject is unsatisfactory. In all cases where a differentiation of color tones is important, Agfacolor materials can be used with advantage in photomicrography. Agfacolor materials are available at the moment as direct transparency reversal color films and as a negative/positive color process. From the point of view of the research worker it is important to note that reversal materials give better color saturation but that the colors cannot subsequently be steered to match the colors of the original if there is exposure aberration. As we shall see later, it is primarily the need to match the record with the colors of the original that is of special importance in photomicrography, particularly since the microscope illuminant is often changed. The negative/positive Agfacolor process permits just this and it has the further advantage that any number of color prints and color transparencies can be reproduced from a single negative color record. Further, the exposure latitude of Agfacolor negative film is greater than with reversal color materials, but reversal materials have the higher resolving power.

For good quality it is advisable to use only those microscope objectives or optical systems which have been expressly corrected for color, such as apochromatic objectives. Color aberration in the optical system will inevitably result in unwanted color fringes in the record, particularly towards the edges of the image field. The light source may be either tungsten or carbon arc, but in both cases it will be necessary to stabilize mains voltage because slight fluctuations are accompanied by changes in color temperature which, if uncontrolled, can adversely influence the color response of the film and hence the quality of the color photomicrograph. The most convenient light source is a low voltage tungsten filament lamp used in conjunction with a transformer and rheostat for controlling the amperage. Carbon arc can be troublesome in the control of constant output and, moreover, only the so-called *white flame* carbon arc should be used. An ammeter should also be used here when regulating the spark gap and centering it correctly in the optical system of the microscope prior to each exposure.

Agfacolor artificial light film (Type K) should be used for tungsten sources and film balanced for daylight (Type T) with white flame carbon arc.

Note that it is not possible to examine the image visually at the maximum output of the light source required for photomicrography because the intensity is blinding. For visual examination and control the light source must be regulated by means of the rheostat, or neutral density filters may be interposed between it and the microscope mirror.

In color photography the first and most important requirement is that the colors of the image should be as objectively correct as possible. This condition, though most important in photomicrography, is not always clearly understood because the human eye undergoes very appreciable accommodation changes in its response to color when viewing a microscope image directly through the eyepiece.

Every microscopist knows that the eye rapidly adjusts itself subjectively to the colors of an object so that the clear parts of the microscope slide, which appeared yellow to him at the first glance, seem clear white if observation is prolonged. Parallel with this change there is a corresponding subjective hue shift in all the other visible colors. It is these colors, as seen by the accommodated human eye, which are normally regarded as the correct ones. And it is with this subjective impression of color that the photographic color record is expected closely to correspond.

It is therefore fundamental to by far the most numerous applications of photomicrography in color, that the color record of a clear portion of the transilluminated microscope slide must be printed in a manner which renders it as a clear white to a daylight adapted eye. For reflected light micrography, such as possible with the Ultropak system, the same condition must apply to the color rendering of a dead white field. The behavior of color film is comparable with that of a physically objective measuring instrument—i.e., its color response is quite independent of the accommodating power of the human eye. However, the Agfacolor negative/positive process permits the colors of the positive to be steered in the desired direction. The variations of the microscope light source from standard daylight illumination can be compensated by appropriate color filtration of the enlarger light source during the making of the positive print.

It will be clear that the co-operation of the color printer is decisive for the quality of the result. In order to facilitate his task it is essential for him to have some reference object. Such a reference object must be provided by the microscopist.

Let us suppose for a moment that it is desired to photograph a translucent microscope slide, such as an histological specimen or a smear from a bacteria culture. The microscope is adjusted to give an optimum image, taking particular care that the image field is very evenly illuminated—control that can be exercised by using a very finely ground glass screen, or by examining the aerial image on a clear glass screen, or even by means of the deflecting prism at the position of a telescopic eyepiece, depending on the type of apparatus available. Once the microscope has been correctly aligned and focused no changes should be made in the positioning of the light source or the load at which it is run, nor should diaphragm settings be altered; microscope objective and eyepiece should also not be interchanged for others of higher or lower power. Either before or after the desired exposures are made, a completely clear section of the microscope slide should be exposed three times to the film: once at the estimated correct exposure, again at $\frac{1}{4}$ this value and once more at an exposure varying between $\frac{1}{10}$th and $\frac{1}{20}$th the normal exposure. For reflected light micrography similar exposure variation should be made to a clear white sheet of baryta, and not to the brightest part of the specimen, after the microscope has been correctly adjusted for this white reference object. For miniature film these exposures would be made on three successive frames but for larger sizes a step-wedge, such as those used in normal monochrome photography, may be used to establish the correct exposure time. This enables the printer at the processing station to decide on the correct enlarger lamp filtration for the test strip. Filtration of the positive is correct if the color print of the three exposure steps is in a neutral gray. This positive filtration will then also be the correct one for the remaining exposures in the same series or on the same strip of film, provided that they were all made under constant microscope settings. In most cases satisfactory color rendition will be obtained by reference to such a step-wedge, but it is not always absolutely necessary to use one. Thus, for instance, in cases where the specimen exhibits large empty areas, overall color rendition will normally be correct if these neutral areas are rendered in a light neutral gray. Only in exceptional cases will it be necessary to supply a specimen color which it is important that the printer should match.

It is, unfortunately, impossible to give hints on exposure times because these are dependent on a variety of factors, such as the thickness and stain of the preparation, the light source used and its load, radiant field stops and iris diaphragms and, lastly, the microscope magnification.

But with a little practice it soon becomes possible to estimate exposure accurately by the brightness of the ground glass image or by the use of Photometers like the Ilford S.E.I. Some may prefer to arrive at an approximation by making a test strip on monochrome material of the same rated speed.

Because of the effects of light and shadow areas, the luminance ranges of larger specimens requiring only macroscopic orders of magnification will in general be found to be considerably greater than the luminance range of a thin microscope section. To bridge the wider luminance ranges of macro-subjects Agfacolor negative film should be developed to a correspondingly flatter contrast. In photomicrography, with its small luminance ranges, Agfacolor negative film can with advantage be developed to higher contrasts, since this is coupled with better differentiation between colors. Such steepening of gradation is achieved simply by prolonging the duration of development of Agfacolor negative films.

It should be mentioned that the brilliant color rendition of the reversal transparency cannot be attained with a positive color print on Agfacolor positive papers. This limitation in the possibilities of rendering high contrasts on paper has already been generally recognized in the production of monochrome photographic prints. In color work this limitation of the brightness range of the print tends to broaden the line of demarcation between colors and can cause difficulty if the color tones of the subject are very similar.

Apart from such exceptions to the rule, it will be found that the color print is well suited to micrography because it offers new possibilities of comparative work at the microscope. With it, it is possible to document phenomena difficult or impossible to record in monochrome and, indeed, to do this in a manner commensurate with the reality, and often the beauty, revealed to those who make a study of the small things on earth.

Ophthalmic Photography

by Dr. Walter Rauh, Professor of Medicine in Giessen Eye Clinic

THERE ARE as yet but very few text-books on ophthalmology containing good photographs of normal and diseased eyes. In many cases the photograph is still unable to replace good monochrome and color sketches of eye detail. There are many reasons why good photographs of the eye are difficult to make. The anterior segment, or visible portion of the eye between the upper and lower lids, has considerable curvature and a shiny surface which reflects the light sources used. These specular reflections can impair the study of fine detail. Since a field depth of at least 4—5 mm. is essential, lenses must be well stopped down. But shutter speed should not exceed a certain maximum exposure value which is conditioned by the light-sensitivity of the eye, especially in cases of abnormality. Further, it is important that the image of the eye on the negative must be in the largest possible image/object ratio, in order to permit considerable enlargement of detail. In cases where it is desired to photograph the various stages of an eye operation it is necessary that there must be continuous and effortless control of focus; and it is essential that the photographer should not in any way impede the surgeon or disturb the patient.

The invention of the speed light and the reliable synchronizing of the Leica camera have greatly contributed to the elimination of the problems posed above. By using a lens of long focus we can ensure that image/object ratio is sufficiently large. In our own work we use a Mannesmann multi-flash unit with an output high enough to permit the use of medium speed panchromatic material, 32...27°, with the lens stopped well down to provide the necessary large field depth for the photography of operations. In close-up work the depth of field is even greater than usually given in Depth of Field Tables, because in this work one can tolerate a disk of confusion slightly larger than the diameter of $1/_{30}$ mm. which is the basis for compiling the tables. To estimate the correct stop for color work we normally do a test on monochrome rated at 32...27° and give an extra whole stop. This is a fairly accurate measure of the difference in rated speeds between the monochrome and Agfacolor negative materials, but it would not necessarily apply exactly if other types of color film are used. The flash duration of $^1/_{5000}$ sec. is so short that even those patients who suffer from eye diseases which force them to shun light can be photographed before the uncontrollable reflex of closing the eyelids has taken place.

Camera techniques for the photography of the anterior segment are comparatively simple. The Leica is mounted on a stand with a rack and pinion traversing movement, such as those found in most eye clinics, while the patient uses a chin rest with a support for the forehead (fig. 14). Focus is controlled by means of the ground glass screen of the Visoflex housing. It is very convenient to use a special pre-selector diaphragm control ring which fits over the lens and is operated by one prong of a coupler release. After focusing at full aperture the pre-selected stop is set automatically by the coupler release an instant or so before the shutter is tripped. The hinged mirror of the Visoflex housing is operated by an additional short coupler at the position of the camera release

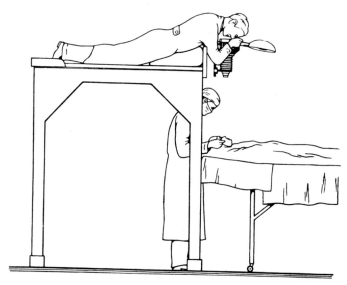

Fig. 1: Arrangement for the photography of eye operations.

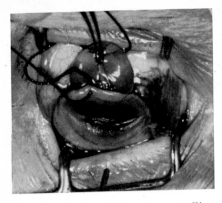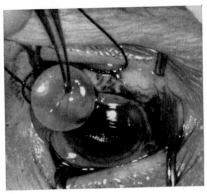

Fig. 2: Cataract operation: the crystalline lens of the eye has been almost totally removed from under the cornea.

Fig. 3: Cataract operation: the crystalline lens is completely removed and is held by capsule forceps. Photos: Th. Kisselbach

button. The photography of operations is rather more complicated because the patient is lying prone, which necessitates some means of positioning the camera vertically above his head. Fig. 1 is a diagram of a suitable camera platform for the purpose. It should be sufficiently large to allow the photographer to lie or sit in a position from which he can comfortably operate the Leica which is again fixed to a transverse rack and pinion on a bracket support, so that it points vertically downwards and can be laterally adjusted. Focusing is again controlled on the ground glass screen of the Visoflex housing by means of the monobar focusing bellows. The magnifier eyepiece is one that bends vision through 90°. The theater lights are bright enough for focusing. Exposures are made to electronic flash tubes.

Fig. 4: Corneal opacity before homo-keratoplasty. Fig. 5: Forceps on the right hold the eyeball steady. A trephine, or cylindrical saw for removal of a disk from the cornea, is brought upto the patient's eye. Fig. 6: A circular hole of 4 mm. diameter has been cut in the cornea. Fig. 7: With the same trephine a corneal disk of a similar size and shape is removed from the donated eye of a person who was blind. Fig. 8: The disk removed from the donated eye rests on a spatula prior to insertion in the hole cut in the patient's cornea for grafting. Fig. 9: A disk of 13 mm. diameter from the cornea of a second donated eye is placed over the section to be grafted and held in position by means of four stitches. This section of cornea is so clear that the small section to be grafted is clearly discernible through it.
Photos: Th. Kisselbach

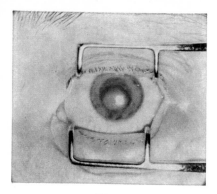

Fig. 4

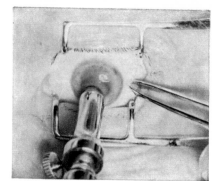

Fig. 5

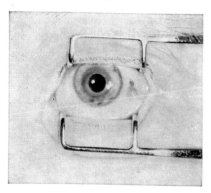

Fig. 6

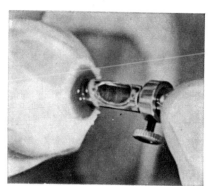

Fig. 7

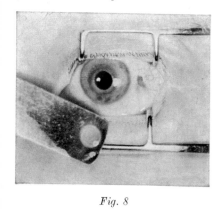

Fig. 8

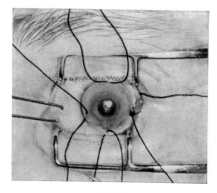

Fig. 9

Photos: Th. Kisselbach

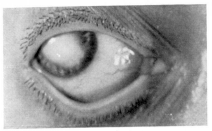

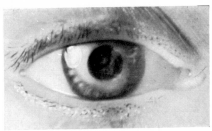

Fig. 10: Corneal opacity before keratoplasty.

Fig. 11: Graft of clear corneal section one year after operation.

The monochrome illustrations of figs. 2 & 3 indicate the available depth of field. They show the stage at which, in an operation for the removal of cataract, the clouded, opaque crystalline lens of the eye is removed after an incision has been made in the upper part of the cornea (intracapsular operation for cataract). Since the definition of the negative has permitted considerable enlargement it can clearly be seen how the capsule forceps have gripped the capsule of the crystalline lens. In the first diagram the crystalline lens is already more than half-way through the incision, while in the second it has been removed entirely from the eyeball; and behind it the cut along the cornea has been allowed to close. The degree of sharpness extending over the crystalline lens, which is more than 4 mm. thick, and beyond to the instruments and detail of the anterior segment gives a good idea of the relatively great depth of field.

Color photography has heralded a definite advance not merely in the recording of changes taking place in diseased eyes but more particularly in the photography of eye operations. An operation which has aroused great interest of

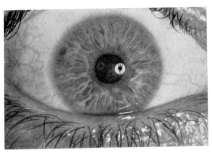

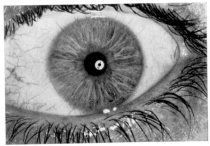

Figs. 12 & 13: Normal irises with small images of the light source in the region of the pupils.

recent years is the homo-keratoplasty, or the removal of a portion of the cornea containing an opacity and the substitution of a clear piece of the same size and shape from another human eye preserved in an eye bank. Here the method is shown in six stages which are self-explanatory. The principle of the operation consists of trephining or removing, with an instrument known as a trephine, the opaque section of the cornea and baring the pupil under it (figs. 4—6). The same instrument is used to trephine a corneal section of the same size and shape from an eye which is blind and has been removed, for one reason or another, from a second person (fig. 7). This section is laid on a spatula (fig.8) for insertion into the opening already made in the eye to be treated. This corneal graft must be securely anchored otherwise it would fall out. This can be done in several ways, for example stitching on the graft, which is only about 1 mm. thick, with nylon sutures. But the method shown in fig. 9 is more elaborate. Here the graft is protected by a second corneal covering of larger diameter also trephined from another eye, and in a shape and size which is a perfect fit for the cornea under treatment. This trephined section is anchored to the cornea by four sutures thus preventing, in a very simple manner, any movement of the graft. This covering section is so clear that the graft is clearly visible through it in the picture (fig. 9) and can also be directly observed during the stages of assimilation and healing. The sutures are removed after about a week and the grafted section is uncovered. The result of such a corneal graft is shown in the monochrome illustrations of figs. 10 & 11. These two pictures were made with the aid of two 500 W photofloods. The eye, which to all intents and purposes is blind due to the corneal opacity, shies away from the light in an uncontrollable movement upwards. The eyelids must, moreover, be held apart since the patient's instinctive reaction to the great intensity of the photofloods is to shut his eyes tightly. Difficulties like these have been overcome by the introduction of electronic flash.

Fig. 11 shows a well-healed graft of a clear corneal section, covering only the pupil, exactly one year after the operation. The original cornea lying beyond the circumference of the pupil is still in its opaque state. In the photograph part of the circumference of the pupil and the adjoining iris are clearly visible.

Sight can thus be restored to eyes blinded by diseases of the cornea.

The photographic methods described go a very long way towards fulfilling the requirements of doctors, surgeons and specialists who need monochrome and color records for instruction and research.

New apparatus for ophthalmic photography of the iris permitting a ratio of magnifications from ×1.5 (total view) to ×3 (sectional detail) has recently been developed by Leitz.

This apparatus consists of a special pillar stand with transverse, vertical and fore and aft adjustments, and it carries a Greenough stereo binocular body (fig. 15) which is readily interchangeable with the photographic equipment. All synchronized f series cameras and the Leica M 3 may be used in conjunction with the Visoflex housing, the monobar bellows and a special version of the 90 mm. Elmar lens equipped with a pre-selector diaphragm control. Any good make of electronic power pack may be used but the tube should be encased in a cylinder with a small aperture, which is fitted to a stand which permits reasonably good vertical and lateral adjustment of the light source (fig. 14). Ring illuminants which encircle the camera lens cannot be used for this purpose because pictures made with them tend to be of low contrast, or very flat. The

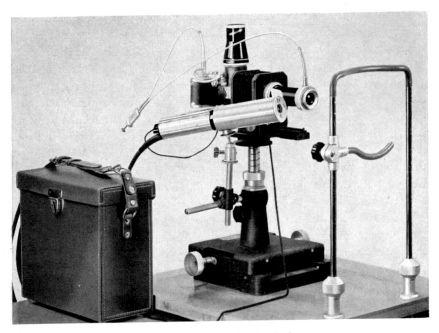

Fig. 14: Apparatus for photography of the iris showing flash source.

horizontal traverse of the light source should be about 3½ in., and the vertical span about 5 in. This would cover every shape of head and every possible interocular distance.

Focusing is by means of the ground glass screen of the Visoflex housing. A pilot light should be used for the purpose and if this is incorporated in the flash head the reflection or catch-light in the eye can be positioned where desired and remain constant for the exposure. An index or serial number may be projected onto the eye, if necessary, and there photographed for easy filing and later reference. A combination of coupler releases adjusts aperture, swings out the mirror, trips the shutter and fires the flash, as already described.

With most modern power packs the lens stop would be around f/16 on film rated at 32...27° and about f/11 on Agfacolor reversal film for total views. For sectional detail these stops would be opened to about f/11 and f/8 respectively. Such data can only be a guide and must naturally vary with the output of the flash head used, but it will in general be found that stops are always small enough to obtain the necessary depth of field in photography of the iris. This apparatus is also suitable for other close-up work in fields such as dermatology and dentistry.

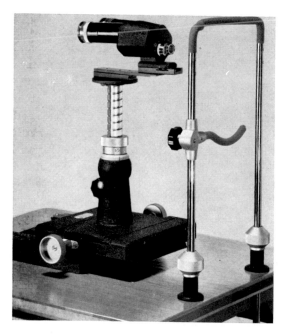

Fig. 15: Greenough stereo binocular body and stand for ophthalmic observation.

The Leica in Dentistry and in Ailments of Mouth and Jaw

by Prof. G. Korkhaus, Bonn

FOURTEEN YEARS have passed since the last edition of this book appeared—
years of war and privation, of political and economic collapse, of reconstruction
that was initially slow and laborious. All the more astonishing is the progress
made in miniature photography; progress that is most apparent when modern
Leica equipment for the documentation and diagnosis of dental conditions and
abnormalities of mouth and jaw is compared with the earlier but still usable
apparatus described in the last edition of this book by Prof. Gerlach.

Those who are conscious of the part the miniature camera plays in dental
photography and are aware of the peculiar difficulties of this field, will not have
been surprised by the decided simplifications of technique attendant on the
application of the Leica camera to dentistry. As in medical work, the miniature
is used to record and classify rare clinical phenomena of interest in research and
instruction; but in dentistry the camera is also used for photographic diagnosis
—with suitable precautions—in much the same way as the X-ray photograph
is used for the diagnosis of ailments. Consider, for example, anomalies of the
bite, for which the appropriate treatment is often first suggested by the photograph. In the orthopaedic treatment of jaw conditions photography has long
been an invaluable aid to the practitioner, and it is now also increasingly
employed in dental surgery and prosthesis and during the conduct of various
facial operations such as, for instance, a gnathoplasty. Here, particularly, the
photograph is now known to be of benefit also to the patient.

Photography of the restricted area of the human mouth, with its single comparatively small oral opening, is not an entirely easy matter. Intraoral exposure
requires intense and well-distributed illumination of the interior of the mouth
through the same small opening through which it must be photographed. This
is a requirement which has only recently been satisfied by the introduction of

the new high tension ring illuminants. These may be said to have solved the problem in a remarkably efficient manner. Such apparatus is available from Langham Photographic Instruments, Ltd. With a ring illuminant surrounding the mount of a long focus lens (135 mm. Hektor) the iris diaphragm may be well stopped down to give the necessary depth of field. The exposure itself is short enough (duration of flash is about $^1/_{500}$ sec.) to prevent blur caused by involuntary movements, for instance of the patient's tongue. The intensity of the flash is high enough to permit the use of color materials, both reversal and negative processes, and this is an improvement that cannot be too highly rated.

Our own equipment for intraoral photography with the Leica (figs. 1 & 2) consists of the following apparatus:

1. A newly designed stand by H. Wertebach, Bonn, as illustrated in fig. 1. Weight and rigidity preclude the possibility of camera shake. The stand is a fixture to one side of the dental chair or operating table. Twin articulated brackets carry the camera, which can be drawn forward or returned in a single uninterrupted movement without introducing unnecessary complications into the treatment of a case. With the camera extended horizontally at a convenient height angular adjustment is made by means of a cine pan and tilt head. Once set whole series can be rapidly exposed and the camera can always be accurately returned to any given position.

2. The camera is a model f Leica fully synchronized for use with high tension discharge tubes.

3. The camera is used in conjunction with the Visoflex and the pentaprism magnifier which bends vision through 45°, a convenience when viewing the image with the camera tilted downwards from the horizontal (fig. 2).

4. Visoflex and camera rest on the platform of the monobar focusing bellows. The lens panel of the bellows carries the 135 mm. Hektor f/4.5. This bellows equipment (fig. 2) has proved to be a very vital improvement in the technique of intraoral photography. It removes the restrictions imposed by the use of fixed focus intermediate collars or extension tubes and permits rapid and continuous focus over a range extending from infinity to natural size. A scale indicates all possible intermediate ratios of reduction (or magnification as the case may be) together with the corresponding exposure factors for lens extension. Magnifications are possible if lenses of shorter focal length are used. Thus with the 50 mm. Elmar focus is continuous from natural size to a magnification of $\times 2.5$, and this may be extended upto a magnification of $\times 6.5$ with the 35 mm.

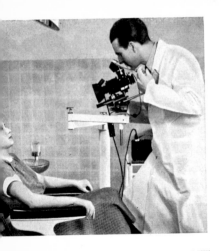

Summaron. In such cases the use of the sliding copier instead of the Visoflex is optional.

If the Visoflex is used control of focus and field through the magnifier on the ground glass screen is possible right upto the instant the exposure is made, thus greatly reducing the margin of possible error. Focus is set in a single operation and for this purpose the mouth may be illuminated by a photoflood or even by the light above the dentist's chair.

5. The light source for the exposure is a high tension ring-shaped discharge tube which clips over the front of the lens mount, encircling the field of view of the lens (fig. 2). The tube is embedded in a parabolic reflector which also does duty as a lens shade.

The Leica is synchronized by selecting the appropriate shutter speed ($^1/_{30}$ or $^1/_{50}$) for the model in use and setting the correct contact number on the synchro-dial (on model M 3 there are no contact numbers because synchronization is automatic). Exposure is made with a coupler release, one prong of which swings the hinged mirror of the Visoflex housing out of the path of the image-forming rays a fraction of a second or so before the other prong trips the shutter. The flash is synchronously discharged during the traverse of the shutter. Any power pack may be used but the Langham model supplied is operated either by dry cell or mains power and output is variable. The advantages are obvious.

Fig. 1: Leica apparatus for intraoral photography on a new articulated stand.

Fig. 2: Leica apparatus for intraoral photography showing monobar bellows, Visoflex mirror reflex housing, 45° magnifier eyepiece and ring illuminant.

Ring illuminants of the type described project a cone of light into the intra-oral cavity, providing very bright illumination of the mouth and pharynx. The flash duration of $^1/_{500}$ sec. is a happy compromise because it is fast enough to stop involuntary movements of tongue and pharynx, even with color film, and yet not fast enough to upset the reciprocity law.

The quite exceptional optical, mechanical and electrical qualities of the apparatus described far transcend anything that has gone before. For the first time it has become possible to expose entirely in color with its attendant advantages in record work. The patient, moreover, suffers the minimum of inconvenience from the flash which does not generate the great heat of tungsten illuminants (fig. 3). Nor is there any delay in manipulation because depth of field tables are unnecessary and focusing is considerably easier. Such equipment has led to a very welcome standardization of technique which always assures good results.

For intraoral and pharynx exposures on color film, both negative and reversal materials, it has been found that the 135 mm. Hektor lens should be stopped down to f/16, but only to f/11 when taking a picture of a whole head. In both types of record there is ample depth of field, but it is advisable to set sharp focus on the front third of the desired field. If monochrome is used the corresponding stops are f/32 for the cavity and f/16 for the head.

In this field of photography color has introduced a factor which cannot as yet be fully evaluated. It is certain that it has greatly helped clinical work, research and instruction by allowing the presentation, in reasonably durable form, of the delicate differences in flesh and mucous membrane tints as well as the angriness of inflammation or of boils. There is no doubt that the color transparency is being increasingly used at medical and scientific congresses, and this might well lead to the wider use of color illustrations in books which are still predominantly illustrated in monochrome.

This stage we have clearly not yet reached. We are still only at the beginning of such a revolutionary development, but we should not allow the frequent disappointments due to the present inadequacy of color negative processes, or the difficulties of four-color printing, to deter us from the goal. Towards this end we must continue to strive and it will be well served only by the continued maintenance of high standards of discrimination in regard to the accuracy of color rendition.

In our experience color reversal material (fig. 4) is truer in its response to natural color and is convenient in use because exposure and processing are

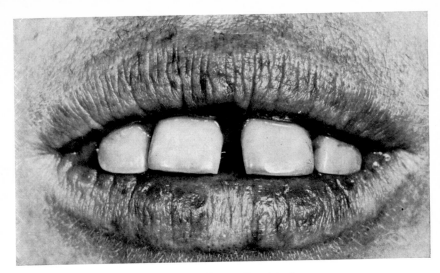

Fig. 3: Photograph of a mouth showing abnormality of incisors.
Ratio of magnification about × 2, at f/32.

reasonably constant factors; but the result is a *single* transparency. Its uses are much more restricted than those of the color negative, from which color (or monochrome) prints can be made on paper; from which transparencies can be made in color (or monochrome), in different sizes and from only sections of the negative if need be, and in any required numbers. The negative process is understandably expensive.

The color balance of prints made from negative color film (figs. 5—7) is entirely dependent on the nature of the positive filtration decided on by the darkroom operator at the processing station. Many an unsatisfactory result is directly attributable to this cause. Though there is little doubt that the process holds much promise for the future, its use for scientific purposes demanding the highest possible quality must at present be confined to those workers who have their own darkrooms and can themselves control the making of the print. I, personally, am convinced that the improved negative/positive color materials now becoming available will greatly reduce the uncertainty hitherto experienced in "steering" the colors of the positive.

To turn now to the photographic evaluation of maxillomandibular conditions requiring orthopaedic treatment it is, first, essential that all prints should

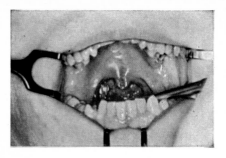 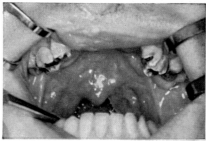

Fig. 4   *Fig. 5*

Fig. 4: Cleft palate one week after operation. Agfacolor reversal film at f/16 with ring illuminant.
Fig. 5: Patient M. Cleft palate after operation. Agfacolor negative film at f/16 with ring illuminant

bear a definite and fixed relationship to each other. Measurements made on different prints should be strictly comparable. Frontal and lateral exposures of the head should always be in a definite ratio of reduction. This system has been adapted to our own use from methods devised for identification photographs by criminologists. Every exposure is made under identical conditions with the head always orientated in a fixed direction. Various types of equipment have been devised with the aim of maintaining a fixed relationship between the camera position and the patient's head, and ways have been sought to simplify correct focus and alignment on certain fixed cephalometric planes. The present writer has found that the wall of a room, with suitable fixtures (fig. 8), is entirely satisfactory for the purpose because camera/subject distance is a constant and focus is always on the desired cephalometric planes.

The patient sits on a low stool, permanently fixed to the wall and rotatable through an arc of exactly 90 degrees. Placed centrally above this stool, and also fixed to the wall, is a sighting ring on rails. This sighting ring has a vertical traverse along a scale graduated in millimeters or inches as the case may be.

On this sighting ring there are two indicators for correctly positioning the ears and a third indicator on the circumference for positioning points on the lower arc of the eye-sockets. With the head so positioned it is said to be in the correct horizontal plane according to the Frankfort Criminological Specification. A second graduated scale is fixed to the wall at a definite distance from the sighting ring (5 or 6 feet). It is against this scale that the height of the camera is adjusted to correspond exactly with the height of the patient's head. The

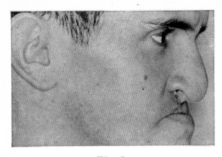
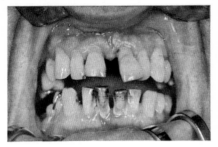

Fig. 6　　　　　　　　　Fig. 7

Fig. 6: Patient M. Harelip. Ring illuminant.
Fig. 7: Patient Dr. X., Extensive paradenitis.
Agfacolor negative film at f/16 with photoflood and reflector.

alignment of the camera is such that a prolongation of the optical axis of the lens passes through the center of the sighting ring, and this is also the plane of critical focus.

With the patient's head correctly positioned and the camera correctly aligned, the sighting ring is hinged upwards before the exposure is made. In this way accurately comparable lateral, semi-lateral and frontal exposures can be made (fig. 9) without having to readjust the camera alignment once it has been set for a particular patient.

The Leica camera has proved to be most suitable for this purpose, as Gerlach has already pointed out in the previous edition of this book. The same excellent combination of apparatus is used as for intraoral photography, namely, model f Leica with monobar bellows and 135 mm. Hektor lens with ring illuminant (fig. 2). Flash duration of $^1/_{500}$ sec., at apertures between f/16 and f/22 for medium speed panchromatic films, 32...27°, guarantees a sharp image, while the great depth of field so characteristic of the miniature more than covers the requirement in this respect. Since the orthopaedic treatment of malalignments or deformities of the jaw is confined almost entirely to child patients the wisdom of using speed flash ring illuminants should be obvious. Twin photofloods in suitable reflectors might be preferred by some, but the comparatively long exposure ($^1/_{30}$ sec.) and the much less favorable aperture (f/5.6) increase the risk of image blur and reduce the depth of field.

Another application of the Leica to dentistry lies in the photography of the plaster casts of upper and lower sets, both separately and in superimposition.

316

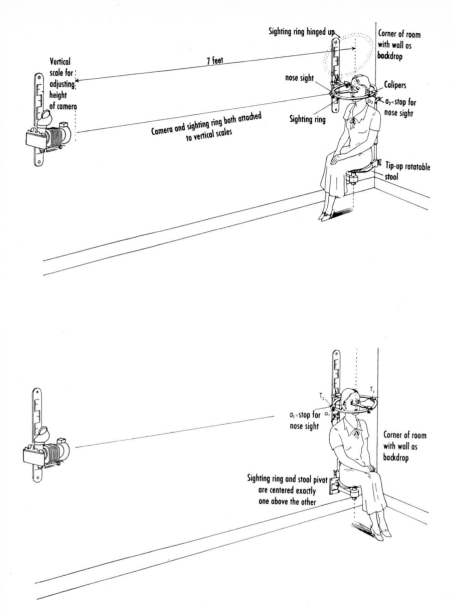

Fig. 8: Author's method of maintaining constant ratios of reduction in the photography of cephalometric planes.

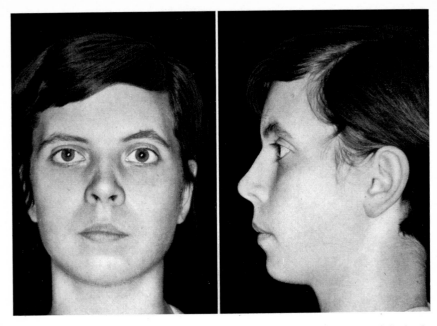

Fig. 9: Cephalometric photographs of antero-posterior and lateral positions of the head, made with the Leica camera.

In my own work I use the Leica with the Reprovit II. The projection focus and simultaneous field delineation of this apparatus greatly simplify photographic procedure. An image of the crossed hairs on a clear section of the ground glass screen is projected onto the plane of the object to be photographed and there sharply focused; or, if desired, the projection lamp can be replaced by a magnifier eyepiece bending vision through 45° for direct visual focus and framing. The latter method might be preferred by those who make a habit of estimating exposure by the brightness of the ground glass image, and it is also useful for controlling the effects of illumination from the four independently operated lamps carried on brackets attached to the baseboard of the instrument. A useful refinement is the double throw change-over switch which operates either the projection lamp or the light sources for the exposure.

Another very useful feature of the Reprovit II is the automatic diaphragm control which sets the aperture to any predetermined lens stop as the camera body is slid over to the position that was occupied, during focusing, by the ground glass screen. The lever which controls the settings can be lifted off, if desired, for manual adjustment of aperture by means of click stops.

Very accurate centralization of the camera on the column assures that the object to be photographed is always in the center of the image field through all the ratios of reduction of which the instrument is capable.

The photography of plaster casts is certainly not easy. The most usual fault is hard illumination with the loss of fine detail and intermediate tones in sudden transitions from light to shade. Here the four independent lamps of the Reprovit II should be used in preference to speed flash. They allow the modulation necessary for correct illumination of the specimen and one soon learns how best to obtain negatives full of the desired detail (fig. 10). Black velvet is quite a good background for plaster casts.

The Reprovit II is a pleasure to use, and it is versatile. It can be used for the microfilming of radiographs *via* a light-box, for negative film, or by means of the standard illuminants for paper prints. Cold light viewing boxes large enough to accept X-ray film upto 12×16 in. are very suitable accessories for microfilming radiographs because they generate little heat and do no damage to the film.

It will be clear that the Reprovit II is adaptable also to the microfilming of documents, illustrations and books. Such records are convenient for filing and may be referred to either by running the microfilm through a microfilm reader or by enlargement back onto paper. A useful accessory for copying books is the Leitz "see-saw" book holder. The open book is placed on a rest which swings it upwards into flush contact with a sheet of plate glass, and pressure on the book is exerted in such a way that both pages are in the same plane (the plane of sharp focus) irrespective of the fact that the two sections of the open book may not be of equal thickness. The copying of books is thus greatly speeded up and the double page on a single frame is both economic and conveniently read on a film reader.

Photomicrography provides yet another illustration of the versatility of the Leica camera in the elucidation of abstruse scientific points and in the provision of lasting records of rare clinical phenomena. The Leica in conjunction with the micro-attachment "Mikas" can be used with specialist apparatus like the "Panphot" microscope or with any other microscope having a standard tube.

There are many advantages in the use of miniature film for micrography. The

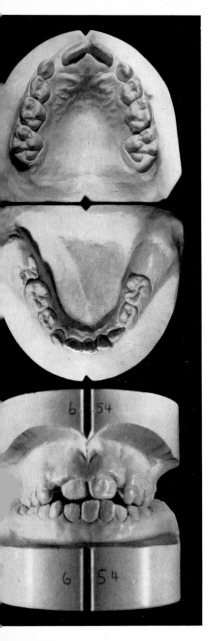

low cost of sensitive material allows the duplication or triplication of exposure at varying shutter speeds to ensure at least one good result from a bracketed set (figs. 11 & 12). Since the Square Law favors the Leica format, shutter speeds in photomicrography are much faster than those possible with larger negative sizes—a factor of considerable importance when microscope slides are of low luminance or can be photographed only by dark field illumination. Both negative and reversal color materials—considerably cheaper in the miniature size—may be used as desired. This is an undeniable advance in the recording of color differences in histological specimens and the color record lives into the future long after the original specimen has faded.

Since dentistry deals with things and their condition it is not surprising that sketches, diagrams and pictures play so important a part in the illustration of papers and lectures on the subject. A good picture conveys more than many words. To be good it must be sharp and sufficiently large; it must be brilliant and exhibit the essentials of a subject in the same manner in which it is normally seen by the eye.

When attending Dental Congresses abroad during the years 1930—35 we always took our Leica transparencies with us. The Leitz projector was dwarfed by the bulky apparatus set up in the congress rooms and lecture halls but the superiority of our screened images was so marked that professional workers in many countries converted to the miniature.

Fig. 10: Photographs of plaster casts in plan and in occlusion.

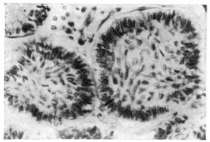 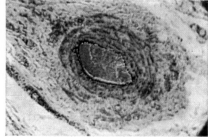

Fig. 11   *Fig. 12*

Fig. 11: Photomicrograph of an adamantinoma.
Magnification about × 380, ×45 microscope objective with × 8 eyepiece and Mikas. Exposure 1 sec., without filter.

Fig. 12: Photomicrograph of a cell from a telangiectatic granuloma.
Magnification about × 100, × 10 microscope objective with × 8 eyepiece and Mikas. Exposure ¹/₅ sec., without filter.

Today the transparency is in universal use. During the International Congress of Dentists held in London in July 1952 the 2-in. square color transparency was predominant and constantly referred to even by small groups of people at the various demonstration tables. In projection the brilliance was such that inadequate screening of windows was hardly noticed.

It is the screen brilliance of the miniature projector which enabled me, in 1939, to lecture in Bonn and Wiesbaden to the International Congress of the European Orthodontic Society without interpreters. Copies of the lecture in various languages were photographed on long strips of Leica film and projected onto three screens during the actual delivery. The congress room was not darkened. This was the first time such a method had been attempted and it was found that none of the foreign delegations had any difficulty in following the thesis—and this without the interminable delays caused by interpreters.

Finally, the value of the Leica transparency in the dissemination of knowledge and the graphic depiction of new methods of treatment was convincingly demonstrated before the war by the Academy for Dental Research, a body which issued a most instructive series of transparencies to all the members of an entire profession. Duplicated in large numbers, these transparencies greatly assisted the valuable work of local groups engaged in dental research and instruction.

Applications of Photography to Surgical Operations

by Dr. Viktor Dostal, Marburg/Lahn

THE IMPORTANCE of exact scientific records in modern research is undeniable Of the many applications of photography to medicine I intend here to deal only with its applied uses in the operating theater. Today every large hospital recognizes the value of a permanent and well-equipped photographic department able to cope with all the technical problems which might arise. I have been able to make a relatively large number of exposures during operations on the abdomen, the chest and the limbs and consider that it might be worth while to report in detail on the methods adopted.

My basic photographic apparatus is the Leica camera, which has proved extremely valuable in medical work because of the wide range of ancillary equipment which adapts it to the most varied applied medical uses. The relatively short focal lengths of the miniature size permit great depth of field.

Long experience in the field of miniature photography has shown that the 24 × 36 mm. frame will always yield good results in surgical work and that it is adaptable with equal success to photomicrography. But however pressed for time or for whatever other reason, it really will not do to develop miniature films in X-ray film developers. This is not entirely unknown!

It can be said with little fear of contradiction that no difference is detectable between the quality of the miniature enlargement and the photograph made from the large negative when the two are compared in the print sizes customary for the monochrome and color records of medical work. The miniature, moreover, allows a series of pictures to be printed on a single large lantern slide for close comparison. This is particularly useful for following the course of treatment. The individual frames can be captioned and it has been found that this procedure is an advantage in the reproduction of microradiographs. Attention should be directed to utilizing the whole of the available frame while confining the record only to the required essentials. It needs no emphasis that clean workmanship is necessary both in the processing of the negative and in the making of the print.

There are two possible approaches: one is to use the Leica with a standard 50 mm. lens such as the Elmar or Summicron and get as near the subject as possible. The limit is set at $3\frac{1}{2}$ feet under normal camera conditions, but an approach to within 18 inches is possible if lens extension is used, and this is supplied by the optical near-focusing device Nooky, which corrects automatically for the pronounced parallax of close-up work. Nooky (code word is Sooky for Summicron) is very suitable for instantaneous exposures (fig. 1) or when very little time is available for photographic preparation. The camera is focused in the normal way by means of the rangefinder. The other possibility is the use of long focal lengths with the Leica. I have found lenses of long focal length, especially the 90 mm. Elmar and 135 mm. Hektor, and occasionally also the 200 mm. Telyt, very suitable for the photography of operations. Very fast lenses (f/1.5) do not offer any advantage here. At full aperture field depth is too restricted so that one is obliged to stop such lenses down in order to obtain all the required detail in good definition. Perhaps the principal advantage of long focus lenses is that they permit relatively large camera/subject distances and hence aseptic surgery. Conditions are much more comfortable both for the patient and for the photographer. The 90 mm. Elmar is most suitable for general views, for example to show a complete incision or the situs of a malignancy.

This lens is focused with the coupled rangefinder. At a distance of $3\frac{1}{2}$ feet the field is about $9\frac{1}{2} \times 14$ inches which corresponds approximately to a camera/ subject distance of 5 feet when using a 135 mm. lens, or to a camera/subject distance of $17\frac{1}{2}$ inches when using a standard 50 mm. lens with Nooky. To use the 135 mm. Hektor in its long mount and directly coupled to the rangefinder offers no advantages over the 90 mm. lens, since the Hektor can then only be focused to 5 feet, but if this Hektor lens is used in conjunction with a mirror reflex housing and monobar bellows it is much the preferred apparatus, because this combination also permits the photography of much smaller fields than that given (figs 2, 5 & 6). If bellows extension is not available the desired lens extension can be obtained by interposing collars, but since these are comparatively clumsy and inflexible (fixed focus) it is advisable to use the monobar bellows for all surgical photography. Its continuous focusing range extends from 1:1 to ∞ and it is quick to operate and adjust. The ground glass image is free from

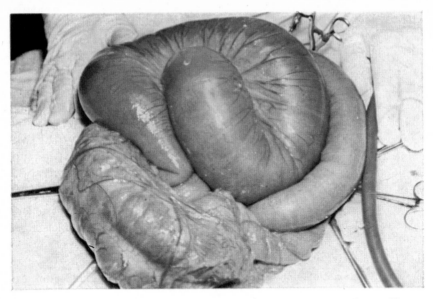

Fig. 1: Intestinal obstruction caused by intussusception. Leica with Nooky and 50 mm. Elmar.

parallax and the image is focused at full aperture before setting the desired stop. A coupler release actuates the hinged mirror and the shutter at a single pressure, thus allowing observation of the image right upto the instant of the exposure, guaranteeing that what one sees one gets. A stand is essential when using long focal lengths (135 and 200 mm.) in this way, but it should be a very rigid one provided with a rack and pinion for height adjustments (fig. 3). With the stand illustrated it is possible to approach close to the operating table and, if necessary, use a crossbar for verticals from this position. Tripods are unsuitable for the purpose.

During the last few years various attempts have been made to simplify surgical photography and arrange things so that the surgeon and the patient suffer the least possible inconvenience. One simplification is that the surgeon operates the camera by means of an electric foot switch. The Leica is housed under the bowl of the theater light and distance, aperture and shutter speed are set before the operation begins. The film is automatically transported, and the shutter wound, by the Leica motor. By adjusting the operating light to any desired angle or position the camera is automatically aimed at the same spot.

The exposure is made to the synchronized discharge of one or two electronic flash tubes also housed under the bowl of the theater light. Various adaptations of the method are possible, such as focusing by means of the mirror reflex housing and a magnifying eyepiece—the operating lamp is moved to a position vertically above the area required and by raising or lowering it the desired field is obtained on the ground glass screen. The method calls for extra effort but it can be very useful in those hospitals where much surgical photography is undertaken. The anaesthetist or some other helper can be detailed to undertake the duties of focusing and positioning the camera while the surgeon operates it with his foot switch.

Another method is to photograph operations through a mirror positioned immediately below the theater light (fig. 4). A Leica with a 200 mm. Telyt lens is positioned near the anaesthetist at the patient's head. Exposure is to two electronic flash tubes positioned one on either side of the mirror. By adjusting the angle of the mirror it is possible to vary the position of the camera to any desired location.

The arrangement shown on p. 303, as used by Prof. Rauh, is very satisfactory. It locates the photographer and his apparatus right above the operating table and out of the way of all those whom he is otherwise likely to disturb or inconvenience. Here the 135 mm. Hektor with bellows and electronic flash would be the most suitable equipment.

Theater lights are not powerful enough for surgical photography. Except in a few special cases it will always be necessary to supplement this illumination. Photofloods in hand-held reflectors have been used for the purpose. Such light sources are balanced for color work and the light output is good. Of recent years some photofloods have been internally silvered to dispense with reflectors. But such light sources generate great heat which can be uncomfortable both for the patient and the surgeon, so spot-lighting (figs. 2 & 5) will usually be preferred. The beam can be focused onto the desired surface. The illustration on page 328 was made with such lighting. It shows a stage in an operation for the removal of a large osteoma from the calvaria or skull-cap (fig. 5). The exposure time may vary between $^1/_{10}$ and $^1/_{30}$ sec., at apertures between f/8 and f/11 for Agfacolor negative film.

I never use expendable wire- or foil-filled flash-bulbs because it is impossible to be certain that the bulb will not explode, with attendant danger of sepsis.

We have already mentioned electronic flash. This is probably the most

Fig. 2: Direct illumination of the operation field by means of spot-lights.
The Leica is shown with Visoflex, bellows and 135 mm. Hektor lens.

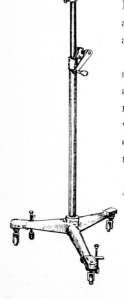

suitable illuminant. The very short flash duration (between $^1/_{1000}$ and $^1/_{5000}$ sec.) simplifies photography even when there is movement. The flash head should not be positioned on the camera. It should be held, either by the photographer or an assistant, at a distance of 2—2½ feet from the patient and angled from above onto the part to be photographed (fig. 8).

With two flash heads the illumination is better and the shadows are softer. Flash heads should always be positioned at a constant distance from the subject to ensure exactly repeatable aperture stops and exposure times. The lens can be well stopped down because of the high intensity, and this, of course, means greater depth of field. The flash is synchronized to Leica shutter speeds of $^1/_{30}$ or $^1/_{50}$ sec. (the latter speed

Fig. 3: Rigid monopost stand with vertical extension.

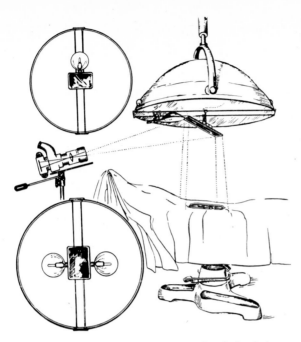

*Fig. 4: Diagrams illustrating a tiltable mirror fixed under the bowl of an operating theater
light. The two plan sketches illustrate how one or two electronic flash heads might be
positioned near the mirror on a crossbar under the bowl.*

for red synchro-dial f models and the Leica M 3). In all my years of experience
I have never known a fault in synchronization. The following table may serve
as a guide to lens stops for various films when using electronic flash synchronized at $^1/_{30}$ or $^1/_{50}$ sec.

My best results have been
obtained with films rated at
32...27°, whether exposed
to photoflood or to speed
flash. I do not consider it
desirable to use faster films
because of increased grain,
lower resolving power and
flatter contrasts. In color we

Sensitive Material	Lens Stop
Perutz Pergrano 10 . . . 22°	11
Perutz Perpantic 32 . . . 27°	32
Agfa Isopan F 32 . . . 27°	32
Agfacolor Negative (T)	16
Agfacolor Reversal (T)	16
Flash/Subject Distance 2—2½ feet	

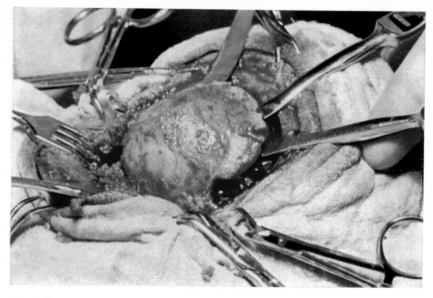

Fig. 5: Removing an osteoma from the calvaria or skull-cap.
Leica with bellows and 135 mm. Hektor at f/11, $^1/_{40}$ sec., to two spot-lights on Agfacolor negative film (Type K)

have a choice of direct transparency or negative processes. My experiences with the negative color processes have been so satisfactory that I always prefer to use negative color film whenever several prints or transparencies of a subject are required. These negatives can also be used for the making of monochrome prints. But the obvious choice for color work is the reversal transparency because of the low cost of each exposure and the greatly improved color response and definition of recent years. In much of pathology the color record is the only satisfactory one. Daylight type color film should be used with speed flash and tungsten type color film with photofloods or spots. In the latter case daylight should be excluded from the operating theater to avoid the ill effects of mixed lighting. Colored objects which might introduce undesirable reflections into the subject should be removed or covered up. It has often proved necessary to lay a clean sheet over the site of the incision prior to exposing.

Fig. 7: General view of a mastotomy.
90 mm. Elmar at f/16, $^1/_{30}$ sec., to speed flash.

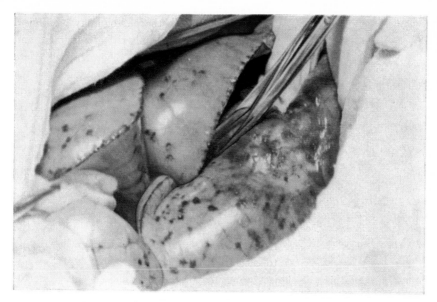

Fig. 6: Record of an old abscess on the basal lobe of the right lung. It was removed by a resection of the lobe. The center of necrosis can be clearly seen in the color record.
Leica with bellows and 135 mm. Hektor at f/16, $^1/_{30}$ sec., to speed flash on Agfacolor negative film.

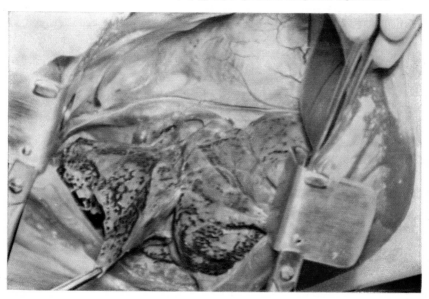

Fig. 8: Diagram illustrates relative positions of camera and flash head when photographing an incision.

Side by side with the photography of surgical operations it is often required that specimens and preparations should also be photographed. Here again the Leica can be used to advantage with the Reprovit I or II. Slimy or moist surfaces which do not present an area lying only in one plane can cause great difficulty because of the numerous specular reflections from parts which it may be required to photograph from several different angles. A polarizing filter may be used to eliminate reflections, but this is successful only if the specimen is illuminated by a single lamp and from a given angle. At certain angles of incidence the reflections are reduced to a minimum, but owing to the fact that such illumination is usually inadequate for lighting the subject properly, the photographic effect is, unfortunately, not as good as it might be. A simpler method of eliminating reflections is to immerse the preparation in a glass container filled with water. It is illuminated by the bundled beam of a spot-light, but here again there may be difficulty if the specimen is fresh, because hemolysis, the adhesion to the surface of small particles of tissue and the continuing flow of blood, reduce contrasts and impede the making of the desired record. The problem is considerably eased if the specimens are preserved by Jore's or Kaiserling's method, either of which prevents alteration of color. Specimens of lower specific gravity than the solution should be weighted.

Any of the various approaches to surgical photography described in this short article will yield good results, but it should be borne in mind that the individual problems of a particular subject will largely determine the method to be used for best results. Other determining conditions are personal preferences, the time factor, the use to which the records are to be put and the space available for photography.

Subject Index

SERVING INDUSTRY

In depicting every aspect of industrial activity, photography performs an essential service for manufacturer and customer alike—and Ilford HP3 provides the leading specialists in this field with the right tool for the job.

Negative on Ilford HP3 by Stewart Bale Ltd., Liverpool & London.

ILFORD *HP3*

PLATES, FLAT FILMS, ROLL & 35 mm FILMS

ILFORD   LIMITED   •   ILFORD   •   LONDON

Trade Showroom: 106/107 High Holborn   •   London, W.C.I   •   Telephone: HOLborn 3401

So Many Reasons Why...

There are so many reasons why the discerning photographer prefers CAMERA WORLD... Because its stimulating, authoritative articles on all aspects of the art and technique of photography are different from the usual run... Because its beautifully reproduced illustrations encompass both the modern and the traditional... Because in its regular feature, "35 mm.", the miniaturist finds a constant source of information and ideas... Because its test reports of latest apparatus are the most detailed and comprehensive available... Because its correspondence pages are the liveliest in photographic journalism... Because its monthly competitions provide continual encouragement to better work... Because it offers a note of adult humour unusual in photographic magazines... Because, in short, it is well written and elegantly presented, and has an individual flavor all its own.

Camera *World* the magazine for the discerning photographer

ls. 6d. monthly. Annual subscription, home and overseas, 20s.; U.S.A. and Canada, $ 4. Published from 46-47 Chancery Lane. London W.C. 2.

FOUNTAIN PHOTOBOOKS

SEND FOR ILLUSTRATED PHOTOBOOK CATALOGUE 46 CHANCERY LANE LONDON WC 2